Wat
Poc
Handbook

The essential guide to property and construction,
as used by professionals since 1983

First published in 1983, the Watts Pocket Handbook is an annual publication.

The editors wish to express their indebtedness to previous editors of the handbook, who laid the foundations on which this 23rd edition has been built.

The editors would also like to acknowledge with thanks the contributions of individuals in the property market and construction industry who send suggestions and comments. Such contributions are always welcome and should be sent to Samantha Rumens, Production Executive, Watts, 1 Great Tower Street, London, EC3R 5AA.

Acknowledgements

Specification data from the BCO Guide, *The British Council for Offices Guide 2005 Best Practice in the Specification of Offices*, is reproduced with permission from the British Council for Offices.

BRE material is reproduced with permission from Building Research Establishment Ltd.

Text from *Constructing for Sustainability – a basic guide for clients and their professional advisors*, is reproduced with permission from the Construction Industry Council.

Crown Copyright material is reproduced with the permission of the Controller of HMSO and the Queen's Printer for Scotland.

No guarantee is given by Watts, RICS Books or any of their employees as to the accuracy of this Pocket Handbook or any information contained in it. No responsibility for loss occasioned to any person acting or refraining from action as a direct or indirect result of any material included in this publication is accepted by the publisher, editors or contributors, and all liability for any such loss is hereby disclaimed to the fullest extent permitted by applicable law. This publication is produced for general information only, and specific advice should always be sought for individual cases. Library and research facilities are (subject to applicable conditions) available at Watts to assist in developing particular lines of enquiry. Where opinion is expressed by any contributor, it is the opinion of the contributor and does not necessarily coincide with the editorial views of Watts.

ISBN 978 1 84219 304 4

Published by RICS Books, an imprint of RICS

Typeset by Cantate Print, Battersea, London

Printed Cromwell Press, Trowbridge, Wiltshire

Cover design work by Art and Industry, Clerkenwell, London

The paper used for this publication is elementary chlorine free and from sustainable managed forests.

Contents

Contents

Contents

Introduction

It is my great pleasure to introduce the Watts Pocket Handbook 2007 – the indispensable guide to property and construction.

Watts Group PLC is in its maiden year of incorporation – just as I am as Non-executive Chairman. Watts traded for 40 years and for 24 of these it has published the Handbook. But neither let the grass grow under their feet. Watts continues to evolve – hence the new 'PLC' status – and to sharpen its service offering and range, while the Handbook continues to satisfy new and wider demands for information; and it does so in an articulate and accessible manner.

The current edition of the Handbook has no fewer than 24 new sections and these include an (even more) comprehensive environmental agenda with added data on renewable energy, Part L, recycling, sustainability and water. Building technology and building defects have been expanded substantially, as has legislative compliance. Of special note, is the section which supports APC students; the Handbook really is a student's best friend.

At this time, too, I must also express my deep gratitude to all contributors who provide their time and contributions for free.

Finally, all technical and legal references are believed to be accurate at the time of going to press. However, we operate in a dynamic industry and to meet the needs of subscribers for real time accuracy, Watts' monthly technical bulletins serve as timely updates to the Handbook.

Whether you are an industry professional, a client or a student, I am confident that you will find the Watts Pocket Handbook an invaluable, quick and reliable work of reference; and as always your comments are welcome. Good luck.

Tony Williams
Chairman
Watts

Commercial and industrial property

Property investment and ownership

Commercial/industrial surveys

See also the RICS guidance note *Building Surveys and Inspections of Commercial and Industrial Property* (3rd edition), 2006. The guidance note also contains example forms and conditions of engagement.

The following checklists are tools for establishing the brief and the extent and method of a commercial or industrial survey:

Identify the reason for and scope of survey

- acquisition or disposal (vendor survey)
- general or specific
- adaptation, extension, change of use
- maintenance programme, expenditure plan
- value as an investment
- insurance assessment
- investment or occupation.

Ascertain the scope and degree of detail required

- delivery, access
- floor loadings, gantry loadings
- security
- fire protection
- means of escape
- environmental control and other matters
- special processes, dangerous or toxic materials
- degree of opening up of concealed areas.

Identify energy conservation requirements

- use of specialists for inspecting, testing, etc.

Agree extent of tests/analysis of materials

- asbestos (type, content, dust counts)
- High Alumina Cement
- calcium chloride
- carbonation
- covermeter or other non-destructive tests
- methane gas
- nature of core materials in composite panels
- quality/constituents
- extent and method of sampling
- making good
- extent of services tests including drainage
- electromagnetic radiation.

Ascertain access for inspection

- ❖ ladder, cradle, hydraulic hoist, abseil, specialist help required
- ❖ public liability insurance and insurance of hire equipment
- ❖ special access requirements for confined spaces.

Ascertain tenure and request relevant documents

- ❖ freehold/leasehold/feuhold
- ❖ copies of leases, deeds and any plans attached
- ❖ advice on effects of repairing covenants, schedules of condition, rebuilding, reinstatement clauses.

Contaminated land

- ❖ possible contaminative uses (but check that professional indemnity insurance (PII) covers this risk).

Ascertain information available

- ❖ history
- ❖ base building specification
- ❖ original architects, engineers, developers, contractors
- ❖ floor plans, other drawings, details
- ❖ maintenance records
- ❖ maintenance personnel
- ❖ collateral warranties
- ❖ building contracts/status of works
- ❖ health and safety file
- ❖ fire certificate or fire risk assessment.

Consider impact of regulations

- ❖ Disability Discrimination Act
- ❖ Workplace Regulations:
  - – fire
  - – glazing
  - – sanitary provisions
  - – lighting
  - – protection from falling
- ❖ Construction (Design and Management) (CDM), health and safety
- ❖ Fire Precautions Act.

Establish if costings are required

- ❖ approximate for budget purposes
- ❖ state limitations on costing information.

Establish and confirm restrictions

- ❖ access arrangements
- ❖ restricted, high security areas
- ❖ means of identification, security arrangements
- ❖ potentially hazardous areas
- ❖ normal working hours/weekend working
- ❖ need to undertake risk assessment.

When surveying property – especially when empty – practitioners should conform to the procedures outlined in 'Practical procedures' under the 'Health and safety at work' section of this handbook.

Real Estate Investment Trusts (REITs)

Real Estate Investment Trusts, or REITs, are listed entities that may hold, manage and maintain properties for investment. They provide a means for both large and small investors to buy shares in a portfolio of residential and/or commercial property with tax advantages, income return and protection from inflation. Portfolios may include retail, industrial and office space as well as rental accommodation.

REITs were first established in the USA in the 1960s and then in the Netherlands and Australia. In the 1990s their popularity started to grow, with 23 countries around the world now having, or proposing to introduce, REIT-type vehicles. REITs are structured differently in each country. America and Australia have the most mature REIT markets, with the American regime being the most liberal. In contrast, REITs in the Netherlands and Belgium are the most restricted. Worldwide, REITs are estimated to account for 48% of listed real estate, valued at more than $500bn (source: RICS Business).

In the UK, the *Finance Act* 2006 confirmed the introduction of REITs in January 2007. A number of property industry bodies, including the British Property Federation, Royal Institution of Chartered Surveyors and Investment Property Forum have been lobbying for the introduction of REITs for some time, believing that commercial property has enormous, previously untapped, potential as an asset class. Pre-REITs, investment in commercial property made up only 7% of pension funds' total share holdings (source: RICS Business). It is anticipated that from January 2007, UK REITs will have widespread investor appeal due to the strong performance of the property sector in recent years.

What are the criteria?

To qualify for conversion to a UK REIT, companies must meet the following criteria:

- ❖ be UK tax resident;
- ❖ be listed on a recognised stock exchange;
- ❖ not be an open-ended investment company, nor a close company;
- ❖ not issue more than one class of ordinary share; and
- ❖ not be funded by a loan that is linked to either the profits or assets of the company, or one with interest or repayment terms that exceed a reasonable commercial return.

A prospective UK REIT must also comply with the following conditions:

❖ it must own at least three properties for property rental purposes;

❖ no one property must exceed 40% of the total value of the portfolio;

❖ it must distribute 90% of profits to shareholders;

❖ it must not hold owner-occupied property;

❖ profits from the tax exempt business must be at least 75% of total profits; and

❖ the value of all assets of the tax exempt business must be at least 75% of total assets held by the REIT.

What are the tax implications?

REITs are tax exempt for both property rental income and for chargeable gains on disposals. However, they will be taxed on other income such as that accrued from property trading and other gains. Tax exemptions also apply to subsidiaries of REITs holding property investments.

When converting to a REIT, a tax charge is payable equivalent to 2% of the market value of the property assets held. This conversion charge can be paid in four instalments: 0.5%, 0.53%, 0.56% and then 0.6% respectively are payable at yearly intervals.

Benefits for investors

From 2007, for the first time, UK investors will be able to diversify their portfolios into a sector that has proved its ability to produce high returns for a small initial stake.

For investors, UK REITs will provide:

❖ a highly liquid method of investing in property;

❖ asset class diversification;

❖ new investment opportunities for major players and small investors alike, many of whom previously could not easily have included property in their share portfolios; and

❖ the ability to invest in a wide range of property types.

When buying shares in REITS, investors do not only take a stake in the ownership of property via increases and decreases in value, but will also benefit from any income generated by the property.

Further information

www.hm-treasury.gov.uk

www.hmrc.gov.uk

Property derivatives and options

Derivatives

A derivative is, in very simple terms, a sale or purchase of a promise. A party will agree to buy from another a promise that at an agreed point in the future (usually one month, six months, a year or five years from the agreement date) the purchaser will buy from the seller an agreed quantity of some asset the buyer wants for a price which is agreed at the time the promise is made.

For the buyer a deal of uncertainty is taken out of the transaction. For example, a major user of electrical power, may want to purchase a derivative for the unit price of electricity. To operate their business they need certainty and are currently exposed to the risk of electricity unit price fluctuations. They are therefore happy to purchase promises that for the next five years they will not have to pay more than a pre-agreed range for electrical units. If the price of the units goes above the defined range then the seller pays the difference to the purchaser; if the price dips below the defined range the user pays the price difference to the seller. There are, as you can imagine various different combinations and complexities of promises but basically there are three different types of general derivatives:

❖ the sale of a promise to deliver an asset in the future – a forward contract;

❖ the sale of a promise either to deliver a quantity of an asset or to pay its market value in the future – a futures contract; and

❖ the sale of a promise to pay the market value of an asset in future – a contract for differences.

However, the property derivatives market in the UK to date has been dominated by two basic instruments:

❖ property total return swaps; and

❖ property structured notes or property index certificates.

A question often asked against this background is: 'Will derivatives make the prices more volatile?' The economics of the arrangements are very detailed but economists have generally concluded that trading in derivatives actually helps to decrease the extremes of market price changes rather than to increase them.

Another attraction is that trading derivatives is arguably more liquid than trading the actual asset, particularly if trading in that asset is likely to be slow. This is exactly what has happened with property. Property was the last major asset investment class without a liquid derivatives market. So in many ways a property derivatives market would seem to be more essential than a similar market in another asset class which is inherently more liquid in its pure form.

Background

Many will be surprised to hear that property derivatives date back to the early 1990s. This initial launch was poorly timed. Property Index Certificates were developed in 1994 but they were not popular and were relaunched in 2004. Property derivatives did not go away but now the climate is more favourable and after a slow start they are here to stay. There are three reasons why the time is now right for property derivatives:

❖ high demand from buyers and sellers at this stage in a property cycle;

❖ clarification of recent tax allowances and treatments; and

❖ a change in regulation that allows insurance companies to use derivatives for capital relief.

One of the reasons that property derivatives have not been successful in the past is that unlike trading some other commodities all properties are different and the market can be slow moving. For the first time now, with a property derivative it is possible to profit by 'betting' on a falling market.

How it all works

A prerequisite to a derivatives market is an independent index correlated to changes of value in the asset class. The United Kingdom has the investment property databank UK property index to fulfil this role and is regarded as a benchmark.

Using the most common swap contract (total return) a buyer of an exposure to property pays what is known as Libor, or London Interbank

Offer Rate, used when one bank borrows from another, plus a spread in return for the total annual return (capital and income) on the Investment Property Databank (IPD) All Property Index (other indices are All Retail, All Office and All Industrial). An alternative is to trade individual sector performance against the All Property Index.

Advantages of property derivatives

The advantages of this investment medium are obvious. Property derivatives allow parties to show a view on a market position without having to trade the base asset. Investors can sell (short) a position without having to actually buy it first and go long (buy) an asset or exposure to it without a cash investment. They dramatically reduce the transaction time and the time taken to form a view on the market by allowing a party to sell or buy immediate exposure to the main property return indices. They also crucially avoid the transaction costs associated with actual property transfers such as Stamp Duty Land Tax (SDLT) and conveyancing costs. Traditionally costs for physical transactions can be 5.75%, whereas for derivatives they are likely to be just 0.5%.

The future and any trends

The trade press have reported that initial take up and overall interest has been quite low. The IPD revealed that as at end of June 2006 the total property derivatives market was almost £2 billion. The commercial sector has taken off and although initially most of the trades were swaps on the All Property level there is now an increase of sector and even subsector trading.

Options

Real property options are opportunities and prior commitments to acquire, develop, refurbish or dispose of property linked real assets at an investment cost determined in the present time with the benefits delivered in the future.

There must be an underlying asset or value in the first place.

Real property call options are chances for the owner or holder of the option to benefit from the upside while only suffering the cost of the premium as the downside.

Put options are the reverse, in other words, chances for the holder to benefit from any down side such as a depressed sale value or depreciation.

Due diligence

Property investment and ownership

Due diligence and the building survey

The term 'due diligence' fell into common use following the US *Securities Act* of 1933. So long as broker dealers conducted a due diligence investigation into a company whose equity they were selling, and disclosed what they found to the investor, they would not be held liable for non-disclosure of information that failed to be uncovered in the process of that investigation.

The building survey is just one part of the process of property acquisition; its significance should not be underestimated. While it may be true to say that the decision to purchase or occupy is often governed more by commercial pressures than by faults in the building, the due diligence process is designed to alert the purchaser to issues that will affect the building as an investment and/or as an asset – to manage the risks that are inherent in property acquisition. The 'conventional' survey may therefore be expanded to encompass a wide range of issues that might, in the normal course of events, be disregarded.

There is no hard and fast rule as to what should be included in the process and what should not; the particular nature of a deal or building will dictate particular investigations. However, the following issues may be relevant:

Occupational considerations

- ❖ Constructional issues relating to fit out and occupation
- ❖ Suitability of space for particular use
- ❖ Ease of subdivision/subletting
- ❖ Contributions from landlord
- ❖ Efficiency of space usage
- ❖ Quality of base build information and accommodation
- ❖ Oversized/undersized
- ❖ Access
- ❖ Parking restrictions
- ❖ Security
- ❖ Service charge levels – past history
- ❖ Workplace Regulations (fire, lighting, glazing, sanitary provision, protection against falling)
- ❖ Disability Discrimination Act
- ❖ Occupancy cost review.

Repairs and defects

- ❖ Patent defects
- ❖ Potential latent defects
- ❖ Compliance with statute
- ❖ Schedules of Condition (and effects thereof)
- ❖ Onerous maintenance issues
- ❖ Deleterious materials
- ❖ Quality of finishes/construction
- ❖ Unusual construction techniques.

Environmental considerations

- ❖ Risk of contamination
- ❖ Previous site use
- ❖ Remediation
- ❖ Power lines
- ❖ Japanese Knotweed
- ❖ Flooding
- ❖ Radon
- ❖ Coast erosion
- ❖ Mining
- ❖ Security
- ❖ Energy consumption/performance.

Legal issues

- ❖ Boundaries
- ❖ Services crossing boundaries
- ❖ Party wall issues
- ❖ Rights to light
- ❖ Restrictive covenants
- ❖ Planning
- ❖ Means of escape over adjoining land
- ❖ Adjoining uses
- ❖ Warranty package
- ❖ Building contract issues
- ❖ Defects liability
- ❖ Title
- ❖ Repairing obligations
- ❖ Lease break provisions
- ❖ Reinstatement obligations
- ❖ Dilapidations liability
- ❖ Fire certification.

Due diligence team members

- ❖ Building surveyor
- ❖ Services engineer
- ❖ Environmental engineer
- ❖ Agent
- ❖ Managing agent
- ❖ Solicitor
- ❖ Planner
- ❖ Space planner
- ❖ Structural engineer
- ❖ Cladding specialist

❖ Project manager
❖ IT consultant
❖ Cost consultant.

Vendor surveys

The traditional approach to selling investment grade property is to release details to the market, consider offers and reach heads of terms which are often subject to survey and legal enquiries. This due diligence process may give the prospective purchaser cause to renegotiate terms with a risk to the vendor in terms of cost and time. If matters proceed smoothly, exchange of contracts and completion can then take place.

The process is time consuming and fraught with risk. To streamline the procedure and manage risks, vendors are increasingly procuring full survey reports prior to sale – the government's 'Home Information Pack' for the residential market is a similar concept albeit the requirement for a Home Condition Report has now been dropped. A vendor survey can be defined as a building and other surveys commissioned by a vendor but primarily for the benefit of a purchaser.

Normally, the vendor's sale pack will include the normal building survey, a phase 1 environmental report or land quality statement, test reports on deleterious materials (where relevant) and probably a report on the building's services installations. For housing transactions, the proposed seller's pack will include:

❖ terms of sale;
❖ evidence of title;
❖ standard searches;
❖ planning and building control certificates;
❖ seller's information form;
❖ warranties; and
❖ Energy Performance Certificate.

Whereas a conventional report may often make recommendations for further investigation, a vendor survey must not invite further questions. Thus, it is very important to either make a judgement and express an opinion based upon the evidence, or commission additional tests and inspections where it is relevant to do so. Similarly, questions that would normally be referred to the legal team should be addressed in advance of the production of the final report. In other words, every effort must be made to 'close' particular issues or observations.

Traditionally, building and other surveys include a number of limitations. The third party clause (where the report can only be relied upon by the client) clearly needs variation with vendor surveys. There is always some scope for discussion, but the usual basis is that the client (or vendor) can rely upon vendor survey reports as well as the first purchaser. A duty is often extended to the first purchaser's bankers. Furthermore, there should be no change of use, as this may have impacts on the building that the surveyor cannot foresee. The purchaser must also accept that the building's condition may have changed since the date of the report. Assignment of the report to the first purchaser is traditionally done by exchange of letters but can also be executed as a deed.

An advantage of a vendor survey is making information on the condition of the property available to the vendor, which is essential for good asset management. Such surveys also take technical due diligence off the critical path, because they are prepared before the property is marketed. Heads of terms can be entered into without being subject to survey. This approach may also give less scope to prospective purchasers who are not sincere in proceeding on the basis of their original offer.

Identifying the age of buildings

This guide cannot pretend to be a comprehensive dissertation on the architectural and construction history of Britain. It is a concise yet wide-ranging guide to clues and explains what to look for when seeking to assess the age of a building. Always remember that, almost without exception, any building, unless of very recent construction, will, at some time in its life, have undergone some form of change, modernisation or conversion that may well hide the age of the original construction.

If you have the time and opportunity, always seek to consult such archival sources as are immediately available. Even if the building is not a historic building, some records of the original date of construction will exist somewhere in the files of the local administration.

If the building is listed as being of Special Architectural or Historic Interest or a Scheduled Ancient Monument, the listing description or entry in the Scheduled Monuments Register will provide some indication of the believed age of the building or monument. A word of caution here is that these believed ages are based in most cases on external inspections only and even the most experienced inspectors of historic buildings and ancient monuments have been known to have been deceived. The problem usually takes the form of putting a more recent age on the structure based on external elevations that are the result of, say, a late Victorian refronting of a Georgian Building, or an early 18th century brick refronting of a Tudor or earlier timber framed building. This last is often referred to as a Queen Anne front on a Mary Anne back, therefore, always ensure that you look at the back of the property as well as the front.

Where to go to find records

Every county in Britain has a County Archivist and contact can be established through the local authority of the area in which the building is situated. Alternatively contact can be made via the relevant heritage authority – English Heritage, Scottish Heritage, Welsh Heritage [Cadw] or the Northern Ireland Heritage Department of The Department of Environment of Northern Ireland. Alternatively the Local Authority Conservation Officer will be able to put you in touch and indeed the relevant conservation or heritage authority or office could be a useful source in their own right.

Archives, be they county or district or more local, down to even parish level, will include one or more sets of the following which may assist:

❖ maps, especially tithe maps, showing down to considerable detail ownerships and the building in outline on each site or plot;

❖ sale documents, especially auction details that themselves give indications of believed age(s) of the building;

❖ newspaper and other articles indicating the believed age(s) of the building;

❖ deeds registers, which can be particularly useful in establishing exact dates for the original building lease from the lord of the manor or landed estate owner, granting the right to the construction of the building being considered;

❖ local authority building bylaw and drainage permissions or approvals to the construction of the building and subsequent alterations. This last one usually only reaches back to the mid-19th century but the equivalent landed estate or manorial records can reach back much further. If the building is still held in freehold or equivalent by the landed estate or manorial estate then such records may still be held by them. However, some such estate records have been transferred to the county or district archives; and

❖ the National Monuments Records Office in Swindon via their website at www.english-heritage.org.uk will link you into 'Online Resources' and the United Kingdom strand of the A2A Archives database currently at www.a2a.org.uk but ultimately to change to www.nationalarchives.gov.uk/a2a which links into 390 record offices. CADW-Welsh Heritage has 'Coflein' on www.rcahmw.org.uk/coflein/shtml. For Scotland try www.rcahmsgov.uk/history/html. For Northern Ireland try www.ehsni.gov.uk.

Published and unpublished archival research

The Victoria County Histories, which should be available in the county or district central reference library may contain a reference to your building.

London has the Survey of London volumes now produced by the Survey of London branch of English Heritage. Those started in the late 19th century only cover a part of the historic areas of London and are available in principal reference libraries and gradually online at www.british-history.ac.uk then link to 'Survey of London'.

Other public and private publications may exist for your particular building. The Dr Nikolaus Pevsner 'Buildings of England/Britain' series may assist.

Local history librarians are a mine of information in such a search. They and the county or district archivists may also be able to assist in pointing you towards unpublished works either held by them or produced by local historians.

Research in specialist public archives can also be extremely positive in producing plans and documentation. For any building that is or has been in government or Crown ownership, the Public Record Office at Kew can be invaluable, with large parts of their catalogues available online.

See www.nationalarchives.gov.uk and enquiry@nationalarchives.gov.uk

For a building by an important architect the V&A/RIBA Drawings Collection at the Victoria and Albert Museum can produce drawings back to the 17th century.

For London, the Metropolitan Archives (T: 020 7332 3820) hold papers dating back to the 16th century.

For any building that has at any point in its life been in the direct ownership of (or occupation by) the Monarchy, the Royal Archives at Windsor Castle can produce vital details unobtainable elsewhere.

The building

Once you have understood the types and forms and materials of construction used in particular periods, as you inspect or survey a building the less altered areas of the building can be very revealing. This is particularly true of roof spaces, basements, rear elevations, back or rear additions or anywhere else that has escaped the 'improver of antiquity' i.e. the previous owner(s) who modernised the property. As you crawl around the building look out for such unaltered places.

Above ground archaeology is the increasingly common term for such on-the-property investigations.

Development monitoring

The need for development monitoring

Development monitors are appointed to oversee a third party's interest in a development. Development monitoring involves identifying, advising on and monitoring construction related risks, which are not under the client's direct control. There is a need for the monitor to actively protect the client's interest during the lifetime of the development. This is particularly important where the client takes a more risk-averse approach to the project than the developer.

A key element of the role is that advice is provided to the client from a party that is independent and not associated with the development or the development team.

The need for development monitoring is diverse and each instruction will reflect the requirements of the client and their relationship to a particular development. Development monitoring is typically undertaken on behalf of investment funds, banks and future occupiers, as summarised in the following table.

Development monitors are also commonly referred to as project monitors, fund surveyors and construction monitors.

Typical clients

Type of organisation	Examples of organisation	Interest in development
Fund	Property investment fund, pension fund, private equity fund, joint venture partner	Will purchase the scheme as an investment on completion, or will acquire the land and fund the development during construction as an investment
Funder/lender	Clearing banks, investment banks	Will earn interest on a loan for the land purchase and/or the building during construction, as well as a pre-agreed arrangement fee and possibly an exit fee
Prospective occupier	Various tenants	Will acquire a leasehold interest in the completed development, which may include full repairing and insuring obligations

The monitoring service

The development monitoring service will depend on the nature of the client's interest in the development and the risks associated with this interest. Therefore, there is no standard service. The client and the monitor must work closely together to ensure the monitor's brief fully meets the specific project requirements.

Where a funder is providing debt finance, the principal focus is likely to relate to the value of the works undertaken and the completion of the works within the agreed budget. Progress of the works during construction will also be an important aspect to monitor. However, where the loan is secured against the property, it is prudent for the funder to ensure that the quality of the works is also considered.

In situations where the client has, or has agreed to, purchase the development, a quality focus is more prevalent. The client will want to ensure that the completed development is of a quality suitable as an investment asset. Where the fund is financing the works, it is common for development and purchase agreements between funds and developers to include maximum cost limits for the fund, or developer profit erosion provisions, which protect the fund from cost overruns.

Progress of the works may be critical if there is an agreement for lease with a future tenant, or tenants. In this instance, close monitoring of the likelihood of achieving the access date(s) for the tenant's fit out works will be required. This can be undertaken on behalf of the fund, funder or future occupier.

In general terms the monitor will comment on the cost, programme and quality of the proposed development, from the initial concept to full design, and throughout the construction period, and into the defects liability period.

The key skills and competencies that should be sought in a development monitor are:

- Diverse technical knowledge of construction
- Thorough understanding of the client's interest in the development, including the development/purchase/finance agreement and the conditions precedent
- Project management and procurement expertise
- Cost management knowledge
- Risk awareness
- Independence from the development team
- Reporting and appraisal skills
- Proactive and a good communicator.

Development monitoring is usually carried out in four stages. Each stage is listed below and is discussed in the following sections.

- Appraisal and risk assessment
- Construction and finance monitoring during the works
- Advice at practical completion and at end of the defects liability period.

Appraisal and risk assessment

The development monitor will request and then review a wide range of information on the proposed development, including the programme, construction cost, design quality, future maintenance requirements, procurement route, selection of consultants and contractors, building contract, provision of warranties, insurances, statutory requirements, neighbourly matters, and land contamination issues. This review is summarised in an appraisal report, which will highlight any potential risks associated with the project.

The focus of the appraisal will reflect the needs of the client and its interest in the particular development. This should be defined in the legal documentation, such as the development/purchase/finance agreement or the agreement for lease. Where possible it is advantageous for the development monitor to provide technical advice to the client on the construction related matters at the pre-agreement stage. Such advice would relate to any potential significant risks associated with undertaking the development that may have an adverse effect on value.

Construction and finance monitoring

Following the appraisal stage and agreement to proceed with the development, monitoring is undertaken during the construction works. This involves periodic site inspections and attendance at site progress meetings, typically on a monthly basis. A formal report will be prepared that comments on a variety of construction issues, including:

❖ construction costs, cash flow and expenditure against budget;

❖ progress of the works against programme;

❖ quality of workmanship on site;

❖ development of the design;

❖ status of any statutory approvals;

❖ status of appointment documents and warranties; and

❖ status of insurances.

The monitor may also be required to monitor expenditure of all development costs against the agreed budget. This can include expenditure such as legal fees, marketing costs and professional fees.

Practical completion and the end of the defects liability period

The role of the development monitor at practical completion and at the end of the defects liability period is usually set out in the development/purchase/finance agreement or in the agreement for lease. A robust role may be specified involving inspection of the completed development and advising the client on whether they should accept the development as complete, or that the end of the defects liability period has been achieved.

Practical completion is particularly critical where a prospective tenant is in place, as practical completion is likely to trigger rent commencement. Furthermore, practical completion is likely to result in payment for the building to the developer (projects which are not interim funded), or payment of the developer's profit.

The monitor can help to ensure that all the necessary handover documentation is in place, such as the health and safety file, as built drawings, the operation and maintenance manuals and warranties.

Housing and residential property

Property investment and ownership

Residential surveys

Readers are urged to follow the advice of the RICS guidance note *Building Surveys of Residential Property* (2nd edition), 2006, which covers taking and giving instructions, preparing for the survey, the inspection, and the report. 'Example Terms and Conditions of Engagement' are also included.

Suggested pre-survey checklist for surveyors:

Confirm instructions

- ❖ nature of the instructions
- ❖ date and time of the survey
- ❖ access arrangements, particularly occupied premises
- ❖ statement of surveyor's intentions
- ❖ limitations.

Bear in mind

- ❖ *Unfair Contract Terms Act* 1977
- ❖ liability in negligence and contract
- ❖ 'requirements of reasonableness'.

Equipment to take – consider the following

- ❖ powerful, robust torch
- ❖ claw hammer and bolster
- ❖ ladder (minimum 3 metres long)
- ❖ pocket probe
- ❖ binoculars or telescope (not more than x8)
- ❖ hand mirror (minimum 100mm x 100mm)
- ❖ moisture meter
- ❖ screwdrivers – assorted
- ❖ measuring rods or tapes, notebook and writing equipment
- ❖ plumbline
- ❖ spirit level
- ❖ first aid kit
- ❖ protective clothing, hard hat and suitable footwear.

Site notes to be recorded

- ❖ notes of defects
- ❖ record of weather, persons present, etc.
- ❖ answers to queries of vendor/neighbours, etc.

Suggested outline of report

Introduction

- ❖ brief
- ❖ limitations
- ❖ general description of property and situation
- ❖ present accommodation.

Structural condition and state of repair

External

- ❖ roofs
- ❖ other defects at roof level
- ❖ eaves
- ❖ flashings
- ❖ external walls
- ❖ likelihood of cavity wall tie failure
- ❖ airbricks (provision and adequacy)
- ❖ damp-proof course
- ❖ foundations and settlement/subsidence/heave
- ❖ rainwater goods
- ❖ soil/waste stacks, gullies
- ❖ other external comments
- ❖ external decorations.

Internal

- ❖ roof spaces
- ❖ partitions
- ❖ plasterwork
- ❖ windows
- ❖ doors
- ❖ joinery
- ❖ ceilings
- ❖ other internal defects
- ❖ internal decorations.

Services

- ❖ plumbing/wiring
- ❖ heating
- ❖ electricity/gas
- ❖ sanitary fittings
- ❖ drainage.

Outside

- ❖ boundaries, pavings, fences, gates and outbuildings
- ❖ noise, contamination and other environmental factors
- ❖ adjoining properties
- ❖ garden/trees – risk of ground movements/mining subsidence
- ❖ garage/car parking
- ❖ probability of flooding.

General

- ❖ compliance with statutory regulations
- ❖ planning situation

- ❖ energy consumption
- ❖ any responsibilities under a lease
- ❖ limitations of report
- ❖ any appropriate approximate costings
- ❖ presence/condition of toxic materials, for example, asbestos
- ❖ general condition and conclusion
- ❖ risk and likelihood of fungal decay, insect infestation or conditions that could give rise to these attacks
- ❖ risk of contaminated land
- ❖ risk of Radon emissions, power lines, etc.
- ❖ any other relevant information.

Golden rules

When drafting the report, endeavour to avoid technical jargon and take care to communicate precisely.

Avoid assumptions and ill-thought out statements.

When describing elements answer the following questions:

1. What is it?
2. What is wrong with it?
3. What will need to be done to put it right?
4. What are the consequences of not putting it right?

Health and safety

When surveying a property – especially one that is empty – practitioners ought to conform to the procedures outlined in 'Practical Procedures' under the 'Health and safety at work' section of this handbook.

See also page 94 and *Surveying Safely* published by the Royal Institution of Chartered Surveyors.

Home Information Packs

The introduction of Home Information Packs (HIPs) as a requirement for buying and selling homes in England and Wales will apply from 1 June 2007. The primary legislation was originally detailed in the *Housing Act 2004*.

Content

The contents of the Home Information Pack are likely to include:

- ❖ terms of sale;
- ❖ evidence of title;
- ❖ replies to standard preliminary enquiries;
- ❖ copies of planning and building regulation consents;
- ❖ copies of warranties, guarantees for work carried out to the property;
- ❖ replies to local searches;
- ❖ an Energy Performance Certificate (EPC);

and, additionally, for leasehold property:

❖ a copy of the lease, recent service charge accounts;

❖ buildings insurance policy details; and

❖ any regulations, memorandum and articles of the landlord or management company may be required.

What is an Energy Performance Certificate (EPC)?

The certificates will give homebuyers and sellers A to G ratings for their home's energy efficiency and carbon emissions. They will tell them current average costs for heating, hot water and lighting in their home, as well as how to cut costs with energy efficiency measures.

Part of the energy performance review will advise consumers on which energy measures – ranging from thicker loft insulation right through to solar panels – could cut carbon emissions from their home and improve their energy rating.

The government have stated that the introduction is due to 'the growing challenge from climate change and rising energy costs ... to improve energy efficiency ... and to help sellers and buyers to cut carbon emissions and fuel bills'. Also, the European Energy Directive requires that from 2009 all homes for sale should have energy certificates.

Recent changes to HIPs

On 18 July 2006, the government announced that a major component of the HIP, namely the Home Condition Report (HCR), would not be mandatory, only voluntary. It was felt by many experienced commentators that the main thrust of HIPs, to speed up the buying process, would not be helped by HCRs. It had been commonly accepted that there might not have been enough trained inspectors by the introduction date of 1 June 2007 and that this was also a reason why HCRs became voluntary. The government have indicated that HCRs will only become mandatory if the voluntary take-up is a success.

Why HIPs?

The aim of HIPs is to remove uncertainty in the house buying and selling process and, in theory, reduce the transaction time. Despite the withdrawal of HCRs, opportunities for gazundering should still be reduced but perhaps less so. Currently, information required by buyers and sellers appears some time after an offer has been made and accepted, increasing the potential for abortive expenditure on surveys, legal fees, searches, etc.

How will HIPs work?

The legislation will require home owners or their selling agents to have an HIP prepared before putting a home on the market and to make a copy of that pack available to prospective buyers on request.

What will it cost?

No firm estimates have been made for the cost of the new HIP. Costs are likely to be lower than the £600–£900 estimated with the HCR and will be determined by the market.

Who will carry out the work?

A stand-alone qualification for Energy Assessors is being developed. It is felt by RICS that the EPCs can be completed by chartered surveyors, with limited further training. RICS also believes that there will be a limited future for the Home Inspector qualification and that Home Inspectors should seek technical membership of RICS.

Penalties

If an HIP is not provided, it is anticipated that the enforcement regime will be based on civil sanctions.

Trading Standards Officers would be given discretion to determine appropriate action in each case – whether to provide information and assistance, issue a warning or a civil fixed penalty notice (initially envisaged by the then ODPM to be around £200). Trading Standards Officers would also be able to notify the Office of Fair Trading (OFT) of any breach by persons acting as estate agents, which could also trigger action by the OFT under the *Estate Agents Act* 1979. Trading Standards Officers would have a duty to do this where a fixed penalty notice had been issued. In addition, a person who breached the HIP obligations would be liable to be sued by prospective buyers for recovery of the costs of obtaining documents which should have been provided in the pack.

Further information

Department for Communities and Local Government (DCLG): www.communities.gov.uk

Royal Institution of Chartered Surveyors (RICS): www.rics.org

Home Information Pack website: www.homeinformationpacks.gov.uk/home.aspx

Housing Health and Safety Rating System

The Housing Health and Safety Rating System (HHSRS) replaced the former Housing Fitness Regime in England and Wales in 2006. HHSRS, which has been introduced under the *Housing Act* 2004, has also superseded the Fitness Standard as an element of the Decent Homes Standard. Surveyors and other construction professionals, particularly those working in the social housing sector, should be aware of these changes and understand the basic principles of the new system.

The Department for Communities and Local Government (DCLG) states that '… the government's aim is that this reform will enable local authorities to address more effectively the hazards to health and safety present in the home'. The regulations are designed to ensure that any residential premises and their environs provide a safe and healthy environment for occupiers and their visitors. The HHSRS works by assessing the risk associated with particular hazards that may be encountered in the home. If there is a significant chance that they could cause harm, a local authority may take action to ensure that the risk is removed or reduced.

Unlike the former Fitness Standard, the HHSRS assessment is not designed to set a standard but to provide objective information which will determine and inform enforcement decisions made by local authorities. The new assessment sets out 29 categories of housing hazard, including factors not covered (or considered to be covered inadequately) by the former Housing Fitness Standard.

A rating is given for each hazard, rather than for the dwelling as a whole or, in the case of dwellings in multiple occupation, for the building as a whole. Hazard ratings use a numerical score which falls within one of ten bands. Scores in Bands A to C are Category 1 hazards. Scores in Bands D to J are Category 2 hazards.

Under the new system, the hazards given priority are:

- ❖ excess cold, damp and mould growth;
- ❖ fire and electrical hazards;

- ❖ carbon monoxide and fuel combustion products;
- ❖ crowding and space;
- ❖ entry by intruders;
- ❖ noise;
- ❖ domestic hygiene, pests and refuse;
- ❖ food safety;
- ❖ personal hygiene, sanitation and drainage;
- ❖ water supply for domestic purposes;
- ❖ structural collapse and falling elements;
- ❖ collision and entrapment; and
- ❖ falls associated with baths, stairs and steps, between levels and on the level.

According to DCLG guidance, 'the HHSRS assessment is based on the risk to the potential occupant who is most vulnerable to that hazard'. For example, when rating stairs, these 'constitute a greater risk to the elderly, so for assessing hazards relating to stairs they are considered the most vulnerable'. A dwelling that is safe for those most vulnerable to a hazard is safe for all, says the DCLG.

Any action taken by the local authority as a result of an HHSRS assessment will be based on a three-stage test:

- ❖ the hazard rating given;
- ❖ whether the authority has a duty or power to act; and
- ❖ that authority's judgement as to the most appropriate course of action to be taken.

New enforcement options are now available to local authorities, taking into account the statutory enforcement guidance.

Authorities can:

- ❖ serve an improvement notice requiring remedial works;
- ❖ make a prohibition order, which closes the whole or part of a dwelling or restricts the number of permitted occupants;
- ❖ suspend these types of notice;
- ❖ take emergency action;
- ❖ serve a hazard awareness notice;
- ❖ make a demolition order*; and
- ❖ declare a clearance area*.

(* not available for Category 2 hazards)

More information can be obtained from www.communities.gov.uk/hhsrs

Contracts and procurement

Development and procurement

Public procurement, Public Private Partnerships and the Private Finance Initiative

Public Private Partnerships (PPP) are, broadly speaking, contractual arrangements where the public and private sectors work together to deliver a project or service. This can include many types of arrangement such as transfer of public undertakings to the private sector and private sector investment in public services.

The Private Finance Initiative (PFI) is a type of PPP where the private sector provides an asset-based service under contract to the public sector. The key features of PFI are that there is an underlying asset, often a building or a series of buildings, and that private finance is used to provide the facility and service. In return, the private sector receives a regular payment from the public sector over the life of the concession, typically 25 – 30 years. PFI is one of HM Treasury's preferred forms of procurement.

This chapter describes some of the key features and mechanisms of PFI and public procurement. Due to the complexity of this field, together with differences in interpretation and practice between contracting authorities, it should be regarded as a guide only and specific advice sought in appropriate cases.

Features of PFI/PPP

- ❖ The private sector contracts not only for the provision of the building or other asset, but for maintenance and services over the life of the concession. This encourages the integration of construction and services provision and investment decisions based on whole life cost, rather than capital cost only.

- ❖ The public sector requirements are expressed as outputs (requirements to be met) rather than inputs (standards to be achieved). This allows the private sector to meet requirements by the most cost effective route and encourages innovation.

- ❖ The private sector is incentivised to deliver the services by a penalty structure which reduces or suspends the regular payment (called the Unitary Payment). Payment reductions may arise from parts of the asset no longer being available (unavailability) or performance failures (e.g. failure to rectify a defect within a prescribed period of time).

- ❖ The public sector remains responsible for the core public service (teaching, healthcare, administration, etc.).

- ❖ The PFI is funded entirely by the private sector in return for the Unitary Payment. In some cases, the public sector may offer long stop guarantees to improve Value for Money (see below).

- ❖ The design, construction, operating and maintenance risks are largely transferred to the private sector. For example, if the project costs more or takes longer than agreed at the outset, the private sector is responsible for the overrun. The assessment, allocation and management of risks is one of the key disciplines in PFI/PPP.

- ❖ The transfer of risk enables public sector authorities to benefit from accounting treatment of the Unitary Payment as revenue expenditure, which does not count against their capital allocations.

❖   The PFI proposal must demonstrate Value for Money (VfM), meaning broadly that PFI has to offer a more cost effective solution to requirements than conventional public procurement. This comparison is made via the construction of a Public Sector Comparator (PSC) financial model for the public sector alternative. A 'shadow bid' is often compiled by the public sector to test the overall value at bid stage.

Key advantages and disadvantages

Advantages

❖   Public service improvements are brought forward by using private capital to offset the shortage of public capital.

❖   Development and operational risk is transferred to the private sector, freeing the public sector to concentrate on the core service.

❖   The private sector is incentivised to provide good quality buildings and services and VfM.

Disadvantages

❖   The cost of private finance is greater than that of public capital, meaning that the PFI must achieve efficiency improvements to offset this.

❖   Major changes in public sector requirements during the concession period may be difficult or expensive to accommodate within PFI.

Projects and clients

The largest single category by value is transport, due in part to the inclusion of the London Underground modernisation programme. Other major sectors include health, education and defence.

Types of projects using PFI include headquarters offices, office roll-out programmes, environmental and waste recycling, transport (road, rail and light railway), education, healthcare, prisons, courts, defence, housing and regional projects. Public sector clients include government departments, local authorities, NHS Trusts and government agencies such as the Inland Revenue.

Because of the long-term nature of the transaction and the cost of the tendering process, PFI is rarely used for projects with a value of less than £20 million. A feature of more recent PFI transactions is the grouping of smaller projects into a single PFI to achieve the appropriate minimum size.

The PFI procurement model has also been adopted by some large private or semi-private clients for their building and facilities provision. This is known as 'corporate', or 'private' PFI.

Project inception

The first formal step in the PFI process is the production of an Outline Business Case by or on behalf of the public sector client. This sets out the project brief and business case for the proposal, and forms the basis for applications for PFI credits from central government where applicable. It is followed up with the output specification which sets out the requirements for the project in performance terms, and in due course this forms a key part of the tender documentation.

A key feature of the output specification is that it is expressed in terms of required outputs, rather than prescribed inputs. Within any constraints set by the public sector, the private sector is free to meet these requirements by means of its own choosing. Sometimes these depart significantly from those envisaged by the client at the outset.

Transaction structure

The parties to a PFI transaction typically comprise the following:

❖ Public sector client: The government department, local authority or other public sector authority contracting for the project.

❖ Private sector partner: Usually a consortium comprising a contractor or developer, a facilities manager or operator, and a bank or other financial institution.

❖ Funders: In addition to the consortium partners, external organisations will normally be involved in the provision of funding. These can include banks or other financial institutions, bond issuers, rating agencies and insurers.

A number of companies with an interest in the PFI market have formed specialist subsidiaries or consortia to participate in contracting, funding or operation, particularly in the field of health care.

The above parties to the PFI will normally be advised separately and a typical consultant team would include a financial adviser, legal adviser and one or more technical advisers.

The organisational structure of a typical PFI transaction is shown in Table 1 on page 35.

Procurement

Public procurement is subject to EU rules which are intended to promote fair competition across the EU and a transparent procurement process. Some differences in practice will nonetheless be encountered between contracting authorities and member states.

For public works and services above certain cost thresholds, a notice must be placed by the public sector contracting authority in the Supplement to the Official Journal of the European Communities (OJ). Most PFI transactions will exceed the cost thresholds. The cost thresholds are reviewed every two years and those applying from 31 January 2006 are shown in Table 2 on page 36.

The Supplement to the OJ is published daily in electronic form and may be viewed on the internet (see useful information sources page 335). Tender information services are available on subscription, and a selection of OJ notices are published from time to time in the construction press.

Tendering procedures

There are three types of tender procedure:

❖ **Restricted**

Expressions of interest are invited and the most suitably qualified are invited to submit a tender.

❖ **Open**

A notice is published and anyone can submit a tender.

❖ **Negotiated**

The contract is negotiated with at least three tenderers, or with the maximum number available. Use of this procedure is subject to justification.

The choice of tendering procedure is made by the contracting authority having regard to the nature of the works or services, and the circumstances under which they are to be delivered. For example, the nature of the service may mean that a specification cannot be drawn up with sufficient precision to allow the use of the Open or Restricted procedure.

An accelerated procedure can be used where justified in conjunction with the Open or Restricted procedure.

Types of notice

Prior Information Notice (PIN): optional notice of intent to invite tenders or expressions of interest later. When placed in accordance with the mandatory timescales, it allows the period for submission of tenders or expressions of interest to be reduced. (The mandatory timescales for the tender process are shown in Table 3 on page 36.)

Contract Notice: main notice providing full information and informing parties how to bid or pre-qualify for the project.

Content of notices

Notices are in a form prescribed by the EU and group information into the following sections:

I. Contracting authority
II. Object of the contract
III. Legal, economic, financial and technical information
IV. Procedure
V. [Spare number]
VI. Other information.

Within these sections, certain information is mandatory. However notices contain more than the minimum information, to encourage a good quality and level of response from bidders.

Certain conventions are used in notices, including CPV (Common Procurement Vocabulary) and NUTS (Territorial Designation). For an explanation of these and other conventions, refer to the SIMAP website: www.simap.eu.int.

The official forms for placing of notices in the OJ can be downloaded from the SIMAP website.

Project processes

The post tender processes can vary widely depending on the project nature and external factors. Typically an Invitation to Negotiate (ITN) will be issued to a shortlist of bidders, and this may be followed by a further bidding round (Best and Final Offer or BAFO). In order to reduce bid periods and associated costs, current practice is to encourage the provision of full information by both parties at the outset, and the use of standard contract terms as far as possible.

At the conclusion of bidding and post bid negotiations, a Preferred Bidder is selected, together with a reserve bidder. The parties then negotiate the remaining details of the project and confirm funding, legal and third party issues. During this period, development of the design and construction proposals continues, and planning permission may be sought. Once the terms are fully agreed and funding secured, contract award (or 'Financial Close') takes place, and the project can proceed.

Funding

PFI transactions are mainly debt financed, and senior debt is normally provided independently of the consortium partners. The main sources of PFI funds are:

❖ Equity – normally provided only in limited amounts by the private sector consortium partners.

❖ Subordinated or mezzanine debt – provided by consortium partners or other funding institutions.

❖ Senior debt – normally the bulk of the funding, provided by bank lending and/or via the capital markets.

The choice between bank and capital market options will depend on the nature and size of the project, and the market conditions at the time of placement. Bank debt is suitable for smaller, shorter life or higher risk projects, and the finance cost is generally higher than the capital markets option.

The capital markets option is particularly suitable for larger, lower risk projects for central government, where the covenant is perceived as strongest. This option requires the issue of an index linked or fixed rate bond which is typically taken up by other financial institutions and pension funds. Although the process of issuing a bond is more expensive than arranging bank debt, this will be recovered over the life of the bond in lower finance costs.

The bond issue is underwritten by a financial institution and may be credit rated by an agency such as Standard and Poor's to improve marketability. As an alternative, or in addition, bonds may be enhanced by private or public sector guarantees, or by the use of credit risk insurance (called monoline insurance). A bond enhanced in this way is known as a wrapped bond.

PFI transactions may be re-financed during the concession period, typically by the renegotiation of debt finance once the development period is over and the project risk profile is reduced. Some PFI contractors have also begun to sell on their equity stakes, creating a secondary transaction market.

Success factors

Some PFI transactions are more successful than others, and some success or failure criteria are subjective. While it is difficult to draw general conclusions, research has identified the six most significant value for money drivers in PFI as: the level of risk transfer; linking the output specification requirements to payment; the length of the contract needed to recoup investment; appropriate performance measures and incentives; a competitive bidding process; and excellent management skills in the private sector.

PFI – an assessment

Since it was inaugurated in 1992, PFI has enabled significant investment in public facilities and services which might not otherwise have taken place. Studies by the National Audit Office have indicated that under PFI, the proportion of projects being delivered late or over budget has fallen from roughly three quarters to a quarter, and that four-fifths of public bodies involved with PFI believe they are achieving satisfactory or better value for money from PFI contracts.

There has been criticism of some early grouped PFI projects on grounds of poor design quality, which has led to a series of design quality initiatives led by the government-sponsored Commission for Architecture and the Built Environment (CABE). Others have criticised PFI on the grounds of doubtful value for money, reduction in safety standards, and dilution of the public service ethos. As the number of PFI projects grows and the process matures, the focus is likely to move from the initial transaction to the quality of FM services and operational management over the life of the concession.

The PFI model, which originated in the UK, has been taken up in several other countries, both in Europe and beyond; and so long as there is a demand for better public services and a continuing shortage of public capital, it seems set to continue and even grow in popularity.

PFI: strengthening long-term partnerships

Published by HM Treasury in March 2006, this report confirms that the government sees PFI continuing to play an important role in the overall objective of delivering modernised public services. In percentage terms, PFI is likely to be used for between 10–15% of total investment in public services, with around 200 projects worth £26 billion in capital value anticipated over the period 2006–2011.

The report also highlights survey-based evidence that PFI is now meeting public service needs across more than 500 operational projects with the following particular conclusions:

❖ 'users are satisfied with the services provided by PFI projects, with 79% of projects reporting that service standards are delivered always or almost always;

❖ public authorities are reporting good overall performance and high levels of satisfaction against the contracted levels of service. Authorities report that the overall performance of 96% of projects is at least satisfactory, and that in 89% of projects, services are being provided in line with the contract or better;

❖ the services contracted for are appropriate with 83% of projects reporting that their contracts always or almost always accurately specify the services required, with this result getting better the more recent the contract; and

❖ the incentivisation within PFI contracts is working. While payment deductions have been low reflecting the general levels of high performance, almost all projects report satisfactory levels of service after a deduction has been applied, and 72% report good or very good performance.'

The quote above is Crown copyright and is reproduced from the report *PFI: strengthening long-term partnerships*, 2006, published by HM Treasury.

Table 1 – PFI Transaction Structure

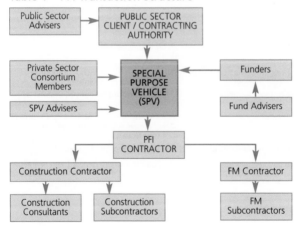

Table 2 – EU thresholds for public procurement

	Supplies and services	Works
Public Contracts Regulations		
Central government bodies	93,738[1]	3,611,319
Other public sector	144,371	3,611,319
Indicative notices	513,166	3,611,319
Small notices	54,738	684,221
Utilities Contract Regulations		
All sectors	288,741	3,611,319
Indicative notices	513,166	3,611,319
Small notices	54,738	684,221

[1] With the exception of the following services, which have a threshold of £144,371 (€211,000):
- Part B (residual) services;
- Research and Development Services (Category 8);
- The following Telecommunications services in Category 5;
     - CPC 7524 – Television and Radio Broadcast services;
     - CPC 7525 – Interconnection services;
     - CPC 7526 – Integrated telecommunications services;
- Subsidised services contracts under regulation 34.

Note: this is a summary of procurement thresholds only. Reference should be made to the current EU Regulations, which contain exceptions and additional categories.

Table 3 – EU Procurement Process

Key Timescales for Publication in OJ and Return of Tenders
(based on Restricted procedure)

Prior Information Notice (PIN)	Between 52 days and 12 months before Contract Notice.
Contract Notice	Period for expressions of interest 37 days (see Note 1).
Tenders	Period for return of tenders 40 days (26 days if PIN issued as above) (see Note 1).
Contract Award Notice	Within 48 days of award of contract.

Note 1: Accelerated procedure can be used where justified and will allow periods for expressions of interest and return of tenders to be reduced.

Table 4
Glossary of Common PFI Terms

BAFO	Best and Final Offer final stage in negotiation prior to selection of Preferred Bidder.
Contract Notice	Main notice placed in OJ Supplement to advertise a public contract.
Financial Close	Stage when all contractual and financial terms have been agreed and private sector funding is in place; formal execution of the PFI agreement.
Gateway Reviews	Project stage reviews by the public sector to review and confirm proposals and acceptability of risk profile.
ITN	Invitation to Negotiate: invitation to the private sector to provide detailed proposals leading to negotiations and a decision on the Preferred Bidder.
KPI	Key Performance Indicator: definition of performance requirement(s), failure events and penalties (deductions from the Unitary Payment).
OBC	Outline Business Case: the PFI project brief and business case, produced by or on behalf of the public sector contracting authority.
OJ	Official Journal of the European Communities (also OJEC or OJEU). The OJ Supplement carries notices of public contracts.
Output Specification	Specification of requirements for the PFI project and service, produced by or on behalf of the public sector contracting authority.
PFI	Private Finance Initiative
PIN	Prior Information Notice: a preliminary notice placed in OJ to advertise a public contract.
PPP	Public Private Partnership
Preferred Bidder	Stage in negotiation where a Preferred Bidder (and usually a reserve bidder) are selected to negotiate the detailed terms leading to Financial Close.
PSC	Public Sector Comparator: a benchmark of the cost of the PFI against the publicly financed alternative.
SPV	Special Purpose Vehicle: the company created and owned by the private sector consortium and which contracts for the PFI project.
Unavailability	Service failure against KPI availability criteria, resulting in a financial penalty to the private sector.
Unitary Payment	The regular user payment made by the public sector client to the private sector SPV.
VfM	Value For Money: the objective of best value, or meeting user requirements at the lowest whole life cost.

Procurement methods

Essentially the function of construction contracts is to assign appropriate levels of risk to those parties best able to deal with them.

Risk is an inherent element of any construction project and therefore risk management is an essential part of contract strategy.

There are currently three main procurement options used within the industry which reflect various ways by which risk is balanced between the parties.

Traditional procurement

A traditional procurement route may be defined as one where the design is largely complete before either the main contractor, sub-contractor or specialist contractors become involved. This may be appropriate for some projects if the client's objectives have been clearly and comprehensively determined. However, it does carry with it the disadvantages of increased economic uncertainty and limited opportunities to refine design and improve cost efficiency. It is also possibly more likely to lead to disputes. Increasingly, when traditional contracts are used, the contractor is selected on a two stage basis to gain some of the advantages that are available from early contractor involvement.

Design and build procurement

One alternative to traditional contracting is design and build procurement, where part or all of the design development and financial outcome responsibility risk is delegated to the constructor. There are many considerations that need to be carefully evaluated in choosing this procurement route, and opinion is divided as to whether it should be used on all types of construction projects. Most commonly this route is used in the procurement of 'spec' buildings, such as industrial units or office buildings when the control of design criteria and building techniques is not a dominant factor for the client.

Management procurement

The key feature of any management contract is that a manager is appointed with the responsibility to manage a project, not just provide advice or consultancy services. Two main derivatives of this form are management contracts and construction management.

Procurement and standard form contracts

Standard form contracts have always been a feature of the construction industry. A summary of the main standard forms relevant to commercial property development is set out below.

Professional appointments

- ❖ Architect: RIBA SFA/99 (revised 2004, new edition due February 2007).
- ❖ Engineers: ACE conditions of engagement 2002 (revised 2004). A suite of conditions to accommodate particular engineering services, including also a short form agreement and sub-consultancy agreement.
- ❖ Consultancy Agreement: BPF May 2005.
- ❖ Quantity/Building Surveyor: RICS Form with guidance notes

1999 for quantity surveying services and RICS Form with guidance notes, 2nd edition 2000 for building surveying services.

❖ Planning Supervisor: The RIBA, RICS and ACE standard form appointments make provision for planning supervisor services. It is common for the architect, quantity surveyor or engineer to also undertake the role of planning supervisor. Sometimes an independent consultant is appointed to undertake the planning supervisor role.

❖ Project Manager: RICS Project Management Memorandum of Agreement and Conditions of Engagement 3rd edition September 1999 and RIBA Form of appointment for Project Manager PM99 (revised 2004).

❖ General: The ICE Professional Services Contract, and Adjudicator's Contract 3rd edition 2005. This is part of the New Engineering Contract.

Construction contracts

1. JCT contracts

The JCT launched its new JCT 2005 suite of contracts in summer 2005. The new forms are as follows:

❖ Major Project Construction Contract (MP) and Guide (MP/G)
❖ Design and Build Contract (DB) and Guide (DB/G)
❖ Standard Building Contract (SBC); Guide (SBC/G); With Quantities (SBC/Q); With Approximate Quantities (SBC/AQ); Without Quantities (SBC/XQ)
❖ Intermediate Building Contract (IC); Guide (IC/G); Intermediate Building Contract With Contractor's Design (ICD)
❖ Minor Works Building Contract (MW); Minor Works Building Contract With Contractor's Design (MWD)
❖ Management Building Contract (MC); Management Works Contract Tender & Agreement (MCWK); Management Works Contract Conditions (MCWK/C); Management Works Contract/Employer Agreement (MCWK/E)
❖ Construction Management Appointment (CM/A); Construction Management Trade Contract (CM/TC); Construction Management Tender (CM); Construction Management Guide (CM/G); Construction Management Trade Contractor Collateral Warranty Funder (CMWA/F); Construction Management Trade Contractor Collateral Warranty for a Purchaser or Tenant (CMWA/P&T)
❖ Prime Cost Building Contract (PCC)
❖ Measured Term Contract (MTC)
❖ Housing Grant Works Building Contract (HG)
❖ Framework Agreement (FA); Framework Agreement (Non-Binding) (FA/N); Framework Agreement Guide (FA/G).

2. JCT subcontracts

There are subcontracts (generally comprising separate agreement and conditions) for each of the JCT main contracts and they should only be used with the relevant main contract. The Short Form of Sub-Contract and the Sub-Subcontract can be used with any of them. A new form of Sub-Contract for use with Minor Works Building Contract with Design is being developed but the publication date is not yet known. The new forms are as follows:

❖ Major Project Sub-Contract (MPSub) and Guide (MPSub/G)
❖ Design and Build Sub-Contract Agreement (DBSub/A); Design and Build Sub-Contract Conditions (DBSub/C); and Guide (DBSub/G)

- ❖ Standard Building Sub-Contract Agreement (SBCSub/A); Standard Building Sub-Contract Conditions (SBCSub/C); Standard Building Sub-Contract with Sub-Contractor's Design Agreement (SBCSub/D/A); Standard Building Sub-Contract with Sub-Contractor's Design Conditions (SBCSub/D/C) and Guide (SBCSub/G)
- ❖ Intermediate Sub-Contract Agreement (ICSub/A); Intermediate Sub-Contract Conditions (ICSub/C); Intermediate Sub-Contract With Sub-Contractor's Design Agreement (ICSub/D/A); Intermediate Sub-Contract With Sub-Contractor's Design Conditions (ICSub/D/C); Intermediate Named Sub-Contract Tender and Agreement (ICSub/NAM); Intermediate Named Sub-Contract Conditions (ICSub/NAM/C); Intermediate Named Sub-Contractor/Employer Agreement (ICSub/NAM/E) and Guide (ICSub/G).

JCT Generic Contracts:

- ❖ Short Form of Sub-Contract (ShortSub)
- ❖ Sub-SubContract (SubSub).

3. Collateral warranties

- ❖ Contractor Collateral Warranty for a Funder (CWa/F)
- ❖ Contractor Collateral Warranty for a Purchaser or Tenant (CWa/P&T)
- ❖ Sub-Contractor Collateral Warranty for a Funder (SCWa/F)
- ❖ Sub-Contractor Collateral Warranty for a Purchaser or Tenant (SCWa/P&T)
- ❖ Sub-Contractor Collateral Warranty for Employer (SCWa/E).

The British Property Federation also publishes warranties which include a consultant warranty.

4. The ICE New Engineering Contract

The ICE launched NEC3, the new NEC suite of contracts, in summer 2005 (republished with minor amendments in 2006). The new forms are as follows:

- ❖ NEC3: Engineering and Construction Contract
- ❖ NEC3: Option A: Priced contract with activity schedule
- ❖ NEC3: Option B: Priced contract with bill of quantities
- ❖ NEC3: Option C: Target contract with activity schedule
- ❖ NEC3: Option D: Target contract with bill of quantities
- ❖ NEC3: Option E: Cost reimbursable contract
- ❖ NEC3: Option F: Management contract
- ❖ NEC3: Engineering and Construction Contract Guidance Notes
- ❖ NEC3: The Engineering and Construction Subcontract
- ❖ NEC3: The Engineering and Construction Short Contract
- ❖ NEC3: The NEC Partnering Option
- ❖ NEC3: The Engineering and Construction Short Subcontract
- ❖ NEC3: Term Service Contract
- ❖ NEC3: Framework Contract.

5. The ACA standard form contract for Project Partnering

PPC2000 (amended 2003)

6. The ACA standard form of Specialist Contract for Project Partnership

SPC2000 – This is a specialist subcontractor version of the PPC2000 form of contract. It can be used with PPC2000 or on its own (amended 2004).

7. The Built Environment (Be) Collaborative Contract (2003).

A partnering contract with a defined 'overriding principle'. Note: JCT is working with 'Be' to produce an improved form of collaborative contract. The publication date is not yet known.

The contract administrator's role

It is a feature of most construction contracts that a person is appointed by the employer to administer the terms of the contract on the employer's behalf.

The contract administrator owes a duty of care to the employer. Under the terms of the contract he or she must undertake a number of administrative functions including the following:

- ❖ managing the client/contractor;
- ❖ coordinating the pre-project, project and post-project phases;
- ❖ instigating client variations;
- ❖ agreeing interim payments; and
- ❖ issuing certificates including payment certificates and practical completion.

The contract administrator has an important role in giving advice and information and also monitoring the work. However, he or she must also remain unbiased in matters such as certification of payments and ensuring that the contract terms are adhered to.

The mandatory nature of these duties is reflected in the contract between the contract administrator and the employer and in contract between the employer and the contractor. As such, there is often considerable scope for disagreement between the contracting parties, both in contract and tort, on whether these duties have been satisfactorily performed.

It is with this background, that those fulfilling the contract administrator's role should be clear on what is required of them.

As a contract administrator the following pre- and post-contract services should be considered important.

Pre-contract

- ❖ Agree detailed brief with client. Agree procedures for modifying the brief as commission proceeds and recording variations.
- ❖ Set budget and project time constraints and establish reporting procedures.
- ❖ Establish clear routes of responsibility for design, drawings and specification and ensure client approval as scheme develops.
- ❖ Prepare tender documents and approve tendering processes with client, including the selection process.

Post-contract

- ❖ Administer the terms of the building contract during operations on site.
- ❖ Inspect the progress and quality of the work on a regular basis.

- ❖ Prepare interim financial reports to client including the effects of any variations.

- ❖ Agree interim valuations with the contractor in accordance with the contract allowing for the submission of interim applications for payment.

- ❖ Convene and chair site progress meetings on a regular basis to principally discuss progress, cost and quality issues. Record all principle matters in minutes distributed to all project team members.

- ❖ Prepare regular progress reports for client, including details of any applications for extensions of time or disputes.

- ❖ Agree practical completion of the works under the contract terms. This may include the preparation of 'snagging' lists detailing the non-completion of minor work items remaining outstanding at practical completion.

- ❖ Administer the contract conditions during the defects liability period ensuring that all items of disrepair are rectified before the issue of the making good defects certificate and release of retention monies.

Contract management

Development and procurement

Employer's agent

Employer's agent duties

Clients routinely wish to procure projects in the pursuit of certainty of cost. Design and build forms of procurement are now in frequent use and these transfer the 'risk' in any development to the contractor, while giving him or her greater flexibility to deliver the product. As an agent acting on behalf of the employer, it is essential that the following pre-contract and post-contract services are provided:

Pre-contract service

❖ Define the responsibilities of the employer, employer's agent and contractor.

❖ Appraise and quantify the risks.

❖ Formulate the employer's brief and identify specific requirements.

❖ Assess the contractor's proposals and ensure compliance with the employer's requirements.

❖ Undertake design audit of the contractor's proposals for compliance with the employer's requirements.

❖ Evaluate the offer, the contract sum analysis and stage payments and assess value for money.

Post-contract service

❖ Set up quality control procedure and report on works carried out on site.

❖ Provide site visits and chair meetings.

❖ Implement changes to the employer's requirements only on written approval of the client.

❖ Agree stage payments and recommendations for payments.

❖ Prepare monthly project control statements and cash flow forecasts to client.

❖ Advise on practical completion, preparation of snagging schedules and component literature.

General exclusions

❖ Checking and verifying contractor's design in terms of adequacy and efficiency.

❖ Checking and verifying contractor's design in terms of fitness for purpose.

In undertaking duties as the employer's agent, it is important to recognise the contractor's freedom to design, while respecting the client's brief and auditing the quality of the end product.

The quantity surveyor's role

Capital project advice

The quantity surveyor is tasked with controlling construction cost by accurate measurement of the works required and the application of expert knowledge of costs of labour, materials and plant required. An understanding of the implications of design decisions at an early stage ensure that good value is obtained for the money to be expended.

Several capabilities are required to fulfil this role:

❖ An ability to predict future costs from limited information and in dynamic market conditions.

❖ An ability to manage the procurement process to ensure that predictions of cost, time and quality are delivered.

❖ An awareness of risk with a capability to assess and manage that risk.

❖ An ability to demonstrate value for money.

Current trends in the industry lean towards cost reductions, with pressure coming from major purchasers; the importance of value for money is undoubtedly here to stay. Fixed out-turn costs are a necessity.

This is against a backdrop of upward cost pressure on suppliers of construction resources. Skills shortages are emerging and price rises are sticking.

The challenge to the construction industry and the quantity surveyor is sizeable. Changes in working practices and culture are inevitable and there needs to be a significant change in emphasis towards:

❖ value rather than cost;

❖ more professionalism in the early stages of project delivery;

❖ effective team work between the construction professions and contractors – adversarial relationships are no longer appropriate and will not survive;

❖ an understanding of the clients' business, and with that, the ongoing costs of the finished project;

❖ an awareness of financial incentives and opportunities available to the client (VAT relief and capital allowances – for details, see relevant sections in the cost management and taxation chapter); and

❖ an awareness on the part of purchasers that effective management of the construction process is a valuable service and does not come cheap.

Partnering

The traditional approach to construction procurement is driven by the terms of a contract. Relationships are imposed rather than developed; cost is focused at the expense of value; problems are packaged into liabilities rather than accepted as joint responsibilities; risk is off-loaded rather than managed. Partnering offers an alternative.

Partnering unites the sponsoring, design and construction teams and it endeavours to drive them forward with a common purpose.

The important characteristics are involvement, ownership and trust. This becomes obvious when one considers the facts:

❖ The parties' objectives are not mutually exclusive.

❖ A construction project should not comprise a discrete stage of design followed by construction.

❖ Generally, parties to a venture perform better if given a measure of control and a share in the action. This is all about ownership and being a stakeholder.

There are several levels of partnering. The simple indicators include the following:

❖ Early involvement of contractors and subcontractors; viewing a construction team rather than a design team and a contractor.

❖ Flexibility – for example, being prepared to accept higher short-term costs in the interests of longer-term value; reducing cost rather than simply transferring it to others.

❖ A willingness to look beyond contractual responsibilities and provide more than is called for. 'The gold service' – going the extra mile.

❖ Concentration upon relationships rather than contractual positions. Actions driven by a common purpose rather than a book of rules.

More formal arrangements are implied in:

❖ project partnering; and

❖ strategic partnering.

The tools implied in partnering usually involve the following:

❖ Two stage tendering – getting the contractor on board early.

❖ Negotiation – allowing the contractor to contribute to the design process rather than having to react to it; gaining a clear understanding of the project's objectives before committing to contract and ultimately being able to reduce the contractor's costs and, in that process, the client's costs. Perhaps more importantly, however, if the process of negotiation is conducted correctly the contractor is afforded the opportunity of understanding the client's definition of value.

❖ Open book – everything competitively tendered but with the leader in the procurement process, the contractor, fully acquainted with the project's decision-making rationale.

❖ A charter – as distinct from the rigidity of a contract, the parties set out what they want to achieve rather than what they are obliged to do.

❖ Performance related reward – allowing the contractor to become a stakeholder in the project budget rather than a conduit through which it flows.

Ultimately of course, partnering is all about attitude. The logic of partnering is inescapable; the extent to which it works will depend on the ability of the parties to shake free from traditional attitudes but also on the ability of the management team to deliver a project in unison and without (necessarily) conventional contract protection.

Development

Development and procurement

Construction management

Under this form of procurement, the client appoints a construction manager who is paid a fee for managing and overseeing pre- and post-contract project activities. Site overheads may be included or paid direct by the client. Separate direct appointments will generally exist for the design team members. Building can begin as soon as the design is sufficiently advanced to allow the initial stages of construction to proceed and to prepare and agree a cost estimate for the entire scheme.

Construction is divided into works packages – either on single or multi-trade lines – and the client enters into direct contracts with each of the individual package contractors. This differs from management contracting where the contracts are between the management contractor and each package contractor. The individual packages are tendered at appropriate times throughout the construction period under the direction and management of the construction manager.

Whether a given project is suited to construction management (CM) will depend on a number of factors, as identified in the following table.

Factors	Considerations
Size	CM is an involved form of procurement and can seldom be justified for small projects of less than £1 million.
Complexity	CM is suited to complex projects with a substantial proportion of specialist package contractor involvement.
Uncertainty	Where the project is being conducted in an uncertain environment, CM affords clients a higher degree of flexibility to make changes during the process while minimising the consequent time and cost penalties.
Time	CM permits overlap between design and construction because tendering of packages can take place on a staggered basis rather than all at once as per traditional arrangements. This can save time and suit a 'fast track' approach. Greater involvement of the client with the CM and package contractors may also improve efficiency and introduce time savings. It should be noted however that time savings may be at the expense of cost risk as the scope isn't fixed until much later in the process.
Cost	Certainty of final cost is possible if the scope is finalised before the package contracts are placed. Obviously this sacrifices some of the flexibility referred to. This basis of contracting (in common with management contracting) should result in the lowest cost at the end of the day because the best price is chosen for each package contract without a main contractor's risk provision. Clients have more options to alter or adapt the design throughout the construction period without leaving themselves at a negotiating disadvantage with a main contractor. There is also greater potential to 'value engineer' the project under these arrangements.
Design	Often clients wish to retain control of the design process and this is facilitated under CM. Changes to design during construction carry less cost and time risk than under other procurement methods.

Achieving excellence in construction

Through the Achieving Excellence initiative, central government clients commit to maximise, by continuous improvement, the efficiency, effectiveness and value for money of their procurement of new works, maintenance and refurbishment.

With this statement, the Office of Government Commerce (OGC) launched 'Achieving Excellence' in 1999 – a programme which aims to incorporate the recommendations of the Latham ('Constructing the Team 1994') and Egan ('Rethinking Construction' 1998) reports into new ways of working for a construction industry that is notoriously resistant to change.

The initiative prescribes best practice for construction procurement in the public sector. Principal themes that run through the guidance are:

- ❖ long-term relationships, encouraging shared learning as a route to improving performance;
- ❖ crisper decision-making;
- ❖ investment in people through skills development then empowering them to take ownership and make decisions;
- ❖ development of 'metrics' so that performance can be measured and compared; and
- ❖ active management of value and risk across the whole life of a built asset – from construction to operation.

Certain factors are seen as critical to success:

Leadership and commitment – the successful project starts at the top with 'ownership' by a senior competent individual and the correct commitment of his or her time. This is seen as absolutely crucial but frequently neglected.

Stakeholder involvement throughout – 'stakeholders' are all those parties with an interest in the project and who will influence its outcome. This may range from bosses to staff to neighbours to the general public. These parties will each have a different perspective on the project. These perspectives need to be understood and reconciled as far as is possible. The successful project aims to exceed the expectations of all these parties.

Roles and responsibilities – each player should know its place in the team and what is expected of it.

Integrated teams – the 'design team' or 'construction team' should be subsumed within the greater group of client, designers, constructors, specialist suppliers and even facilities managers, operating as a single development team with common overriding goals and objectives. This means investment in bringing the parties together and building the team ethos.

Integrated processes – in which design, construction, operation and maintenance are considered as parts of a whole rather than separate activities.

Design quality – that which achieves whole-life value by combining functionality with serviceability while respecting the environment. Design Quality Indicators (DQIs) have been developed as tools to give measurability to this multi-faceted dimension of individual projects.

Health and safety – a commitment to excellence, because it is ethical, shows respect to the team and community and makes business sense.

Procurement strategies – adopting those that ensure an integrated team and process approach. The Private Finance Initiative, Prime Contracting and Design and Build are those preferred by the government for this reason. Traditional routes of procurement should only be used if they can be fully justified by business case.

Risk and value management – These are interrelated activities that should involve the integrated team in constructive collaboration to deliver best value throughout the project. The independent key stage, or 'gateway' review process has an important role to play here.

Whole-life business perspective – business decisions should be made based on the balanced long term costs of site acquisition, design, development and operation, rather than short term costs only. This is consistent with the integrated process approach.

Continuous improvement – this requires a genuine commitment allied to schemes of measurement, key performance indicators (KPIs) and benchmarks so that levels of performance can be established and trends tracked.

Sustainability – Construction has a major impact on the environment and project teams have an important responsibility in this respect in areas such as quality of life, flexibility, creating desirable environments and ensuring the efficient use of resources.

The Achieving Excellence initiative is supported by a suite of publications and a web-based toolkit. They jointly comprise perhaps the most comprehensive best practice 'manual' in the history of the industry. They are all available on the OGC website at www.ogc.gov.uk.

How successful is the initiative proving? Consistent with the emphasis on measurable performance, a strategic target was set for the period 2003-5 that 70% (by volume) of public sector construction projects should be delivered on time, within budget, exceeding consumer and stakeholder expectations and with zero defects.

The National Audit Office, reporting in March 2005, presented an encouraging picture that between April 2003 and December 2004, 55% of projects were delivered to budget as compared to 25% in 1999. Also, 63% were delivered on time, compared with 34% in 1999. While it is recognised that these improvements have a combination of sources, the adoption of the OGC guidance is identified as a major contributing factor – particularly the shift towards partnering and collaborative approaches.

In the avoidance of direct overspend alone, this benefit is estimated at £800m over that 22-month period. With similar improvements over the entire public sector, the NAO estimates that savings of between £500m and £2.6bn pa could be achieved. This is a strong endorsement of the Achieving Excellence initiative and has reinforced government resolve to press on with these reforms.

Project management

Project management can be defined as the direction of any complex of activities that have a defined beginning and an end. This process has a direct application to all industries and particularly to the construction process. The application of project management techniques in construction has developed rapidly over the past 25 years in response to the growing complexity of projects and the need to coordinate an increasingly fragmented and specialised industry.

The first task of a project manager is to define precisely the scope of the project, including the gaining of an understanding of the fundamentals of the client's business plan for the anticipated scheme.

The second is to gain an understanding of the client's objectives in terms of time, cost, quality and perceived risk. These objectives should be specified by means of a precise brief and schedule of target dates, a master budget, a risk register and specification standards. The relative priority that the client gives to each of these measures should also be understood. For example, a client may have an overriding need to complete by a certain date, so requiring the expenditure of additional funds to make this event a greater certainty. The project manager needs to reflect these factors in a strategy and plan for the project, usually termed the Project Execution Plan (PEP).

The third task is to assemble a competent team to deliver the project. The team needs to be briefed on the client's objectives and their precise role in such delivery. Coordination and reporting routines should be clearly defined at this point.

An effective project manager will be skilled in leading and directing a team drawn together specifically for the duration of the project. This requires personal, managerial, presentational and, above all, communication techniques. Stimulation of coordination in the project team and control of time, cost and quality requires the establishment of master control documents, such as the PEP, information flow tracking tools, risk registers, project master budgets and programmes. These are invaluable tools to enable the project manager to promote coordination, monitor progress, evaluate status and manage delivery.

Successful construction project management entails:

❖ strong balanced leadership;
❖ an empowered client project sponsor;
❖ project team focus on client's objectives;
❖ strong team relationships and motivation;
❖ a strong business case;
❖ a clear and developed brief and schedule;
❖ identification of measurable time, cost and quality objectives;
❖ defining roles and communicating objectives throughout the team;
❖ establishment of strategic as well as detailed controls;
❖ recognition that only the remaining time, cost and performance can be managed;
❖ management apportionment of risk;
❖ awareness of opportunity;
❖ robust project management practice – alive to risks and opportunities;
❖ an appropriate procurement and delivery methodology;
❖ an appropriate project contractual matrix;
❖ balanced risk apportionment;
❖ early established use of project control documentation;
❖ dynamic programme management;
❖ use of gateway review techniques;
❖ open, truthful and transparent lines of communication;
❖ continual challenge to ensure best quality, long-term value and programme;
❖ active management; and
❖ regular review to ensure long-term value.

Quality management and professional construction services

ISO 9001:2000 has superseded the previous 'triple pack' of ISO 9001:1994, ISO 9002:1994 and ISO 9003:1994. To maintain accreditation, organisations whose quality management systems were compliant with the 1994 standard had until 15 December 2003 to undergo a transition to ensure compliance with the 2000 standard.

The revised title, *Quality management systems – requirements*, reflects the change from assuring quality to producing a quality management system. The requirements of the 2000 standard are more generic in nature and it is intended to be more relevant to all categories of product and professional services and size of organisation.

ISO 9001:2000 is intended to be simpler and more flexible for organisations to adopt and use. The main difference is that it is process driven and a management system standard which integrates quality management with business management.

The content has been arranged into five main sections instead of the original 20. The five sections are identified as follows:

Quality management system. An organisation needs to establish what its processes are, how they interact, what resources are required to provide the product and how the processes are measured and improved. Once this has been established then a system for the control of documentation has to be established along with the Quality Manual and controls for looking after records.

Management responsibility. This requires management to set policies and objectives, to review the systems and to communicate to the organisation the effectiveness of the system.

Resources management. An organisation needs to identify the resources it needs to ensure that the customer receives what has been agreed. This means not only people but also the physical resources such as equipment, premises and any support services required.

Production realisation. This deals with the processes required to deliver to the customer the product/services required. These processes cover activities such as taking the instruction from the client, the design and development of the particular service/product, the purchasing of services and materials, and the delivery of the services and products.

Measurement analysis and improvement. This is the measurement and monitoring of the management system, the products and services and customer satisfaction and the analysis of data for the continuing improvement of the system.

The implementation of BS EN ISO 9001:2000 is on the basis of the 'plan-do-check-act' principle:

Plan:
- identify customer needs and expectations;
- strategic planning; and
- set policies and objectives.

Do:
- implement and operate the processes.

Check:
- collect business results;
- monitor and measure the processes; and
- review and analysis.

Act:
- continually improve process performance.

Latent defects insurance

Latent defects insurance is commonly required on construction projects by developers, purchasers, tenants and funders. The objective of the policy is to provide cover for latent defects that existed prior to practical completion, but remained undiscovered at that time, and became apparent during the period of the policy (usually 10 to 12 years). These policies include defects in design, materials and/or workmanship.

Latent defects insurance is also known as decennial insurance (10 years cover), wrap up insurance and BUILD (building users' insurance against latent defects).

The basic policy covers physical damage to the structure of the building, or damage that resulted from the latent defect in the structure. Weatherproofing (e.g. roof coverings) and waterproofing cover is usually incorporated, however the policy wording should be verified. Cover for non-structural elements and mechanical and electrical services can usually be purchased as an addition. The policy will not cover works that were outstanding at practical completion, therefore these outstanding works should be kept to a minimum. In addition, cover is not included for defects that occur after practical completion. Policy exclusions, such as business interruption and loss of profit, should also be carefully reviewed.

The cost of a policy is generally between 0.65% and 1% of the contract value for the basic cover. Adding cover for the non-structural elements and the mechanical and electrical services would increase the premium to between 1% and 2%, which is relatively expensive.

The developer usually takes out the policy, however it can be assignable to future owners, tenants or funders.

For a successful claim, insurers will usually pay for the repair costs, emergency works, professional fees, site clearance and compliance with statutory requirements. The insurance will provide almost immediate funds for repairs which minimises disruption. The developer does not need to rely on proving a claim against the designers' or contractor's professional indemnity insurance for inherent defects. Furthermore, the insurance helps to provide a no-blame approach that aids the resolution of the defects in a less confrontational environment.

The insurer will want to make an independent assessment of the design and construction of the project. They will generally appoint a technical monitoring surveyor to act on their behalf throughout the duration of the project.

Contract insurance

Construction contracts, by their very nature, give rise to risks of injury to persons and damage to property. On a large construction project the financial implications can be enormous. It is critical that the right insurance provisions are in place.

Contract insurance is one of the principle features of a construction contract and ensures that certain risks are clearly covered by one or other of the parties. However, it is also one of the most complex elements and great care should be exercised when advising on the correct insurance requirements.

On 14 January 2005, the Financial Services Authority (FSA) introduced the *Insurance Mediation Directive Regulations*, requiring anyone who carries out certain regulated activities (such as advising on choice of contract insurance) to be authorised by the FSA. Providing advice when not authorised by the FSA, is in breach of the regulations and is a criminal offence. Consequently specialist assistance is often required.

Within the construction industry there are two main types of insurance; a liability insurance policy and a loss insurance policy.

Liability insurance policies

A liability insurance policy provides protection against claims, arising from negligence or inappropriate action, resulting in injury to persons or property damage.

Liability of contractor

Under the JCT traditional forms of contract, the contractor is required to take out and maintain a liability policy in respect of:

❖ personal injury or death of any persons, which is caused by the carrying out of the works, unless that is due to act or neglect of the employer or its agents; and

❖ injury or damage to property (with the exception of the works) that is due to negligence, omission or default of the contractor, subcontractor or its agents.

Liability of employer *(non-negligence cover)*

This type of policy covers liability of the employer if damage is caused to any property, other than the works, by the carrying out of the works. The provision is usually optional and operates when damage that occurs is not due to negligence on the part of either the employer or contractor.

In the case of *Gold v Patman & Fotheringham Ltd* [1958] 2 ALL ER 497, the employer was found liable in nuisance to the neighbouring property for subsidence damage caused by the works. It was found that the contractor had not been negligent in carrying out the works and therefore the employer was liable for third party costs. Hence the need for insurance.

When deciding on whether to select this type of policy, it is important to consider the surrounding environment and location of adjoining properties, together with the nature of the works.

Loss insurance policy

The general principle of construction contracts is that they place a commitment on the contractor to complete the works. If the contract works become damaged or destroyed then the contractor is obliged to repair or reinstate the works at its own cost. Under a loss insurance policy the insured party is able to recover its losses from the insurers.

Insurance of the works

Typically under the JCT traditional forms of contract, insurance of the works is split between 'new buildings' or 'existing structures'.

For new building works, either the contractor or the employer may take out a joint names policy covering 'all risks' insurance. This is insurance against physical loss or damage to work and site materials, including theft and vandalism, however it excludes a list of industry standard exclusions such as war or nuclear contamination.

When works are undertaken to existing buildings, it is usual for the employer to take out a joint names policy covering 'specified perils' rather than 'all risks'. Specified perils includes a finite list of events such as fire, explosion, storm, flood, civil commotion, riot, etc. and is narrower than that of an all risks policy.

Joint names policy

Construction contracts often require that a 'loss' insurance policy is taken out in the joint names of the employer and contractor. The purpose of a joint names policy is to protect both parties whereby the insurers have no right of subrogation against one or other of the parties if damage occurs due to the other party. Subrogation is an important legal principle relating to insurance and is the right of the insurers to stand in the shoes of the insured party and recover the loss.

In practice, it is not always possible for a policy to be taken out in the joint names of both parties. In this instance, a 'subrogation waiver' may be obtained to prevent the insurers seeking compensation from the defaulting party.

Further information

Financial Services Authority (FSA) website: www.fsa.gov.uk

Building legislation and control

Legislation

Acts of parliament and regulations

England and Wales

There are hundreds of Acts relating to the design, construction and maintenance of buildings in England and Wales. Listed below are some of the more relevant.

The *Access to Neighbouring Land Act* 1992
The *Agriculture (Miscellaneous) Act* 1968
The *Ancient Monuments and Archaeological Areas Act* 1979
The *Anti-social Behaviour Act* 2003
The *Arbitration Act* 1996
The *Building Act* 1984
The *Building Regulations* 2000
The *Building (Amendment) Regulations* 2001, 2002, 2003 and 2004
The *Building (Amendment) (No 2) Regulations* 2002 and 2004
The *Building (Approved Inspectors) Regulations* 2000
The *Building (Approved Inspectors etc.) (Amendment) Regulations*
2002, 2003, 2004 and 2006
The *Building (Prescribed Fees) Regulations* 1994
The *Capital Allowances Acts* 1990 and 2001
The *Celluloid and Cinematograph Film Act* 1922
The *Chronically Sick and Disabled Persons Act* 1970
The *Chronically Sick and Disabled Persons (Amendment) Act* 1976
The *Civil Procedure Rules* 1998
The *Clean Air Acts* 1956, 1968 and 1993
The *Clean Neighbourhoods and Environment Act* 2005
The *Climate Change and Sustainable Energy Act* 2006
The *Coal Mining Subsidence Act* 1991
The *Commonhold and Leasehold Reform Act* 2002
The *Companies Act* 1985
The *Construction (Design and Management) Regulations* 2007
The *Construction (Health, Safety and Welfare) Regulations* 1996
The *Consumer Protection Act* 1987
The *Contaminated Land (England) Regulations* 2000 and 2006
The *Contaminated Land (England) (Amendment) Regulations* 2001
The *Contaminated Land (Wales) Regulations* 2001
The *Contracts (Rights of Third Parties) Act* 1999
The *Control of Asbestos Regulations* 2006
The *Control of Lead at Work Regulations* 2002
The *Control of Noise at Work Regulations* 2005
The *Control of Pesticides Regulations* 1986
The *Control of Pollution Act* 1974
The *Control of Pollution (Amendment) Act* 1989
The *Control of Substances Hazardous to Health Regulations* 2002
The *Control of Substances Hazardous to Health (Amendment)*
Regulations 2003 and 2004
The *Control of Vibration at Work Regulations* 2005
The *Countryside and Rights of Way Act* 2000
The *Data Protection Act* 1998
The *Defective Premises Act* 1972
The *Disability Discrimination Acts* 1995 and 2005
The *Disability Discrimination Act 1995 (Amendment) Regulations*
2003
The *Disability Discrimination (Premises) Regulations* 2006
The *Disability Discrimination (Providers of Services) (Adjustment of*
Premises) Regulations 2001
The *Disabled Persons Act* 1981
The *Education Act* 1996
The *Education (School Premises) Regulations* 1999
The *Electricity Acts* 1947, 1957, 1972 and 1989
The *Electricity at Work Regulations* 1989
The *Energy Act* 2004

The *Environment Act* 1995
The *Environmental Protection Act* 1990
The *Environmental Protection (Duty of Care) Regulations* 1991
The *Estate Agents Act* 1979
The *Factories Act* 1961
The *Finance Acts* 1989, 2001, 2004, 2005 and 2006
The *Fire and Rescue Services Act* 2004
The *Fire Safety and Safety of Places of Sport Act* 1987
The *Food Safety Act* 1990
The *Gambling Act* 2005
The *Gas Safety (Installation and Use) Regulations* 1998
The *Health and Safety at Work etc. Act* 1974
The *Health and Safety (Miscellaneous Amendments) Regulations* 2002
The *Health and Safety (Safety Signs and Signals) Regulations* 1996
The *Highways Act* 1980
The *Highways (Amendment) Act* 1986
The *Historic Buildings and Ancient Monuments Act* 1953
The *Housing Acts* 1957, 1961, 1964, 1969, 1974, 1980, 1985, 1988, 1996 and 2004
The *Housing and Building Control Act* 1984
The *Housing Associations Act* 1985
The *Housing Defects Act* 1984
The *Housing Grants, Construction and Regeneration Act* 1996
The *Insolvency Act* 2000
The *Landlord and Tenant Acts* 1927, 1954, 1985, 1987 and 1988
The *Landlord and Tenant (Covenants) Act* 1995
The *Land Registration Act* 2002
The *Latent Damage Act* 1986
The *Late Payment of Commercial Debts (Interest) Act* 1998
The *Law of Property Act* 1925
The *Law of Property (Miscellaneous Provisions) Act* 1989
The *Leasehold Property (Repairs) Act* 1938
The *Leasehold Reform, Housing and Urban Development Act* 1993
The *Licensing Act* 2003
The *Limitation Act* 1980
The *Local Government Acts* 1963, 1972, 1985, 1992, 1999, 2000 and 2003
The *Local Government and Housing Act* 1989
The *Local Government Finance Acts* 1988 and 1992
The *Local Government (Miscellaneous Provisions) Acts* 1976 and 1982
The *Local Government Planning and Land Act* 1980
The *London Building Act* 1930
The *London Building (Amendment) Acts* 1935 and 1939
The *Management of Health and Safety at Work Regulations* 1999
The *Management of Health and Safety at Work and Fire Precautions (Workplace) (Amendment) Regulations* 2003
The *Management of Health and Safety at Work (Amendment) Regulations* 2006
The *Management of Houses in Multiple Occupation (England) Regulations* 2006
The *Management of Houses in Multiple Occupation (Wales) Regulations* 2006
The *National Heritage Acts* 1980, 1983 and 2002
The *National Lottery Act* 1998
The *New Roads and Street Works Act* 1991
The *Offices, Shops and Railway Premises Act* 1963
The *Party Wall etc. Act* 1996
The *Petroleum (Consolidation) Act* 1928
The *Planning and Compensation Act* 1991
The *Planning and Compulsory Purchase Act* 2004
The *Planning (Consequential Provisions) Act* 1990
The *Planning (Hazardous Substances) Act* 1990
The *Planning (Listed Buildings and Conservation Areas) Act* 1990

The *Planning (Listed Buildings and Conservation Areas) (England) (Amendment) Regulations* 2003

The *Planning (Listed Buildings and Conservation Areas) (Amendment) (England) Regulations* 2004 and 2005

The *Prescription Act* 1832

The *Private Places of Entertainment (Licensing) Act* 1967

The *Property Misdescriptions Act* 1991

The *Public Contracts Regulations* 2006

The *Public Health Acts* 1936 and 1961

The *Regulatory Reform (Fire Safety) Order* 2005

The *Rights of Light Act* 1959

The *Safety of Sports Grounds Regulations* 1987

The *Scheme for Construction Contracts (England and Wales) Regulations* 1998

The *Special Educational Needs and Disability Act* 2001

The *Sustainable and Secure Buildings Act* 2004

The *Theatres Act* 1968

The *Town and Country Planning Act* 1990

The *Town and Country Planning (Environmental Assessment and Permitted Development) Regulations* 1995

The *Town and Country Planning (Environmental Impact Assessment) (England and Wales) Regulations* 1999

The *Town and Country Planning (Environmental Impact Assessment) (England and Wales) (Amendment) Regulations* 2000

The *Town and Country Planning (Fees for Applications and Deemed Applications) (Amendment) (England) Regulations* 2005 and 2006

The *Town and Country Planning (General Development Procedure) Order* 1995

The *Town and Country Planning (General Development Procedure) (Amendment) (England) Order* 2005 and 2006

The *Town and Country Planning (General Permitted Development) Order* 1995

The *Town and Country Planning (Use Classes) Order* 1987

The *Town and Country Planning (Use Classes) (Amendment) (England) Orders* 2005 and 2006

The *Unfair Contract Terms Act* 1977

The *Value Added Tax Act* 1994 (as amended)

The *Warm Homes and Energy Conservation Act* 2000

The *Waste Management (England and Wales) Regulations* 2006

The *Water Act* 2003

The *Water Industry Act* 1999

The *Water Resources Act* 1991

The *Wildlife and Countryside Act* 1981 (as amended)

The *Work at Height Regulations* 2005

The *Workplace (Health, Safety and Welfare) Regulations* 1992

Northern Ireland

There are over 100 national Acts relating to the design and construction of buildings in Northern Ireland.

The *Building (Prescribed Fees) Regulations (Northern Ireland)* 1997

The *Building Regulations (Northern Ireland)* 2000

The *Building (Amendment) Regulations (Northern Ireland)* 2005 and 2006

The *Construction (Design and Management) Regulations (Northern Ireland)* 1995

The *Construction (Design and Management) (Amendment) Regulations (Northern Ireland)* 2001

The *Control of Asbestos at Work Regulations (Northern Ireland)* 1988 and 2003

The *Control of Asbestos at Work (Amendment) Regulations (Northern Ireland)* 2000

The *Control of Lead at Work Regulations (Northern Ireland)* 1998 and 2003

The *Control of Noise at Work Regulations (Northern Ireland)* 2006
The *Control of Substances Hazardous to Health Regulations (Northern Ireland)* 2000 and 2003
The *Control of Substances Hazardous to Health (Amendment) Regulations (Northern Ireland)* 2003 and 2005
The *Defective Premises (Landlord's Liability) Act (Northern Ireland)* 2001
The *Disability Discrimination Act 1995 (Amendment) Regulations (Northern Ireland)* 2004
The *Disability Discrimination (Northern Ireland) Order* 2006
The *Disability Discrimination (Providers of Services) (Adjustment of Premises) Regulations (Northern Ireland)* 2003
The *Factories Act (Northern Ireland)* 1965
The *Fire Precautions (Workplace) Regulations (Northern Ireland)* 2001
The *Gas Safety (Installation and Use) Regulations (Northern Ireland)* 1997 and 2004
The *Hazardous Waste Regulations* 2005
The *Health and Safety (Safety Signs and Signals) Regulations (Northern Ireland)* 1996 and 2003
The *Housing (Northern Ireland) Order* 1992
The *Management of Health and Safety at Work (Amendment) Regulations (Northern Ireland)* 2006
The *Northern Ireland Act* 1998
The *Management of Health and Safety at Work and Fire Precautions (Workplace) (Amendment) Regulations (Northern Ireland)* 2003
The *Office and Shop Premises Act (Northern Ireland)* 1966
The *Planning (Compensation, etc.) Act (Northern Ireland)* 2001
The *Planning (Hazardous Substances) (Northern Ireland) Act* 1993
The *Pollution Prevention and Control Regulations (Northern Ireland)* 2003
The *Pollution Prevention and Control (Miscellaneous Amendments) Regulations (Northern Ireland)* 2006
The *Safety of Sports Grounds (Northern Ireland) Order* 2006
The *Scheme for Construction Contracts (Northern Ireland)* 1999
The *Wildlife (Northern Ireland) Order* 1985 (as amended)
The *Work at Height Regulations (Northern Ireland)* 2005
The *Workplace (Health, Safety and Welfare) Regulations (Northern Ireland)* 1993

Scotland

There are some 120 national and 50 Scottish Acts relating to the design and construction of buildings in Scotland.

NB: amending Acts (those shown with certain Acts) have important effects and should be read with them.

The *Building (Procedure) (Scotland) Regulations* 2004
The *Building (Scotland) Acts* 1959 and 1970 as amended by the *Housing (Scotland) Acts* 1986 and 2003
The *Building (Scotland) (Amendment) Regulations* 1997
The *Building (Scotland) Regulations* 2004
The *Building Standards (Scotland) Regulations* 1990 (including amendments 1993–99)
The *Building Standards (Scotland) Amendment Regulations* 2001
The *Building Standards (Scotland) Amendment Regulations 2001 Amendment Regulations* 2002
The *Building Standards and Procedure Amendment (Scotland) Regulations* 1999
The *Celluloid and Cinematograph Film Act* 1922
The *Chronically Sick and Disabled Persons Act* 1970 as extended by the *Chronically Sick and Disabled Persons (Scotland) Act* 1972 as amended by the *Chronically Sick and Disabled Persons (Amendment) Act* 1976
The *Cinemas Act* 1985
The *Civic Government (Scotland) Act* 1982
The *Clean Air Acts* 1956, 1968 and 1993

The *Contaminated Land (Scotland) Regulations* 2000 and 2005
The *Control of Pollution Act* 1974
The *Control of Pollution (Amendment) Act* 1989
The *Electricity (Scotland) Act* 1979
The *Factories Act* 1961
The *Fire Safety (Scotland) Regulations* 2006
The *Fire (Scotland) Act* 2005
The *Food Safety Act* 1990
The *Gambling Act* 2005
The *Gas Acts* 1972, 1986 and 1995
The *Health and Safety at Work Act etc.* 1974 as amended by the *Building Act* 1984
The *Housing (Scotland) Acts* 1987, 1988, 2001 and 2006
The *Land Reform (Scotland) Act* 2003
The *Late Payment of Commercial Debts (Scotland) Regulations* 2002
The *Licensing (Scotland) Act* 2005
The *Local Government and Housing Act* 1989
The *Local Government and Planning (Scotland) Act* 1982
The *Local Government etc. (Scotland) Act* 1994
The *Local Government in Scotland Act* 2003
The *Local Government (Miscellaneous Provisions) (Scotland) Act* 1981
The *Local Government (Scotland) Acts* 1973, 1975, 1978 and 1994
The *National Heritage (Scotland) Act* 1985
The *Offices, Shops and Railway Premises Act* 1963
The *Planning and Compensation (Scotland) Act* 1991
The *Planning (Consequential Provisions) (Scotland) Act* 1997
The *Planning (Hazardous Substances) (Scotland) Act* 1997
The *Planning (Listed Buildings and Conservation Areas) (Scotland) Act* 1997
The *Pollution Prevention and Control (Scotland) Regulations* 2000
The *Pollution Prevention and Control (Scotland) Amendment Regulations* 2004
The *Public Contracts (Scotland) Regulations* 2006
The *Regulatory Reform (Fire Safety) Order* 2005
The *Renewables Obligation (Scotland) Order* 2006
The *Roads (Scotland) Act* 1984
The *Safety of Sports Grounds Regulations* 1987
The *Scheme for Construction Contracts (Scotland) Regulations* 1998
The *Scotland Act* 1998
The *Sewerage (Scotland) Act* 1968
The *Theatres Act* 1968
The *Town and Country Planning (Listed Buildings and Buildings in Conservation Areas) (Amendment) (Scotland) Regulations* 2006
The *Town and Country Planning (Scotland) Act* 1997
The *Water Environmental and Water Services (Scotland) Act* 2003
The *Water Industry (Scotland) Act* 2002
The *Water (Scotland) Act* 1980
The *Water Services etc. (Scotland) Act* 2005

Statutory instruments and orders

Many acts of parliament empower secretaries of state and ministers to publish Statutory Instruments and Orders to implement legislation which, although on the Statute Book, requires 'enactment'. The Building Regulations are a prime example. In these cases guidance is given as to how acts ought to be interpreted.

The Regulatory Reform (Fire Safety) Order 2005

The *Regulatory Reform (Fire Safety) Order* 2005 (RRFSO) received Parliamentary Approval on 7 June 2005 and came into force on 1 October

2006. The main effect of the Fire Safety Order is a move towards greater emphasis on fire prevention in all non-domestic premises. However, the RRFSO does apply to the common parts of residential accommodation. The Fire Safety Order applies in England and Wales while Northern Ireland and Scotland have devolved responsibility for safety law (see subsequent sections below).

The Order is not in fact 'new' but a reform of all current fire safety law, which is contained in over 100 separate pieces of legislation. The reform was brought in to simplify, rationalise and consolidate existing legislation in respect of fire safety. The aim is to reduce burdens on businesses caused by previous multiple overlapping fire safety regimes and consequently, the overlap of the responsibilities of enforcing authorities. Accordingly, this reduces the number of enforcing authorities dealing with general fire safety matters.

Under the reform, as of 1 October 2006, fire certificates were abolished and cease to have legal status. Instead, under the RRFSO, a 'responsible person' for each premises is required to carry out an assessment of fire risk and take reasonable steps to reduce or remove that risk. As with previous Fire Risk Assessments required under the former *Fire Precautions (Workplace) Regulations* 1997 and *(Amendment) Regulations* 1999 (which are now revoked), these will need to be kept under review.

Responsibility for complying with the Fire Safety Order rests with the 'responsible person'. There is no separate formal validation process for higher risk premises, although fire authorities will base their inspection programmes on premises that they consider to present the highest risk.

Multi-tenanted buildings

Where two or more responsible persons share or have duties in respect of premises, the RRFSO requires cooperation and coordination between the parties. For example, the landlord will generally be responsible for the common parts and the tenants responsible for their respective demised areas, with coordination between all of the parties concerned, ideally managed by the landlord.

Definition of 'responsible person'

Article 3 of the RRFSO defines 'responsible person' as:

    (a) 'in relation to a workplace, the employer, if the workplace is to any extent under his control;

    (b) in relation to any premises not falling within paragraph (a)

        (i) the person who has control of the premises (as occupier or otherwise) in connection with the carrying on by him of a trade, business or other undertaking (for profit or not); or

        (ii) the owner, where the person in control of the premises does not have control in connection with the carrying on by that person of a trade, business or other undertaking.'

Fire safety duties

Under article 8 of the RRFSO, the 'responsible person' must:

    (a) 'take such general fire precautions as will ensure, so far as is reasonably practicable, the safety of any of his employees; and

    (b) in relation to relevant persons who are not his employees, take such general fire precautions [as described below] as may reasonably be required in the circumstances of the case to ensure that the premises are safe.'

General fire precautions

The RRFSO cites, under article 4, the meaning of 'general fire precautions' as:

(a) 'measures to reduce the risk of fire on the premises and the risk of the spread of fire on the premises;

(b) measures in relation to the means of escape from the premises;

(c) measures for securing that, at all material times, the means of escape can be safely and effectively used;

(d) measures in relation to the means for fighting fires on the premises;

(e) measures in relation to the means for detecting fire on the premises and giving warning in case of fire on the premises; and

(f) measures in relation to the arrangements for action to be taken in the event of fire on the premises, including –

    (i) measures relating to the instruction and training of employees; and

    (ii) measures to mitigate the effects of the fire.'

Crown Copyright material is reproduced with the permission of the Controller of HMSO and the Queen's Printer for Scotland.

Risk assessment

The 'responsible person' is required to undertake a risk assessment, which will need to address, among other things, the following:

- ❖ assessed risks of young persons employed (i.e. under 18 years of age);
- ❖ elimination or reduction of risks from dangerous substances;
- ❖ fire fighting and fire detection provision;
- ❖ emergency routes and exits; and
- ❖ evacuation of disabled people.

The government has produced 11 guidance documents which deal with fire safety in different types of premises and which reflect the new legislation.

In addition to the above, the 'responsible person' will (in most cases) need to appoint a competent person to assist him or her in undertaking the risk assessment and fulfilling the obligations under the Order.

Enforcement

The enforcing authority under the RRFSO will depend upon the type of premises. The enforcing authorities include the fire and rescue authority for the area in which the premises falls, the Health and Safety Executive, the fire service, the relevant local authority, fire inspector or any other person authorised by the Secretary of State. The enforcing authority is empowered to serve a prohibition notice, an alterations notice or an enforcement notice. Failure to comply with the RRFSO is an offence resulting in a fine up to the statutory maximum limit and/or imprisonment for a maximum of two years.

Amendments to existing legislation

The following primary legislation has been revoked/repealed under the new RRFSO. Note: This list is not exhaustive:

- ❖ the *Fire Precautions Act* 1971;
- ❖ the *Fire Certificate (Special Premises) Regulations* 1976;
- ❖ the *Fire Precautions (Workplace) Regulations* 1997; and

❖ the *Fire Precautions (Workplace) (Amendment) Regulations* 1999.

Northern Ireland

Sections 1 and 2 of the *Regulatory Reform (Fire Safety) Order* were implemented in May 2006 following public consultation and approval by Parliament. These sections are relevant to the Northern Ireland Fire Brigade only. Section 4 is currently under consultation and will concentrate on the operational side of the Fire Authority. Section 3 will enforce the need for a relevant risk assessment to be carried out to all workplaces by a relevantly trained competent person. The Fire Authority are currently retraining their staff to ensure they are prepared to review fire risk assessments. Consultation is still ongoing. The Fire Authority were originally advised to prepare for the implementation of section 3 in January 2007, however, it is unlikely that the new Regulations will come into play until mid-spring 2007 following an awareness campaign and a lead-in period.

Please refer to the website for the Northern Ireland Assembly www.ni-assembly.gov.uk for an updated position on the fire legislation.

Scotland

The *Fire (Scotland) Act* 2005 received Royal Assent on 1 April 2005. The 2005 Act came into force on 2 August 2005 with the exception of Part 3 which introduces a new fire safety regime in Scotland and came into force on 1 October 2006.

The main purpose of the Act is to reform fire safety legislation in Scotland, modernising fire and rescue services. It also provides for the implementation of the provisions of a number of EU Directives on health and safety at work.

The new Act revokes/repeals the following legislation:

❖ the *Fire Precautions Act* 1971;

❖ the *Fire Certificate (Special Premises) Regulations* 1976; and

❖ the Workplace Fire Precautions Legislation, in respect of: the *Fire Precautions (Workplace) Regulations* 1997 ('the 1997 Regulations') and the general fire safety provisions of the *Management of Health and Safety at Work Regulations* 1999 ('the 1999 Regulations') (the health and safety provisions of these regulations will be unaffected).

The Act does not include private dwellings but common areas of private dwellings will be dealt with.

The Act consolidates existing legislation relating to duties of employers to their staff and in respect of premises. Provision is made regarding fire safety measures, risk assessment and enforcement.

Provision is also made for a Fire and Rescue Framework for Scotland that will set out priorities and objectives for the relevant authorities. This document will be designed to promote public safety and the efficiency and effectiveness of the rescue authorities.

The introduction of the Act has allowed enabling orders and regulations to be made. In conjunction with Part III of the Act, the *Fire Safety (Scotland) Regulations* 2006 came into force on 1 October 2006. The Regulations, inter alia, cover fire safety, means of fighting fire, means of escape, procedures in dangerous areas, maintenance of premises and equipment, and information to and training of employees.

Please see www.scotland.gov.uk for up-to-date news on the Act and the accompanying Regulations.

Fire, residential property and houses in multiple occupation (HMOs)

Purely domestic properties are excluded under the RRFSO, however, it still applies to the common areas of houses in multiple occupation and the common parts of flats. Residential landlords also have a general common law duty to keep tenants' homes fit for them to live in and to ensure that they do not endanger tenants' health, including ensuring that there are no fire hazards. Where a house is in multiple occupation and meets the 'HMO' classification, there are additional fire safety responsibilities. This will include the provision of adequate fire precautions such as fire alarms and extinguishers and with suitable and sufficient means of escape, usually providing at least 30 minutes protection. The local council or Fire and Rescue Service can inspect the property to see whether the landlord or managing agent is complying with the law. If the property is not an HMO, there are no specific fire safety laws to comply with, although there is a general duty to keep the property habitable. There is also an obligation to ensure that the property is properly maintained, so for example, a fire hazard does not occur as a result of a faulty electrical installation. There is also a requirement to ensure that upholstered furnishings provided in the property are fire resistant.

The Disability Discrimination Act

Disability facts

- ❖ There are estimated to be more than 10 million disabled people in Britain.
- ❖ The annual spending power of disabled people is £80 billion a year.
- ❖ There are more than 2 million disabled people in employment in the UK.
- ❖ There are at least another million disabled people who want jobs but are out of work – many of whom are equally skilled as those who have jobs.
- ❖ Only 50% of disabled people of working age are in employment compared to 81% of non-disabled people.
- ❖ Disability is too often associated with wheelchairs: in fact only 5% of disabled people use wheelchairs.

The DDA (the Disability Discrimination Act 1995 as amended by the Special Educational Needs and Disability Act 2001 and the Disability Discrimination Act 2005)

The *Disability Discrimination Act* 1995 (DDA) came into force on 2 December 1996. It brings in measures to prevent discrimination against disabled people. The *Disability Discrimination Act* 2005 (which further amends the DDA 1995) received Royal Assent on 7 April 2005, increasing and creating new rights for disabled people.

Territorial coverage of the DDA

The DDA 1995 applies to England, Wales, Scotland and (with modifications) to Northern Ireland. The DDA 2005 extends to Great Britain only with the exception of section 9 (Blue badge parking provisions) and section 16 (Improvements to let dwellings) which extend only to England and Wales. The 2005 Act does not extend to Northern Ireland since disability discrimination and transport are classed as 'transferred matters' under the *Northern Ireland Act* 1998.

The provisions in the Act relating to education and special educational needs extend to England and Wales only. The provisions on rights for disabled people in education extend to England, Wales and Scotland, although there is no duty to produce an accessibility strategy or plan in Scotland. The education provisions (SENDA) do not extend to Northern Ireland.

The Act

The DDA 1995 is split into different sections.

- ❖ Part 1 – defines the term 'disability'.
- ❖ Part 2 – deals with discrimination in employment, trade organisations and qualifications bodies.
- ❖ Part 3 – deals with discrimination in the provision of goods, facilities and services to members of the public and the disposal and management of property. The DDA 2005 further amends Part 3 to now include public authority functions, private clubs with more than 25 members and letting of premises. More recent changes as a result of the DDA 2005 amend the Part 3 duties to clarify the scope of the exemption in relation to transport providers. Therefore, the Part 3 duties now extend to certain types of transport vehicles.
- ❖ Part 4 – deals with provisions for education.
- ❖ Part 5 – deals with provisions for public transport.
- ❖ Part 6 – deals with the setting up of the National Disability Council.
- ❖ Part 7 – supplemental provisions, (details duties and responsibilities covering Codes of Practice, victimisation, liability of employers, help for people suffering discrimination, aiding unlawful acts and exclusion for acts done with statutory authority or done for the purpose of safeguarding national security.)
- ❖ Part 8 – miscellaneous provisions, (including government appointments, regulations and interpretation).

Part 1 – Definition of disability within the Act

A physical or mental impairment, which has a substantial and long-term (12 months' minimum) adverse effect on a person's ability to carry out normal day to day activities. The DDA 2005 extends the definition to include people with HIV, cancer and multiple sclerosis, from the point of diagnosis.

Part 2 – Employment, trade organisations and qualifications bodies

Employment

This section of the Act came into force on 2 December 1996 and applies when a disabled person is employed, or an employee becomes disabled. The Act places a duty on all employers (the previous threshold exemption of less than 15 employees being removed from 1 October 2004) to make reasonable adjustments to enable disabled employees to carry out their work. (The armed forces are excluded under the employment provisions.)

An employer is expected to take reasonable measures to allow a person to do his or her job. This may involve:

- ❖ making adjustments to premises;
- ❖ moving a disabled person's place of work;

- ❖ altering hours of work;
- ❖ reallocating a disabled person's duties;
- ❖ acquiring or modifying equipment; and
- ❖ providing a reader or interpreter.

In addition to the above, employers should ensure that their equal opportunities policy addresses disability, in addition to preparing a disability statement and policy. Employers are not required to make changes in anticipation of employing a disabled person, however the code of practice suggests that employers should take opportunities to make improvements as they arise, e.g. as part of planned maintenance or refurbishment works. In addition, employers must not unjustifiably discriminate against current employees or job applicants on the grounds of disability, and may have to make reasonable adjustments to their employment arrangements or premises if these substantially disadvantage a disabled person.

There are also significant improvements to the legislation, which became effective as of 1 October 2004. The October 2004 changes also include people who are not technically employees, i.e. whereby a contract of employment does not exist. Contract workers, office holders, police officers, partners in firms, barristers and advocates and people undertaking practical work experience for the purposes of vocational training are now included. Others to whom Part 2 of the Act applies are contained within the revised 2004 Code of Practice.

Trade organisations and qualifications bodies

Qualifications bodies is an alteration to the trade association provisions of the DDA. These have come about as a result of a European Directive on discrimination in employment, which includes disability. These changes are contained in the *Disability Discrimination Act 1995 (Amendment) Regulations* 2003, which were implemented in October 2004.

The duty of a trade organisation or qualification body to make reasonable adjustments applies in respect of its disabled members and, also, in respect of any disabled person who is, or who has notified the organisation that he or she may be, an applicant for membership. Further information can be found within the revised 2004 Code of Practice.

Part 3 – The provision of goods, facilities and services including discrimination in relation to premises

(Note: A new Code of Practice for Part 3 came into force in December 2006, see www.drc-gb.org).

The Act covers:

- ❖ any place where the public may enter;
- ❖ accommodation in hotels, boarding houses, etc.;
- ❖ all retailers or tradesman's premises;
- ❖ any building owned by a public authority; and
- ❖ facilities for entertainment or recreation.

Discrimination is deemed to have arisen if a provider of services treats a disabled person less favourably than he or she would treat others and:

- ❖ cannot show the treatment in question was justified; and
- ❖ failed to undertake his or her duty to make adjustments as described below.

Part 3 came into force in three distinct sections.

The following duties came into force in December 1996:

- ❖ a duty not to discriminate;
- ❖ a duty not to refuse service;

- ❖ a duty not to provide a worse standard of service; and
- ❖ a duty not to offer worse terms.

The following duties came into force in October 1999:

- ❖ a duty to change practices, policies and procedures that are discriminatory;
- ❖ a duty to provide extra help such as auxiliary aids; and
- ❖ a duty to overcome physical restrictions by the provision of alternative methods.

The following duties came into force in October 2004:

Where a physical barrier makes the use of any service which is offered to the public impossible or unreasonably difficult, a service provider must take reasonable steps to:

- ❖ remove the feature;
- ❖ alter it so it no longer has an effect;
- ❖ provide a reasonable means of avoiding the feature; or
- ❖ provide a reasonable alternative method of making the service available to disabled people.

The Act does not specify what is reasonable, as it varies according to the characteristics of each area of provision. Account may be taken of:

- ❖ the type of services being provided;
- ❖ the nature of the service provider and its size and resources;
- ❖ the effect of the disability on the individual disabled person;
- ❖ the amount of time that the service provider has had prior to that date to make preparations;
- ❖ whether taking any particular steps would be effective in overcoming the difficulty that disabled people face in accessing the services in question;
- ❖ the extent to which it is practicable for the service provider to take the steps;
- ❖ the financial and other costs of making the adjustment;
- ❖ the extent of any disruption which taking the steps would cause;
- ❖ the amount of any resources already spent on making adjustments; and
- ❖ the availability of financial or other assistance.

The Act does not require a service provider to take any steps which would fundamentally alter the nature of its service, trade, profession or business.

Further interpretation of 'reasonableness' is expected through the courts, although there is currently limited case law. The latest update on this can be found at the Disability Rights Commission website: www.drc-gb.org

Public authority functions

The DDA 2005 introduces new duties (which amend part 3 of the DDA 1995) in respect of public authority functions. The Act now prohibits discrimination in relation to every function of a public authority. The new duties came into force on 4 December 2006.

Disability Equality Duty

The DDA 2005 introduces a duty on public authorities to promote disability equality to cover disabled people in every area of their work. The duty is not necessarily about alterations to buildings or adjustments for individuals.

There are both general duties and specific duties under the Disability Equality Duty. The general duty came into force on 4 December 2006. Primary schools in England have until 3 December 2007 to publish their

Disability Equality Scheme and all schools in Wales must publish their schemes no later than 1 April 2007. The Secretaries of State, National Assembly in Wales and Scottish Ministers must produce their first report by December 2008.

DRC guidance on the Disability Equality Duty can be found at www.dotheduty.org

Private clubs

A further amendment to Part 3 affects private clubs with more than 25 members, which have been included since December 2005. The duty to make reasonable adjustments to policies, practices and procedures with the provision of auxiliary aids and services was introduced from December 2005, under the first stage of the new DDA 2005. The second stage came into force on 4 December 2006, where private clubs with more than 25 members will be required to undertake reasonable adjustments to physical features.

Discrimination in relation to letting of premises (housing)

The DDA 1995 duties have been extended under the DDA 2005, from December 2006, (in relation to letting of premises), to include a duty to make reasonable adjustments to policies, practices and procedures and to provide auxiliary aids and services, where reasonable to do so. Landlords will therefore have a duty to take reasonable steps to facilitate access for disabled tenants and leaseholders. Reasonable adjustments might include:

❖ changing a 'no dogs' policy to allow assistance dogs;

❖ changing a term in a lease prohibiting the undertaking of any alterations where the term makes it impossible or unreasonably difficult for a disabled person to enjoy the premises or make use of an associated benefit or facility; or

❖ providing a clip-on receiver, that vibrates when the doorbell rings, for a tenant with a hearing impairment.

However, landlords will not be under any duty to carry out adjustments to physical features of the premises. Furthermore, the cost of any reasonable adjustments that a landlord may have to make (in respect of policies, practices, procedures, auxiliary aids and services) cannot be recovered by way of increased rent or service charges.

Landlord responsibilities for common parts under the DDA

The duties of landlords under Part 3 of the DDA 1995 is unclear. The Code of Practice (Part 3) states that 'there is no legal duty to make reasonable adjustments to premises which are sold, let or managed'. In addition, 'those who are selling, letting or managing premises do not have to make adjustments to make those premises more suitable for disabled people'. The issue surrounding landlords' responsibilities is complex and therefore landlords of premises with more than one occupier should not assume that they are not service providers for the purposes of the Act. The Code of Practice states that 'they should anticipate that they may have responsibilities to make the common parts accessible to disabled people. They are advised to keep up to date with how the law in this respect is being interpreted'. The code of practice goes on to say 'if tenants are providing services to the public in their own right from the premises, they will have a duty under the Act to take reasonable steps to make the services accessible to disabled people'. However, landlords should be careful in the extent of works that they carry out where they would seek to recover the cost of such works from the tenants through service charge provisions.

Disability Discrimination (Providers of Services) (Adjustment of Premises) Regulations 2001

These apply to service providers and landlords of premises occupied by service holders. The regulations prescribe particular circumstances in which it is reasonable or unreasonable for service providers to make physical alterations to the premises they rent or own or for lessors to withold their approval to same. The provisions of the original DDA 1995 have been extensively amended and extreme caution should be taken when referring to material that may now be out of date. There is no substitute for professional legal advice in an environment where incorrect interpretation of the provisions is widespread.

Part 4 – Education (as amended by the Special Educational Needs and Disability Act)

Provision of education was excluded from Part 3 of the Disability Discrimination Act (Provision of Goods, Facilities and Services) as the *Education Act* 1996 made comprehensive educational provision for children with special educational needs, to which LEAs and governing bodies have a duty to comply. However, the *Special Educational Needs and Disability Act* 2001 (SENDA) was given royal assent on 11 May 2001 and came into force from 1 September 2002. The Act removes the previous exemption of education from the *Disability Discrimination Act* 1995, ensuring that discrimination against disabled students will be unlawful. The Act is an amendment to the existing DDA 1995 and only protects people defined as 'disabled' according to that legislation. This definition is based on an individual's ability to carry out normal 'day to day' activities, and so may exclude some students who are usually considered disabled by the support systems within their institutions. Education providers need to be aware of the *Learning and Skills Act* 2000, as they may need to make different provision for people covered by this legislation.

Construction professionals should note particularly the differing requirements between schools and post-16 education. Duties under post-16 education apply to higher education, further education, adult and community education, schools providing further education for adults (but excluding sixth form) and youth and community services.

SENDA (post-16 duties)

The duties of SENDA are being implemented in three stages.

The main new sections of the Act came into force on 1 September 2002. These sections make it unlawful to discriminate against disabled people or students by treating them less favourably than others. In addition, they require responsible bodies to provide certain types of reasonable adjustments to provision where disabled students or other disabled people might otherwise be substantially disadvantaged.

A duty on responsible bodies to make adjustments involving the provision of auxiliary aids and services came into force on 1 September 2003.

The duty on the responsible body to make adjustments to physical features on premises where these put disabled people or students at a substantial disadvantage came into force on 1 September 2005.

Duties under SENDA apply to higher education, further education, adult and community education, schools providing further education for adults (but excluding sixth form) and youth and community services.

SENDA (schools)

The disability discrimination duties provide protection for disabled pupils by preventing discrimination against them at school on the grounds of disability. There are two key duties involved in ensuring that schools do not discriminate against disabled pupils. These are:

❖ not to treat disabled pupils less favourably; and

❖ to take reasonable steps to avoid putting disabled pupils at a substantial disadvantage.

The reasonable adjustments duty does not require the responsible body to provide auxiliary aids and services, nor does it require the responsible body to make alterations to the physical features of the school. The reasonable adjustment duty does not apply to auxiliary aids and services because it is anticipated that in schools in the maintained sector, such provision will be made through the SEN framework. Physical alterations to schools are not required under the reasonable adjustments duty as it is anticipated that these will be achieved through a longer term and more strategic approach to improving access to school buildings through the planning duties.

The planning duties require that schools prepare and develop accessibility plans, which should address three distinct elements of planned improvements in access for disabled pupils:

- ❖ improvements in access to the curriculum;
- ❖ physical improvements to increase access to education and associated services; and
- ❖ improvements in provision of information of a range of formats for disabled pupils.

The planning duties also update the requirement on governing bodies to provide information in their annual reports about arrangements for disabled pupils at the school.

The DRC has published two Codes of Practice that set out, separately, in detail, the duties and responsibilities for both schools and post-16 education. The codes warrant detailed examination for those who are involved in educational establishments as they provide clarification and examples of potential scenarios covering the various duties and responsibilities under the Act.

The codes are available on the DRC website (www.drc-gb.org) and are titled:

- ❖ Code of Practice for schools – DDA 1995: Part IV
- ❖ Code of Practice for providers of Post-16 education and related services – DDA 1995: Part IV.

Part 5 – Public transport

Part 5 of the Act allows the government to set access standards for buses, coaches, trains, trams and taxis. Regulations have been introduced by the government to apply minimum access standards. Part 5 of the DDA applies specifically to the actual means of transport and does not include, for example, railway stations, ferry terminals, bus stations, airports and the like. These are covered under Part 3 of the Act. Under the Code of Practice, the following example is given: 'A wheelchair user has no protection under Part 3 of the Act if a ferry on which he wishes to travel is not accessible. However, if he is refused service in the buffet bar of the ferry terminal because of his disability, this is likely to be unlawful.'

The *Disability Discrimination Act* 2005 will result in further changes and improvements including extending some areas of Part 3 to include public transport. The 2005 Act provides a flexible framework which has allowed the introduction of regulations to include forms of transport into Part 3 of the DDA. The 2005 Regulations apply to breakdown recovery vehicles, hire or rental vehicles, private hire vehicles, public services vehicles (such as buses and coaches), rail vehicles (including underground rail and trams), taxis and vehicles used on a system using a mode of guided transport (e.g. monorails and guided buses). They do not yet currently include aircraft and shipping vessels, although the Act empowers the government to lift the transport exemption in respect of any form of transport service.

The transport duties introduced under Part 3 of the DDA, as amended by the *Disability Discrimination Act* 2005 and its supporting regulations, came into force on 4 December 2006. Section 6 of the DDA 2005 requires rail vehicles to be accessible by 2020.

Providers of transport services in respect of the provision or use of a vehicle covered by the 2005 Regulations are now deemed providers of services to the public for the purposes of Part 3 of the DDA.

Codes of practice and advice notes

The government has drawn up various codes of practice to help implement the Act and interpret its requirements. The codes can be downloaded from the Disability Rights Commission website at www.drc-gb.org

The DDA and the Building Regulations

Where a physical feature of a building is covered by Approved Document M of the Building Regulations, if that feature conforms or is deemed to conform to the requirements of the edition current at the time of approval or installation, a 10-year exemption applies to that specific feature from the date of installation or construction. This exemption applies to service providers only. It also used to apply to the employment provisions of the DDA although, on 1 October 2004, the Building Regulation exemption was removed from the Part 2 (Employment provisions) of the DDA.

BS 8300:2001

British Standard 8300:2001 *Design of buildings and their approaches to meet the needs of disabled people – Code of Practice* was amended in June 2005. This is an important document in the field of access for disabled people and provides extensive and detailed guidance on good practice in the design of and access to buildings and their approaches. It forms the basis for much of the amendment to the Part M Approved Document under the Building Regulations. This document is much more comprehensive than the Approved Document and, therefore, it may not be sufficient to rely uniquely on Part M.

Part M Approved Document

This recently revised guidance is based on and is complementary to BS 8300:2001, although the BS contains much additional material that is not included in the new Part M Approved Document. In some cases, the guidance in the Part M Approved Document differs from the recommendations in BS 8300. Compliance with the recommendations in the BS, therefore, while ensuring good practice, is not necessarily equivalent to compliance with the guidance in the Part M Approved Document and appropriate care should be taken when dealing with both documents.

The National Register of Access Consultants

The National Register of Access Consultants (NRAC) was established in 1999 to accredit access auditors and access consultants. Its website can be accessed at www.nrac.org.uk. There are two levels of membership: auditor or consultant. The fundamental difference between an auditor and a consultant is that consultants are required to have construction-related qualifications. Therefore, there are some limitations to the extent and detail of the advice that auditors can provide. Construction professionals such as surveyors and architects are therefore well placed to advise in this field.

The Royal Institution of Chartered Surveyors (RICS) 'Certificate in Inclusive Environments'

The RICS scheme was introduced spring 2006 to 'promote excellence in the field of inclusive environments'. The scheme is similar to that of the NRAC with the setting up of a register of individuals with appropriate knowledge, experience and skills in inclusive environments. However, it is focused at RICS members, in particular, chartered building surveyors. See www.rics.org for more information.

Case law

Since the DDA was introduced, there have been a number of cases brought forward, although case law, particularly covering Part 3, is still largely undeveloped. Please refer to the full list of DRC cases to be found on the Disability Rights Commission website www.drc-gb.org

Legislation update

It must be noted that the DDA is complex, particularly so with the DDA 2005 amendment and the introduction of new regulations and codes of practice. Care must be taken when referring to the above in light of continuing changes and developments in the DDA and the access field. In any event, legal advice may need to be sought in respect of interpretation of the law.

Access Statements

Essentially, an Access Statement is a document which shows how an applicant is addressing accessibility issues within the design of a building or space. The document would usually start off as being prepared to submit with a Planning or Building Regulation Application. Eventually, the document would be handed over to the end user to assist him or her in addressing the occupational side of access for disabled users. The statement should provide details as to the level of accessibility to be provided and in particular, document any deviation from current regulations and best practice. The reasons for deviating from these standards must also be explained. Where these are approved by the local authority, this will assist an end user by providing supporting documentary evidence as to why this has not been possible. This is particularly important where the end user has duties under the DDA.

As of 10 August 2006, an Access Statement is required to be submitted with all planning applications with the exception of householders and changes of use. Access statements are recommended to be submitted with all Building Regulation applications and should certainly be provided where the applicant deviates from Approved Document M.

Building and construction regulations

Legislation

The Building (Amendment) Regulations 2004

Building Regulations state-of-play table

Part A Structure	Approved Document A – Structure (2004 edition), in effect from 1 December 2004
Part B Fire safety	In effect from 1 March 2003 2000 edition consolidated with 2000 and 2002 amendments
Part C Site preparation	New Regulations made 28 May 2004, in effect from 1 December 2004
Part D Toxic substances	1992 edition
Part E Resistance to the passage of sound	Amended 2004 to include clarifications and correction of errors in the 2003 edition
Part F Ventilation	Revised Part F from April 2006
Part G Hygiene	1992 edition
Part H Drainage and waste disposal	2002 edition
Part J Heat producing appliances	2002 edition
Part K Protection from falling collision and impact	1998 edition
Part L Conservation of fuel and power	Parts L1A, L1B, L2A and L2B published in February 2006, and came into force in April 2006
Part M Access to and use of buildings	2004 edition
Part N Glazing	1998 edition
Part P Electrical safety	2006 edition Excludes work carried out by an approved competent person and work of a minor nature
Regulation 7	1992 edition

Part L 2006 compliance

The only way in which the international community will limit the rise in carbon emissions is if governments, industry and individuals take into account the costs associated with the emissions for which they are responsible. A key role for Government is to put in place a framework which, by placing a value on carbon, provides a financial incentive for business and households to incorporate the climate change impact in their activities.

The quote above is Crown copyright and is reproduced from the energy review report *The Energy Challenge*, published by the DTI in 2006.

Putting our contribution to the world's carbon emissions into perspective, with just 1% of the world's population the UK produces 2.3% of the world's CO_2. (Source: Friends of the Earth, 2006.)

Overview of Part L

The revised Part L was implemented in April 2006 to improve the energy efficiency of new and existing buildings, thereby contributing to the reduction of greenhouse gas emissions that are known to cause global warming. The updated Regulations are the means by which articles 3 to 6 of the EU *Energy Performance in Buildings Directive* (EPBD) are being implemented in the UK.

EPBD articles 7 to 10 will be implemented in stages by January 2009:

❖ for the provision of energy performance certificates for new and existing buildings;

❖ for the provision of regular inspection of boilers and air-conditioning plant; and

❖ for the provision of independent experts to certify, recommend improvements and inspect boilers and air-conditioning systems.

Part L 2006 Building Regulations are implemented through four separate Approved Documents, these are:

❖ AD L1A Work on new dwellings;

❖ AD L1B Work on existing dwellings;

❖ AD L2A Work on new buildings other than dwellings; and

❖ AD L2B Work on existing buildings other than dwellings.

Flexibility is afforded to designers in selecting a means of compliance to achieve the minimum national energy performance targets for new and existing buildings. These targets must be reviewed within intervals of no longer than five years. The next review of Part L is likely to be undertaken in 2010 and is predicted to reduce the emissions benchmark by a further 25% of the 2006 requirements.

The Regulations focus upon whole building energy performance to control carbon emissions in use. No prescriptive technical guidance is provided within the Approved Documents. Therefore, designers are referred to technical data from a range of sources, such as CIBSE, BRE and HVCA. These sources are described as 'Second Tier guidance documents' that are published to assist with achieving target carbon emissions and energy efficiency.

The Regulations legislate for new and existing buildings and dwellings. New buildings and dwellings are required to comply with whole building carbon emissions targets, while existing buildings are required to comply with elemental performance targets.

A provision is made to include a contribution from low or zero carbon (LZC) technologies to achieve emissions targets, such as solar hot water heating, wind turbines, biomass heating and combined heat and power systems. All of these LZC technologies are subject to their own specific efficiency, feasibility, planning and cost issues and in some buildings the cost could be a significant proportion of the total construction cost.

New buildings should be designed and constructed:

❖ to conserve fuel and power to minimise CO_2 emissions in connection with occupancy and operation;

❖ to avoid overheating in summer particularly with regard to unconditioned buildings;

❖ to reduce heat losses and heat gains through the external building fabric and also from pipes, ducts and vessels used for building services;

- ❖ to avoid unwanted and excessive solar gain and to reduce the requirements for mechanical cooling;
- ❖ to incorporate renewable and/or decentralised energy systems where feasible;
- ❖ to limit air leakage through the external fabric and ductwork;
- ❖ to demonstrate compliance upon construction completion by the undertaking of commissioning activities and providing certification; and
- ❖ to have operation and maintenance manuals and log books in place to ensure that efficiency of the installed systems is maintained in operation.

National calculation methodology (NCM)

A calculation methodology is a requirement of EPBD article 3 for validating a building's compliance. The implementation of this in the UK is through the Simplified Building Energy Model (SBEM). SBEM is the Part L specified national calculation software tool created by the BRE for calculating carbon emissions for dwellings over 450m² and for all buildings other than dwellings. The process for calculation involves inputting all aspects of the building design into the SBEM software to establish the emissions rate, which must be within the Target Emission Rate (TER) set for the type of building being considered. The Part L specified calculation method for dwellings under 450m² is the Standard Assessment Procedure 2005 (SAP).

The target carbon dioxide Emission Rate (TER) is the measurement of a building's efficiency and this is measured as the mass of CO_2 emitted per year, per square metre of the total useful floor area of the building shown as kg/m²/year. The type of fuel to be used for a building will have a direct impact upon the carbon emissions calculation. Natural gas, for example, has an equivalent CO_2 emission of 0.194kg CO_2/kWh, whereas grid supplied electricity has an equivalent CO_2 emission of 0.422kg CO_2/kWh. The fuel factor applied to grid electricity is higher than natural gas when calculating building carbon emissions due to the inefficient nature of its production and delivery. The use of fuel factors will have a direct impact upon the Emissions Rate for a building.

There are a number of commercial software tools now available which have been approved for use by the Department for Communities and Local Government (DCLG) which can assist with checking for Part L compliance. These tools are designed to be more flexible, user friendly and quicker to input data than the SBEM tool.

Emissions calculations will need to be undertaken around outline design stage to ensure the building design being considered is likely to fall within the TER and by what margin, before progressing into more detailed design – to avoid abortive design works. When the design becomes fixed, the calculations should then be updated to serve as a final check for design compliance with the TER. This is likely to impose limitations for the design team to make substantial changes to the design later on, if they are to avoid abortive work and costs.

It is important to note that building compliance must be proved at building control submission stage and then again upon completion of the building. There is a risk that, if the construction deviates from the prescribed specification and workmanship upon which Part L compliance relies upon, the completed building could fail to comply and may potentially be costly to remedy.

Design features to achieve whole building energy performance

The specifications listed below can contribute to achieving Part L compliance:

❖ Solar shading to reduce solar gain, through external shading and/or double wall facades, for example. This would reduce cooling loads, particularly when natural ventilation is incorporated.

❖ Low 'e' glazing.

❖ Orientate the building in accordance with the direction of the sun and its angle during each of the seasons.

❖ High boiler and chiller efficiencies.

❖ High external envelope air tightness.

❖ High artificial lighting efficiency and lighting control systems which utilise occupation and daylight sensors.

❖ High fan and pump efficiencies.

❖ Maximise heat recovery using heat exchangers or run around coils, for example.

❖ Narrow plan floor plates, to maximise natural daylight together with shading control, for example, enabling luminaires to be switched on only when daylight is insufficient for occupant activity.

❖ Utilise exposed thermal mass of structure and fabric together with night-time ventilation/purging for passive cooling.

❖ Combined heat and power systems.

❖ Heat pumps for heating and cooling; either through traditional mechanical plant or ground coupling.

❖ Building-integrated renewable energy systems.

❖ Enhanced thermal insulation levels to walls, floors, roofs and glazing.

❖ Optimise the proportion of facade and roof glazing and the type used to limit perimeter and roof heat gains in summer, and losses in winter.

❖ Triple glazing.

❖ Maximise alternative means of ventilation and cooling involving 'mix mode' ventilation and 'free cooling' where feasible.

❖ Effectively use Building Energy Management Systems to optimise services efficiency and energy monitoring.

❖ Specify direct current/low energy fan coil systems.

❖ Specify chilled beam or chilled ceiling systems.

None of the above items listed are particularly revolutionary and indeed have been incorporated into pre-2006 Part L designed buildings. The Part L Regulations provide the flexibility to consider any and all of the specifications above, however the design solution selected will be a consequence of the most cost effective and practical solution that achieves the TER whilst still meeting the design brief provided by the client.

Regulations compliance for existing buildings

Where a building undergoes alteration, renovation and refurbishment, the types of work listed below fall within the remit of Part L.

Extensions – an extension over 100m² and greater than 25% of an existing building qualifies as a new building and must comply with AD L1A. Extensions to buildings can also trigger certain requirements to achieve minimum thermal and energy efficiency standards, these are called 'consequential improvements' and are discussed further below.

Material alteration and change of energy status – such as where work would lead to non-compliance of a building or service that previously complied and therefore minimum energy efficiency standards must be achieved.

Material change of use – such as conversion of private commercial building to a public building.

Extension, alteration or revision of a controlled (thermal) element – captures windows, doors, walls and conservatories, for example, and prescribes minimum energy efficiency standards.

Extension, alteration or revision of a controlled service or fitting – captures lighting, mechanical ventilation and cooling systems, heating and hot water systems, etc. and prescribes minimum energy efficiency standards.

Consequential improvements – for existing non-domestic buildings with a floor area over 1,000m², where a new extension is to be constructed or there will be an increase in the capacity of fixed building services, 'consequential improvements' may have to be implemented to upgrade an existing building's thermal performance. Consequential improvements will be required even where the existing building is not directly affected by the proposed building works. The extent of consequential improvements as advised in the Approved Documents is limited to works that are technically, functionally and economically feasible and not more than 10% of value of principal works, with a simple payback of not more than 15 years.

For an extension, consequential improvements of not less than 10% of the value of the principal works should be spent (when practical and economically feasible) on measures such as:

❖ upgrading heating, cooling or air-handling systems that are more than 15 years old;

❖ upgrading general lighting systems that cover an area in excess of 100m² which have a lamp efficiency of less than 40 lamp-lumens per circuit-watt;

❖ installing energy metering;

❖ upgrading thermal elements with high U-values;

❖ replacing existing windows to achieve lower U-values; and

❖ incorporate on-site low and zero-carbon energy generating systems to provide at least 10% of a building's energy needs.

There are different requirements for historic buildings, particularly those of a listed nature. Listed or 'protected' buildings are exempt from Part L compliance. For buildings which are not exempt the local authority may require certain works are undertaken providing that the original historic character of the building is not affected or compromised.

In assessing the scope of work required, the carbon emissions approach can be used, in addition to elemental performance compliance, to demonstrate that the modified building meets its target.

The approach to achieving compliance for existing buildings is not straightforward. The assessment of the appropriate scope of improvement works for existing buildings will be, by necessity, a trade-off between the ease of implementation, the effectiveness in achieving the TER and of course the capital cost measured against cost-in-use. The energy survey carried out as part of a project to identify and assess the challenges and opportunities will be a key aspect of this process.

How will the Part L compliance affect the way new dwellings and buildings are designed?

Will architects still be able to specify office buildings with fully glazed facades and Fan Coil or VAV air-conditioning systems?

There are two schools of thought on this subject: either that compliance will not be possible if the combination of 100% glazing and fan coil or VAV are designed, or that compliance will be possible with a little bit of creative design with other parts of the building specifications. The overriding factor which determines compliance is the extent to which the flexible design approach is exploited. This is likely to involve new innovative and energy efficient approaches to design and also incorporating alternative technologies.

When designing buildings with full air conditioning, a key consideration in energy use is the perimeter heat gains in summer and heat losses in winter. These are a function of the proportion of facade glazing and also the type of glazing used in conjunction with the level of shading provided at the facades. If Part L compliance cannot be achieved with conventional air-conditioning systems, then alternative solutions may have to be explored for ventilation and cooling such as 'mix mode' ventilation and active and passive cooling where the design permits.

The thermal mass or inertia of a structure and its thermal elements will become more important in achieving compliant design solutions in the future to reduce the reliance upon totally mechanical ventilation solutions and thus reducing carbon emissions. This is because natural passive or mix-mode ventilation solutions can be utilised to harness the thermal mass of a building to regulate changes in temperature without the intervention of total mechanical temperature control. The thermal properties of a structure will determine how swiftly the internal temperatures will respond to heat gains and losses and also how sensitive the internal environment is to temperature fluctuations. Generally speaking, heavyweight structures such as concrete and brick have a high thermal mass and lightweight structures such as cladding, curtain walling and steel have a low thermal mass.

The indications so far are that it will still be possible to specify buildings with 100% glazed facade, however a significant improvement in other aspects of the building performance would be necessary to ensure compliance with Part L. It is still apparently possible to incorporate electric heating into apartments, but again efficiencies must be incorporated elsewhere into the design if compliance is to be achieved.

An easy and low cost way to contribute to achieving Part L, particularly for offices, is to include energy efficient lamps within all luminaires to reduce energy consumption and cooling loads. This is because installing efficient lighting does not require the building envelope to be upgraded and provides a cost effective contribution to carbon reductions.

Improving the thermal performance of the external fabric and glazing is only generally cost effective up to a point and does not significantly contribute to the reduction of carbon emissions for many buildings, particularly when compared to improvements that can be made to the efficiencies of building services installations and providing an airtight facade. Making improvements to the efficiency of building services and the provision of an airtight facade may have a greater capital cost implication, however, the building would benefit from greater energy efficiency and this could lead to downsizing of central plant, thus reducing operational costs over the life of a building.

In dwellings, hot water generation produces a significant proportion of domestic total carbon emissions. Therefore, incorporating enhanced hot water tank insulation, high efficiency heat source(s) and solar hot water heating can provide the necessary scope for achieving the carbon emissions targets.

Air leakage testing is a crucial test of compliance with Part L, and dwellings and buildings that fail the air pressure tests will be subject to prescribed methods of retesting. Establishing liability for failures may be difficult, particularly in relation to poor design detailing or poor workmanship on site. Somebody has to pay to rectify the air leakage paths that caused the air test failures and responsibility has to be established. Air leakage testing takes place when a building is almost or entirely complete, therefore the discovery of significant failures could have a significant impact on the completion programme due to additional time spent carrying out remedial works and retesting.

Revised Part F

It is important to briefly summarise that Part F *Ventilation* was also revised and implemented in April 2006 in line with Part L because airtightness requirements for buildings have increased and therefore designers must ensure that adequate ventilation is provided within the occupied spaces. Part F and Part L are closely linked and strategies for compliance by way of a combination of extract ventilation, whole building ventilation and purge ventilation can be adopted to provide the required rates of fresh air and extract.

Will Part L cost more?

The indications are that it will cost more to build new or refurbish existing buildings to comply with Part L 2006 than it would cost to build Part L 2002 compliant buildings. A general range of up to a 5% addition to the construction cost is estimated, although the cost uplift is entirely dependent upon the design strategy adopted to achieve the carbon performance requirements. The additional costs could be significantly over the 5% for PFI schemes where life cycle performance is particularly crucial. There is also the influence of consequential improvements to be factored into a budget if an existing building falls within this jurisdiction.

Where designs include a high contribution from LZC technologies and/or highly innovative design solutions in the architecture, the stated 5% addition would almost certainly be exceeded. Therefore, close collaboration between all members of the design team to work towards achieving the most cost efficient and practical compliance solution is essential.

Important note

Note that this section is a brief summation of the Part L 2006 Building Regulations and its applications. Therefore, the Approved Documents and their specified 'Second Tier Guidance Documents' should be referred to in the first instance for specific project application.

Further information

ODPM (now Department for Communities and Local Government), *Low or zero carbon energy sources: Strategic guide*, 2006:

www.planningportal.gov.uk/uploads/br/BR_PDF_PTL_ZEROCARBONfinal.pdf

ODPM (now Department for Communities and Local Government) *Regulatory Impact Assessment report*, 2006:

www.communities.gov.uk/pub/308/RegulatoryImpactAssessmentPartLandApprovedDocumentF2006_id1164308.pdf

ODPM (now Department for Communities and Local Government) Approved Documents Parts L1A, L1B, L2A and L2B:

www.planningportal.gov.uk/england/professionals/en/1115314110382.html

Part L explained – The BRE guide, BrePress, 2006

See also the Planning Portal: www.planningportal.gov.uk

Airtightness

Parts L1 and L2 of the Building Regulations contain, among other things, a requirement for minimising air leakage from buildings.

Achieving an airtight building means following three essential steps:

❖ design for airtightness;

❖ build for airtightness; and

❖ test for airtightness.

It is not practicable to construct a building and then try to make it airtight. Remedial sealing can be difficult and costly. By designing in airtightness at the drawing stage you can deal with air barrier continuity and sealing details at critical elements – and ensure long-term performance by specifying the correct seal or sealant.

The main air leakage problems in buildings occur typically:

❖ around doors, windows, panels and cladding details;

❖ in gaps where the structure penetrates the construction envelope;

❖ in service entries: pipes, ducts flues, ventilators;

❖ in porous construction: bricks, blocks, mortar joints; and

❖ in joist connections within intermediate floors.

Designers should identify all the problem areas, for example, sealing around pipe entries, and spell out responsibility for finishing off in the contract documents.

Constructing the building to the airtightness specification is then down to the main contractor and subcontractors. For this to be successful all of the workforce should be aware of airtightness issues in the same way as safety issues and codes of conduct are dealt with.

Inspection during construction is essential. Talking to and working with contractors is the best way of ensuring that the team understands the importance of the airtightness layer and how to incorporate it.

The only real way to be confident that the building meets an airtightness specification is to carry out a fan pressurisation test prior to handover as required in the proposed revisions to Part L. Large buildings, for example, hypermarkets or industrial buildings, need specialist larger capacity equipment.

If the three essential steps listed earlier are followed, the building should pass the test. In the event they are not and the building fails, the proposals in Part L state: 'If on first testing the building fails to comply, the major sources of air leakage should be identified using the techniques described in TM23 [CIBSE Technical Memorandum].' This usually requires specialist help.

Despite improved understanding of construction techniques, few buildings are sufficiently airtight – this is true of new buildings as well as old. In a recent survey, only one out of 39 buildings tested met a good practice benchmark for airtightness. While the degree of leakage varies considerably from building to building, it is not unusual for the problem to be equivalent to having a 9m² hole in the building envelope.

Both the government and CIBSE regard airtightness as a serious issue and encourage protective measures.

Airtightness testing

CIBSE has produced a guide titled *Testing Buildings for Air Leakage* (TM23: 2000).

The technique that is most commonly used to measure air leakage is 'fan pressurisation testing'. This involves a specially designed system of fan units that blow air into the building, and the measurement of air leakage from the building at various air pressures.

Testing can be carried out on any building from a large hypermarket, multi-storey office block or factory to a small store, office or even an individual room within a building. Testing a large office or superstore takes about three hours and is generally done out of business hours when the premises are closed.

Health and safety at work for surveyors

Essential legal duties

The *Health and Safety at Work etc. Act* 1974 requires all surveyors to ensure, so far as is reasonably practicable, the health and safety of themselves and any other people who may be affected by their work.

In essence, the places where surveyors' work must be safe and working practices must be clearly defined, organised, and followed to avoid danger. This requires safety training and the distribution of relevant information, followed up by diligent and regular supervision.

These duties extend to anyone who uses surveyors' professional services.

Those who lease part of their premises to other businesses also may be responsible for them with regard to safety matters.

In addition, all working people whether employees, managers, partners or directors (self-employed or not) must behave in a way that does not endanger themselves or others.

Health and safety policy statement

Every firm of surveyors which employs five or more people is obliged by the Act to draw up a health and safety policy statement, which should be kept up to date, with any significant revisions being notified to employees.

The Health and Safety Executive (HSE) in *Writing your health and safety policy statement: how to prepare a safety statement for smaller businesses* describes what the document should say and gives a useful pro-forma.

It is suggested that employees, especially when taking a new job, should satisfy themselves that they have seen and understood the company's policy statement and have been made familiar with safe working practices. If they consider that the Health and Safety at Work Act is not being followed, they ought to say so, and if necessary ask advice from their local HSE office (listed in the telephone directory).

Practical procedures

Surveyors should identify the hazards they may encounter in practice, carry out a risk assessment and plan accordingly. The way they proceed will depend upon the working environment: when surveying old and derelict buildings, for example, there may be holes in floors, parts of the structure may be unstable or there may be health hazards. Particular care should be taken to protect against personal attack.

The Control of Substances Hazardous to Health Regulations 2002

The purpose of the *Control of Substances Hazardous to Health Regulations* 2002 is to safeguard the health of people using or coming into contact with substances that are hazardous to health.

Substances are classified as being very toxic/toxic, harmful, corrosive or irritant. Under these regulations employers are required to evaluate the risk of all products used that may be harmful to the health of their employees and take appropriate measures to prevent or control exposure.

The 'Six Pack' Regulations

This set of original six sets of regulations were introduced in 1993. They were wide ranging and, with some minor exceptions, apply to all places of work, replacing and consolidating various individual acts or regulations applicable to individual industries or sectors of industry, such as the *Factories Act*, the *Offices, Shops and Railway Premises Act*, and the *Construction Regulations*.

Workplace (Health, Safety and Welfare) Regulations 1992

These apply to all workplaces. The regulations set out the minimum requirements in respect of the provision and maintenance of the environmental conditions, space allocation, sanitary and welfare provision of employees. In addition, they impose particular safety requirements on forms of construction or circumstances which are considered to be high risk. They do not apply to construction sites.

Provision and Use of Work Equipment Regulations 1998

These apply to all workplaces. Basically, all existing and new work equipment which includes everything hired or purchased second hand, must comply with the regulations.

Every employer must ensure that all work equipment is so constructed or adapted as to be suitable for the purpose for which it is used or provided. They identify specific hazards that the employer must prevent or adequately control.

Manual Handling Operations Regulations 1992

These require the employer to try to avoid the need for employees to undertake any manual handling operations at work that involve a risk of their being injured. Where this is not reasonably practicable the risk must be assessed and suitable provision made, including equipment, instruction and training for safe manual handling.

Management of Health and Safety at Work Regulations 1999

These regulations are of a wide-ranging general nature and overlap with many others. They require the employer to carry out an assessment of the risks of the hazards to which his or her employees are exposed at work or to others arising from or in connection with this work. The employer must instigate appropriate protective or preventive measures, reviewing and amending these as necessary.

The employer must appoint a 'competent person' to provide assistance in respect of these duties. Emergency procedures must be put in force to deal with any serious and imminent danger. Employees must be informed of these measures and suitably trained where required. They are obliged to comply with these instructions and warn of any situation considered to be a serious and immediate danger to health and safety.

Personal Protective Equipment at Work Regulations 1992

Under these regulations the employer has a duty to provide and maintain suitable personal protective equipment including adequate instruction and training on its correct use when risks to health and safety cannot be avoided by other means. Employees have a duty to make full and proper use of such equipment provided and to report any loss or obvious defects.

Display Screen Equipment Regulations 1992

The need for the regulations is primarily the evidence of repetitive strain injury that is reported by keyboard users, the amount of time lost due to other causes of sickness among users and, of course, the European Directive.

These regulations target full time users of visual display units, mainly in the banking, insurance and data processing sectors but, given that most of the medium and larger companies will have in their offices a number of full time or habitual users, then these regulations will apply. They will also apply in the office facility of a construction site, if any persons are habitual users of visual display units.

The Construction (Health, Safety and Welfare) Regulations 1996

The CHSW Regulations came into force on 2 September 1996, to form a single set of regulations applicable to construction work and construction sites. They consolidate, modernise and simplify much of the previous legislation and complete the EC Directive on construction.

Their aim is to protect the health, safety and welfare of everyone 'carrying out construction work' and also to protect those affected by the work.

The regulations impose requirements with respect to:

- ❖ the provision of safe places of work and safe access and egress thereto (regulation 5);
- ❖ the provision of suitable equipment to prevent falls (regulation 6);
- ❖ working on or near fragile material (regulation 7);
- ❖ the prevention of injury from falling objects (regulation 8);
- ❖ the stability of structures (regulation 9);
- ❖ the carrying out and supervision of demolition and dismantling and the use of explosives (regulations 10, 11);
- ❖ the safety of excavations, cofferdams and caissons (regulations 12, 13);
- ❖ the prevention of drowning (regulation 14);
- ❖ the movement of pedestrian and vehicular traffic (regulation15);
- ❖ the construction of doors, gates and hatches (regulation 16);
- ❖ the use of vehicles (regulation 17);
- ❖ the risks from fire, the provision of emergency routes and exits, the preparation and implementation of evacuation procedures and the provision of fire-fighting equipment, fire detectors and alarms (regulations 18, 19, 20, 21);
- ❖ the provision of sanitary and washing facilities, a supply of drinking water, rest facilities and facilities to change and store clothing (regulation 22);
- ❖ the provision of adequate fresh air, reasonable temperature and weather protection (regulations 23, 24);
- ❖ the provision of lighting, including emergency lighting (regulation 25);
- ❖ the marking and good order of a construction site (regulation 26);
- ❖ the safety and maintenance of plant and equipment (regulation 27); and
- ❖ training and supervision (regulation 28).

Points to note (including changes of current practice)

Application of the regulations

The Health and Safety Executive is, in certain circumstances, able to issue exemption certificates subject to conditions or time limitations deemed appropriate and which may be subsequently revoked if considered necessary.

Subjective requirements

As with other recent health and safety legislation, the regulations have moved away from prescriptive demands and most of the requirements are, to the extent that they are 'suitable and sufficient', to be determined on the basis of a risk assessment of the particular circumstances. In addition, many are qualified by their 'reasonable practicability', which means that the action to be taken should be proportionate to the risk involved.

Scaffolding

This is one instance where the requirements are prescriptive and the measurements stated mean that virtually all scaffolding and working platforms will require an intermediate guard rail or other means of physical protection, such as a brick guard.

Welfare

The responsibility for the provision of suitable and sufficient welfare facilities is now that of the 'person in control of a construction site' as well as the employer of the site operatives or the self employed.

The washing facilities are to be appropriate to the nature of the work and there is an inference that showers may be required in certain circumstances.

The Health and Safety Executive is paying great attention to the adequacy of welfare facilities on sites and has pointed out that some wash hand basins will need to be of sufficient depth to enable the complete forearm to be immersed for proper cleaning. On occasion, basins have been kept deliberately shallow to minimise the water required.

Falls

Particular emphasis is put on the measures to be taken to prevent persons falling from a height and the regulations set out a hierarchy of alternative methods by which this may be achieved. This takes into account practicability, physical constraints and the duration of the work. The use of safety harnesses, as with all personal protective equipment, should be a last resort.

Prevention and control of emergencies

There are specific requirements to plan for unforeseen circumstances that may arise on construction sites. To prevent risk from fire, explosion, flooding and asphyxiation, procedures for evacuating the site must be established, including emergency escape routes and, where necessary, fire fighting equipment, fire detectors and alarm systems must be provided.

Traffic movement

There are requirements to ensure the safe use and movement of vehicles used in connection with construction work and the provision of safe traffic routes generally.

Further information

For further details, reference should be made to the regulations themselves (ISBN 0 11 035904 6 available from HMSO or www.opsi.gov.uk/si/si1996/Uksi_19961592_en_l.htm).

In addition, the HSE has produced a guidance publication *Health and Safety in Construction* which describes practical ways of complying with the regulations (ISBN 0 7176 1143 4).

The Construction (Design and Management) Regulations 1994

The *Construction (Design and Management) Regulations* 1994 (CDM) provide the framework for managing health and safety during the construction, repair, maintenance and demolition of civil engineering and building works.

They impose statutory duties on clients, designers and planning supervisors and contractors.

The principal objectives are to:

- ❖ ensure proper consideration and coordination of health and safety issues at every phase of a project, from feasibility study to demolition;
- ❖ obtain adequate allocation of resources (including sufficient time) to enable duties imposed by the regulations to be met;
- ❖ involve directly, allocate and share responsibilities between all participants (including the client); and
- ❖ promote the appointment of competent (from a health and safety viewpoint) designers, planning supervisors and contractors.

To achieve its aims, for each new project to which the regulations apply, two documents are required:

Health and safety plan – in two stages, planning and construction, to convey health and safety information to the contractor during the tender and construction phases of the project.

Health and safety file – a record of information relevant to health and safety to be retained by the client, made available and used throughout the life of the building or structure to assist its safe maintenance, alteration or demolition.

The client must appoint a health and safety coordinator. This role is separated for the pre-contract planning and post-contract implementation phases of the project: i.e. the planning supervisor, who is ultimately responsible for the preparation and coordination of the safety plan, up to the appointment of the principal contractor. The principal contractor takes over responsibility for developing and implementing the safety plan during the construction phase of the project.

Revised Approved Code of Practice 'Managing Health and Safety in Construction' published by Health and Safety Commission (HSG 224)

The current ACOP came into effect on 1 February 2002.

Its aim is to rectify confusion and shortcomings identified in the previous publication, in particular to improve the focus of work carried out by the various duty holders and reduce bureaucracy.

The ACOP has been reformatted in a more logical, user-friendly layout and emphasises the financial and other benefits of the CDM regulations, provided they are implemented appropriately.

It clarifies a number of matters which were previously often misinterpreted, by listing those matters which are not required to be included in health and safety documents or which are excluded from the responsibility of particular duty holders, by giving examples of both good and bad practice and by changing the emphasis of particular issues.

The topics where there are significant changes are summarised below and, for each, the concern to be addressed is described, followed by the suggested means of improvement.

Competence and resources

Expense and wasted effort arising from use of assessment questionnaires and processes that are often excessive, unnecessary and inappropriate. Assessments should:

- ❖ form part of the more general checks routinely carried out (for example, quality, finance and viability),
- ❖ focus on the particular project, and
- ❖ be proportionate to the risks, size and complexity of the work.

Time and programme

Duty holders not appointed early enough in the project, design considerations made too late and (design and construction) programmes unrealistic.

- ❖ Planning supervisor, principal contractor and other key people must be appointed as soon as possible.
- ❖ Design risks to be identified and removed or reduced early in the design process, at the concept and scheme stages, not left until detail design.

Design and designers

Using unnecessarily sophisticated risk analysis techniques; identifying risks but not adapting the design to remove or reduce them and overlooking less obvious 'designers'.

- ❖ A team approach to risk consideration is recommended.
- ❖ ACOP lists untypical designers, including temporary works engineers, interior designers, shop fitters, trade contractors and manufacturers of purpose-made products.
- ❖ ACOP lists ways in which the designer can have direct positive influence on risks and circumstances in which relevant information must be provided to others together with those matters which are not the designer's responsibility.

Clients

Failing to appreciate the full scope of the definition of a 'client'; unnecessarily monitoring performance of others and not providing information, either at all or in sufficient time.

- ❖ ACOP gives examples of other parties who may be 'project originators' and thus take on 'client duties'.
- ❖ No legal duty under CDM regulations to review assessments, monitor performance of appointees or continued adequacy of the health and safety plan during the construction phase.
- ❖ ACOP provides examples of relevant information to be provided to the planning supervisor early enough for implications to be assessed by the designer.

Health and safety plan and file

Inclusion of unnecessary and irrelevant information that can affect detrimentally the ease of identification and significance of crucial details.

- ❖ Appendix 3 contains a list of matters that should be included or addressed within the health and safety plan, where relevant to the work proposed. This is in tabular format with those of the pre-tender stage alongside those of the construction phase under the same topic headings, to illustrate and compare the appropriate requirements for each.
- ❖ Appendix 4 has a similar list of contents of the health and safety file and the ACOP also lists those topics that do not need to be included.

Consultation of construction workers

Decisions on health and safety arrangements are often made without consulting workers.

ACOP extols the necessity for and the benefits of obtaining feedback from workers' formal or informal safety committees or representatives, by addressing common problems, reviewing accidents and near misses, and identifying and considering how risks should be addressed on site.

Proposals for radical changes to CDM Regulations

The consultation period ended in July 2005 and at the time of going to print the new regulations have been delayed to Spring 2007.

The current regulations are too bureaucratic and HSE want to consolidate construction H&S regulations and extend responsibility of client in respect of project management.

Differences between current and proposed regulations:

Application of regulations to projects

Project is either notifiable or not (only by virtue of time, no distinction for demolition or numbers employed on project).

Client

❖ Must appoint 'coordinator' before design or planning and ensure they perform.

❖ Ensure suitable project management arrangements are in place.

❖ Cannot appoint agent in his or her place.

❖ Must ensure suitable welfare facilities are in place prior to works commencing.

Coordinator

❖ Replaces 'planning supervisor' as the advisor and 'friend of the client' to assist the client, designer(s) and principal contractor.

❖ Must advise client on measures required.

❖ Coordinates the 'information pack' – coordination rather than current production of generic paperwork.

Information Pack

❖ Replaces the 'Pre-construction H&S Plan'.

❖ This is a 'flow of information' contributed by all the various parties, rather than a single document, which is to be used to obtain tenders from Principal Contractor and others.

Principal Contractor

❖ Duties as before.

❖ No requirement to be a 'contractor'.

Construction Phase Plan

❖ Replaces 'Construction health and safety plan' and has same requirements.

❖ Mandatory for 'demolition or dismantling' even if project is not notifiable.

Health and Safety File

No change except requirement for a file for each site or structure rather than just one for whole project.

The Workplace Regulations - Glazing

The *Workplace (Health, Safety and Welfare) Regulations* 1992, regulation 14, require that glazed doors (and gates) be fitted with safety materials where any part of the glazing is below shoulder height. This requirement applies to glazing in the panels at the sides of the doors (and gates) because these areas are often struck or pushed when mistaken for part of the door.

The requirements also apply to windows, walls and partitions where there is glazing below waist height.

In situations where the width of the glass panel exceeds 250mm then safety materials must be used. Safety materials include:

❖ polycarbonates, glass blocks or other materials that are inherently robust; or

❖ glass that will break safely (i.e. shatters without a chance of sharp edges) or ordinary annealed glass that is of sufficient thickness relative to its area, as outlined in the following table.

Nominal thickness	Maximum size
8mm	1100 x 1100mm
10mm	2250 x 2250mm
12mm	3000 x 4500mm
15mm	Any size

Therefore, just because annealed glass exists, it does not follow that additional protection is required.

Glazing should always comply with British Standard BS 6262: Part 4: 2005 *Glazing for Building: Code of practice for safety related to human impact.*

In circumstances where glazing does not comply, it will be necessary to replace it with safety materials or to provide some physical protection that will ensure that it meets the impact performance levels required by BS 6262, Part 4: 2005.

A cheaper alternative would be to apply safety film to achieve the BS 6262 standard. Manufacturers of film should be consulted to ensure an appropriate grade of material for glass size.

All glass should be suitably marked as being of a safety standard. Where glass is protected by film, labelling should identify this.

Identification

Laminated and toughened glass can be detected using proprietary glass testing kits.

Note that ordinary Georgian wired glass does not comply with safety standards, but Georgian wired safety glass does.

The Workplace Regulations – Provision of sanitary facilities

The *Workplace (Health, Safety and Welfare) Regulations* require that sanitary provision shall be suitable and sufficient for the numbers and types of workers employed.

BS 6465: Part 1: 1994 sets out the minimum requirements.

It contains numerous tables illustrating the number and types of sanitary appliances required for a variety of different circumstances, depending on: the number of workers, and where relevant, customers; the ratio of males to females; and the different primary uses of the building in question.

The types of building include offices, shops, factories, restaurants, cafes, canteens and fast-food outlets, swimming pools, stadia, public houses, licensed bars, other places of public entertainment and non-domestic premises.

Comparison of requirements for 100 people evenly divided between the sexes (not including wheelchair users)								
Building type	Male			Female		Total		
	wc	urinal	whb	wc	whb	wc	urinal	whb
Workplaces	3	2	3	3	3	6	2	6
Workplaces (dirtier conditions)	3	2	3	3	5	6	2	8
Shops (customers) 1000 – 2000m²	1	1	1	2	2	3	1	3
Shops (customers) 2000 – 4000m²	1	2	2	4	4	5	2	6
Restaurants	1	1	2	2	2	3	1	4
Public houses, etc.	1	2	2	3	2	4	2	4

wc = water closet   whb = wash hand basin

The Workplace Regulations – Falls from height

Falls from height are the most common cause of fatal injury and the second most common cause of major injury to employees in the workplace. Most falls are the result of poor management rather than equipment failure.

Common examples include:

❖ failure to recognise a problem;

❖ failure to provide safe systems of work;

❖ failure to ensure that safe systems of work are followed;

❖ failure to provide adequate information, instruction, training or supervision;

❖ failure to provide safe plant or equipment; and

❖ failure to use appropriate equipment.

HSE has produced a number of free leaflets on falls from height that can be downloaded from their website at www.hse.gov.uk/falls. These include general advice such as 'Safe use of ladders and stepladders' as well as the use of specific equipment such as 'Safety in window cleaning using rope access techniques'.

The principles of good practice to prevent falls are contained within the *Work at Height Regulations* 2005.

The Work at Height Regulations 2005

These regulations came into operation on 6 April 2005.

They apply to all work where there is a risk of a fall liable to cause personal injury, even if the fall is at or below ground level.

The regulations place duties on employers, the self-employed and anyone who controls the work of others.

Employers must do all that is reasonably practicable to prevent falling by following a hierarchy for managing and selecting appropriate equipment:

- ❖ Avoid work at height if possible.
- ❖ If not, use work equipment to prevent falls.
- ❖ Where risk of fall cannot be eliminated, use equipment or other measures to minimise the distance and consequences of any fall.
- ❖ Select collective measures to prevent falls (e.g. guardrails and working platforms) before measures which may only mitigate the distance and consequences of a fall (e.g. nets or airbags) or which may only provide personal protection from a fall (e.g. fall arrest lanyards).

Employees must report any safety hazards and properly use the equipment supplied to them.

Duty holders must ensure that:

- ❖ all work is properly planned and organised;
- ❖ work activities take account of weather conditions;
- ❖ persons involved are trained and competent;
- ❖ the place of work is safe;
- ❖ equipment is appropriately inspected; and
- ❖ risks arising from fragile surfaces and from falling objects are properly controlled.

The Workplace Regulations – Lighting

Regulations

The key provisions relating to lighting can be found in the following Regulations:

- ❖ **The Workplace (Health, Safety and Welfare) Regulations 1992**
  - Lighting in workplaces should be suitable and sufficient to enable people to work and move about safely. If necessary, local lighting should be provided, and at places of particular risk, such as crossing points of traffic routes.
  - Lighting shall, so far as is reasonably practicable, be by natural light.
  - Lighting and light fittings should not create a hazard.

- Automatic emergency lighting, powered by an independent source, should be provided where sudden loss of light would create a risk.

❖ **Health and Safety (Display Screen Equipment) Regulations 1992**
  - Satisfactory lighting and appropriate contrast between screen and background to suit type of work and visual requirements of the operator.

❖ **Provision and Use of Work Equipment Regulations 1992**
  - Again, these Regulations require lighting to be both suitable and sufficient.

❖ **Building Regulations Part L**
  - Applies to all new non-domestic buildings over 100 square metres and certain buildings undergoing a change of use. Excludes exterior lighting.
  - Includes requirements for energy-efficient lighting, lamps and luminaries and controls. Aims to encourage maximum use of daylight and avoid unnecessary lighting when spaces are unoccupied.

Guidance

The Chartered Institution of Building Services Engineers (CIBSE) and the Society of Light and Lighting (SLL) (see www.cibse.org for both) have published a number of useful and authoritative guides:

❖ Guidance Note (GN2:1993) *Healthy Workplaces – on compliance with the Workplace Regulations*;

❖ *Code for Interior Lighting* generally, and other task-specific guides e.g. LG1: *Industrial Environment*;

❖ LG3: *Areas for visual display terminals*; and

❖ TM12: *Emergency Lighting*.

ISO 9241 *Ergonomic requirements for office work with visual display terminals (VDTs)*.

BS 5266 – covers minimum levels and for emergency lighting.

The absolute minimum lighting level for particular tasks is set out in HS(G)38 *Lighting at Work* published by HSE.

Other considerations

Other considerations to take into account in relation to lighting would include:

❖ safe access for cleaning and maintenance;

❖ temperature of fitting(s);

❖ reflection and glare; and

❖ ease of control.

Surveying safely

The RICS publication *Surveying Safely – your guide to personal safety at work*, is available as a free PDF download from www.rics.org/management/Healthandsafety/surv_safe.htm.

The guide comprises ten sections:

❖ General statement of employers' and employees duties.

❖ Safety of employees.

❖ Your workplace.
❖ Identifying hazards and undertaking risk assessments.
❖ Before visiting premises/sites – lists 13 situations/factors to be taken into consideration including 'lone working' and the environment.
❖ Upon arrival and during visits to premises/sites – lists common hazards under ten subheadings.
❖ Safety of you and others.
❖ Your legal duties.
❖ Case studies – five examples of criminal and civil prosecutions and punishments for health and safety breaches.

Town and country planning in England

Planning and Compulsory Purchase Act 2004

The Planning and Compulsory Purchase Act 2004 is the cornerstone of the planning system in England and Wales. It represented the first major legislative change to the planning system for nearly 14 years and gave effect to the government's policy of reforming planning and creating 'sustainable communities'. Sustainable development is now the core principle underpinning planning.

This Act introduced powers for the reform and speeding up of the development plan system and increasing the predictability of planning decisions.

The publication of the *Barker Review of Land Use Planning* in December 2006 suggests that further reforms of the planning system are imminent. A White Paper is expected in the spring of 2007 in response to the Barker Review.

Development applications and fees

Development comprises the carrying out of building, engineering, mining or other operations in, on, over or under land or the making of any material change in the use of any buildings or other land. The demolition of buildings also comprises development. Planning permission is required for undertaking development. However, certain categories of minor development and demolition are granted permitted development rights and are therefore do not require planning permission.

Other minor forms of development are expressly excluded from requiring permission by the provisions of the Planning Acts. Such works include the maintenance, improvement or other alteration of any building of works which affect only the interior of a building, or do not materially affect the external appearance of a building

Permitted development rights are confirmed in the *Town and Country Planning (General Permitted Development) Order* 1995 and demolition controls in the *Town and Country Planning (Demolition – Description of Buildings) Direction* 1995. Both regulations have been subject to review and are therefore likely to be amended.

There are a number of parallel consents that are required in the case of special buildings or areas. Buildings which are listed as of special historic or architectural interest (Grades I, II* and II) may not be altered (or demolished) in any way that might affect their character without a separate grant of listed building consent. Unlisted buildings within conservation areas may not be demolished without conservation area consent. Scheduled Monument consent is required for works affecting a Scheduled Ancient Monument. Consent is also required to display an advertisement, although there exist a number of deemed consents for certain categories of advertisement.

Fees are payable for planning and advertisement applications. The current fees are prescribed in the *Town and Country Planning (Fees for Applications and Deemed Applications) (Amendment) (England) Regulations* 2005. Some exemptions from fees are granted. For example, applications submitted within 12 months following a withdrawal or refusal of a previous application for the same development on the same site and submitted by the same applicant are not subject to a fee. No fees are liable for applications for listed building or conservation consent. There are no fees for submitting an appeal against the refusal of planning permission, but a fee is due for lodging an appeal against an enforcement notice.

Planning application fees are subject to regular increases and the last increase in 2005 was significant and resulted in a new maximum fee ceiling of £50,000.

Appeals and called-in applications

Rights of appeal exist in respect of a refusal of planning permission, a conditional grant of permission or the failure of a local planning authority to determine an application within the statutory time period – 8 weeks for most applications, but 13 weeks for major applications and 16 weeks in the case of development proposals that are subject to Environmental Impact Assessment.

Appeals against a refusal or conditional approval must be made within six months of the decision date. In the case of an appeal against the failure of the authority to determine an application, this must be lodged within six months of the date when the decision was due.

Appeals are determined by independent Inspectors employed by the Planning Inspectorate, a government agency specialising in the administration and determination of all appeals.

There are three types of procedure for processing an appeal. Written representations are the simplest and are processed on the exchange of written submissions. Informal hearings allow an opportunity of an oral presentation of evidence, but in an informal session; whilst public inquiries require the evidence to be submitted orally and then subjected to cross examination by the opposing party.

There are stringent timescales and procedures imposed by secondary legislation which govern the appeal process. Guidance on the appeal processes is provided in Circular 05/00. Whilst each party to the appeal is expected to bear its own costs, an opportunity to apply for an award of costs is available in the case of inquiries and informal hearings. However, awards are normally only contemplated when one party has behaved unreasonably and Circular 08/93 contains guidance on the situations where an award of costs may be justified.

The majority of appeals in England are decided by Inspectors. A small percentage are however decided by the Secretary of State for Communities and Local Government. Clarification of the type of appeals which are likely to be recovered by the Secretary of State was provided in a Parliamentary Statement in July 2006. In general the recovery criteria relate to major or controversial development proposals.

Development plans and monitoring

Since 1991 the planning system in England has been plan-led, requiring that where the development plan contains relevant policies, planning applications should be determined in accordance with the plan unless material considerations indicate otherwise. This requirement is now embodied in section 38(6) of the *Planning and Compulsory Purchase Act* 2004.

The *Planning and Compulsory Purchase Act* 2004 introduced a new system of development planning based on Local Development Frameworks (LDFs) and Regional Spatial Strategies (RSSs). In due course structure and local plans and unitary development plans and regional planning guidance will be replaced by LDFs and RSSs. All local planning authorities are engaged on a review of their existing development plans and preparation of LDFs. These review processes, therefore, provide opportunities for submitting representations to promote development opportunities or minimise development constraints and this is a critical component of sound estate management.

General Development Order and Use Classes Order

Town and Country Planning (General Permitted Development) Order 1995

The GPDO grants permission for certain defined classes of development or use of land. These are mainly of a minor nature. The most commonly used class permits a wide range of small extensions or alterations to dwellings, and there are many other minor permitted developments.

The permitted developments granted under the GDPO can be withdrawn in a defined area under the terms of an article 4 direction made by the local planning authority or Secretary of State.

Town and Country Planning (General Development Procedure) Order 1995 (as amended)

This Order details procedural matters in respect of planning applications, including a full list of statutory consultees, as well as requirements for a register of applications, specimen copies of forms and guidance on appeal submissions.

Town and Country Planning (General Development Procedure) (Amendment) (England) Order 2005

Further procedural arrangements in respect of planning applications were introduced by the *Planning and Compulsory Purchase Act* 2004 to complement those contained in the 1995 Order. These powers included:

- ❖ the power to decline to determine repeat applications;
- ❖ the duration of permission and consents which require that development or works must be begun within three years from the date when permission is granted;
- ❖ a duty to respond to statutory consultations; and
- ❖ confirmation that Regional Planning Bodies are statutory consultees on major development proposals.

Town and Country Planning (General Development Procedure) (Amendment) (England) Order 2006

This Order introduced further procedural changes to the development control system. These included:

- ❖ powers for local planning authorities to make local development orders;
- ❖ changes to the outline planning permission process with the result that additional information is required to support an application for outline permission;
- ❖ a requirement that applications for certain types of development must be accompanied by design and access statements;
- ❖ powers controlling internal floorspace additions such as mezzanines; and
- ❖ changes to the decision period for determining major planning applications.

Town and Country Planning (Use Classes) Order 1987

Section 55 of the 1990 *Planning Act* provides that changing the use of some buildings or land does not constitute development and that this applies to changes of use where both the existing and proposed use fall within the same use class as defined within the *Use Classes Order* 1987. In addition some changes of use between different use classes are also permitted development.

There are some uses which do not fall within any use class and these are referred to as sui generis uses.

The use classes have been subject to amendment and in the *Use Classes Amendment Order* 2005 the following changes were made:

- ❖ retail warehouse clubs and nightclubs are excluded from any use class;
- ❖ internet cafes are included within the A1 shops class; and
- ❖ the former use class 'food and drink' is divided into three separate classes:
  - restaurants and cafes;
  - drinking establishments; and
  - hot food takeaways.

One effect of these changes is that it is necessary to apply for planning permission to change from a restaurant or café to a drinking establishment such as a bar or pub or to a hot food takeaway.

Planning policy guidance notes, policy statements and circulars

Planning Policy Guidance Notes (PPGs) and Planning Policy Statements (PPSs) set out the government's national policies on different aspects of planning in England. PPSs are gradually replacing PPGs and they are a material consideration in the preparation of development plans and in the determination of individual planning applications. PPSs are aimed at providing a more succinct statement of the government's planning policies.

Planning Policy Guidance Notes or Statements are particularly relevant when the development plan is out-dated and does not reflect current government planning policies.

There are at present 25 Planning Policy Guidance Notes or Statements. Many are under review and therefore the national planning policy content is subject to change. A check on the current status of a PPG or PPS is therefore advisable and this can be undertaken on the DCLG website (www.communities.gov.uk). From May 2006 the Department for Communities and Local Government (DCLG) assumed responsibilities for planning and Building Regulations in England from the Office of the Deputy Prime Minister (ODPM).

In June 2004 the government committed to a review of specific PPGs with a commitment to review others as and when necessary. With the exception of PPG4 *Industrial, commercial development and small firms*, all of the old-style PPGs that were targeted for review have either been replaced or a draft replacement has been published for consultation. The following table lists all of the PPGs/PPSs with those that are in the format of Statements highlighted.

PPG/PPS number	Title	Date
1	Delivering Sustainable Development	2005
2	Green Belts	1995 (amended 2001)
3	Housing	2006
4	Industrial, commercial development and small firms	1992
5	Simplified Planning Zones	1992
6	Planning for Town Centres	2005
7	Sustainable Development in Rural Areas	2004
8	Telecommunications	2001
9	Biodiversity and Geological Conservation	2005
10	Planning for Sustainable Waste Management	2005
11	Regional Spatial Strategies	2004
12	Local Development Frameworks	2004
13	Transport	2001
14	Development on unstable land	1990
15	Planning and the historic environment	1994
16	Archaeology and planning	1990
17	Planning for Open Space, Sport and Recreation	2002
18	Enforcing planning control	1991
19	Outdoor advertisement control	1992
20	Coastal planning	1992
21	Tourism – cancelled September 2006	
22	Renewable energy	2004
23	Planning and Pollution Control	2004
24	Planning and noise	1994
25	Development and Flood Risk	2006

Some PPGs/PPSs are supplemented by further guidance in the form of annexes or *Good Practice Guides*. PPS1 is accompanied by a statement on *The Planning System: General Principles*. PPS3 is accompanied by a statement *Delivering Affordable Housing*. Circular 06/05 and a Good Practice Guide complement the guidance provided in PPS9. PPG12 which was published in 1999 remains in force for those development plans that are still being prepared under the 'old-style' development plan regulations. Circulars 01/01 and 09/05 amend the guidance contained in PPG15 in respect of the arrangements for handling heritage applications. *A Good Practice Guide on Planning for Tourism* published in May 2006 provides national planning guidance on tourism and replaces PPG21 which was cancelled in September 2006.

An additional PPS on *Planning and Climate Change* has been published for consultation and will form a supplement to PPS1.

Government policy on minerals and planning issues is contained within Minerals Planning Guidance Notes (MPGs) and their replacements, Minerals Policy Statements (MPSs). In Wales, the Welsh Office issues Technical Advice Notes containing policy on planning. In Scotland, the Scottish Office also produces separate planning advice notes.

Regional Planning Guidance has now been replaced by the Regional Spatial Strategy which, following the enactment of the *Planning and Compulsory Purchase Act* 2004, is now part of the statutory development plan. Each of the regions in England is subject to either a RPG or Draft RSS. Where RPGs have not yet been reviewed they have been renamed and now form part of the statutory development plan for the region.

In Greater London the regional spatial strategy is provided by the London Plan which was published in February 2004. The Plan has been reviewed and is subject to two separate Alterations. The *Early Alterations* were subject to 'Examination in Public' in June 2006 and the *Further Alterations* were published for consultation in September 2006.

Departmental Circulars are also material considerations in the discharge of planning powers, but are more restricted and focus on advice on legislative matters and planning procedures.

Key Circulars are as follows:

No	Title	Summary of content
04/06	The Town and Country Planning (Flooding) (England) Direction 2007	Explains the procedures for notifying the Secretary of State for any application for major development in a flood risk area that a local authority is minded to approve
02/06	Changes to Planning Regulations for Casinos	Provides guidance on the impact on casinos of the *Use Classes Amendment Order* 2005 and the removal of casinos from a specific use class
01/06	Guidance to Changes in the Development Control System	Provides guidance on further changes to the development control system introduced by the *Planning and Compulsory Purchase Act* 2004
11/05	The Town and Country Planning (Green Belt) Direction 2005	Contains a formal direction requiring referral to the First Secretary of State for certain planning applications for development within the Green Belt
08/05	Guidance on Changes in the Development Control System	Provides guidance on the operation of the development control provisions introduced by the *Planning and Compulsory Purchase Act* 2004
05/05	Planning Obligations	Provides guidance on the use of planning obligations under section 106 of the *Town and Country Planning Act* 1990 as substituted by the *Planning and Compensation Act* 1991
03/05	Changes of Use of Buildings and Land – The Town and Country Planning (Use Classes) Order 1987	Provides guidance on the *Use Classes Order* as amended by Statutory Instrument in 2005

No	Title	Summary of content
01/05	The Town and Country Planning (Residential Density) (London, South East England, South West England, East of England and Northamptonshire) Direction 2005	This Circular accompanies the Direction which extends the geographical area that is subject to a Secretary of State intervention on planning applications for housing that involve a density of less than 30 dwellings per hectare net. This intervention previously applied in London and the South East
05/00	Planning appeals procedures (including inquiries into called-in planning applications)	Provides guidance on the procedures for handling planning appeals
02/99	Environmental impact assessment	Provides guidance on the effect of the *Town and Country (Environmental Impact Assessment) (England and Wales) Regulations* 1999
11/95	Use of conditions in planning permission	Provides guidance on the use of conditions in planning applications and contains model conditions
08/93	Awards of costs incurred in planning and other (including compulsory purchase order) proceedings	Provides policy guidance on the award of costs in planning and certain other proceedings

A number of circulars have been subject to review and consultation and are likely to be superseded. Consultations have been undertaken on:

- ❖ revised circular on Environmental Impact Assessment; and
- ❖ the introduction of a 'Planning Gain Supplement' and changes in the process of securing planning obligations.

Listed buildings and conservation areas

Listed buildings 'buildings of special architectural or historic interest' have long been recognised as a major asset in the built environment.

The joint RICS, British Property Federation and English Heritage publication *Heritage Works* concluded for example that 'listed office buildings can be a sound financial investment'.

In a world increasingly concerned about reducing carbon emissions and protecting the environment, the 2002 study by the investment property databank for English Heritage and the RICS Foundation concluded that 'the creative new use of historic buildings can bring a return on investment as good as any other type of building and is certainly the best form of "green" development'.

This very much connects with the emphasis in PPG15 on keeping historic buildings in active use and urging planning authorities to be flexible and imaginative in their approach to achieve the right balance between protecting the building's special architectural and historic interest and adapting it for different uses.

The replacement of the present PPG15 by a projected Planning Policy Statement on the Built Heritage in 2007 is part of the comprehensive review of legislation and policies for heritage protection which is to be the subject of a forthcoming White Paper as regards England. (At the time of publication, it is anticipated that this will be published by the Department for Culture, Media and Sport at some time in the spring of 2007.)

This is intended to build on the results of two major consultation papers:

❖ *Protecting our historic environment and making the system work better (2003)*; and

❖ *The review of heritage protection, the way forward (2004).*

The latter document included both immediate and long-term measures for comprehensive changes to the heritage protection process in England. The only immediate matter was the transfer in 2005 of the process for new listings of buildings to English Heritage.

The key proposals for implementation post the White Paper and relevant primary legislation in England are:

1. **The new unified register of historic sites and buildings of England (RHSBE)** – This is intended to offer a holistic approach to the statutory protection of the historic environment through a single designation regime and a new definition of 'historic assets'.

2. **A reformed heritage consent regime** – This is to be implemented by local authorities with assistance from English Heritage. It is presently understood that this process is likely to distinguish between the following three categories:

   • below ground (and water) archaeology and monumental structures;

   • historic buildings and structures suited to adaptive reuse; and

   • historic landscapes and seascapes.

3. **Voluntary heritage partnership agreements** – These are intended to provide an alternative management regime for:

   • large assets;

   • complex entities that comprise many similar or several different assets;

   • assets of similar type and single ownership and management but in dispersed locations; and

   • assets better managed alongside other regimes.

4. **New statutory requirements relating to Historic Environment Records (HER)** – Local authorities will be required to maintain or ensure that they have access to an HER that meets nationally defined standards.

For Scotland there are tentative proposals by the Historic Environment Advisory Council for Scotland (HEACS) (in a report to the Scottish Parliament in August 2006) for a review to consider changes similar to those being implemented in England.

This is, however, all in the future and for the present the provisions are as follows.

Listed buildings in the United Kingdom

The principal current legislation is the *Planning (Listed Buildings and Conservation Areas) Act* 1990, in Scotland the *Planning (Listed Buildings and Conservation Areas) (Scotland) Act* 1997. This sets out the statutory framework relating to listed buildings and conservation areas.

Listed Building or Conservation Area Consent is not required for a material change of use. Change of use is covered under the *Town and Country Planning Act* 1990.

Grade I: (Grade A in Scotland)

Buildings of exceptional interest (about 2% of listed buildings).

Grade II*: (Grade B in Scotland)

(There is presently a threat in England to remove the II* grading.) Particularly important buildings of more than specialist interest (about 4% of listed buildings).

Grade II: (Grade C(S) in Scotland)

Buildings of special interest which warrant every effort being made to preserve them.

Listing

The basic criteria for listing are set out in PPG15 and 'spot listing' will still be considered for individual buildings overlooked or under threat, by reference of details by any member of the public to English Heritage, Historic Scotland, CADW (Welsh Heritage), the Northern Ireland Environment and Heritage Service. Note in the near future the criteria to identify potential buildings for listing will alter. The list reviews will concentrate on finding the best examples of types and periods of buildings under-represented in the current list.

What is a listed building?

A listed building is any structure or erection, and any part of a building including any object or structure within the curtilage that forms part of the land and did so before 1 July 1948. There are of course 'Modern Movement' Listed Buildings that postdate 1948.

Material change of use

It is accepted that new uses for old buildings, the 'adaptive reuse of historic buildings', may often be the key to their conservation. In some instances, it may be appropriate that controls should be relaxed where this would enable historic buildings to be given a new lease of life.

The best use for an historic building is obviously the use for which it was designed and, wherever possible, the original use should continue.

Works for which listed building consent is necessary

Demolition of a listed building, or its alteration or extension in any manner that would affect its special architectural or historic interest, requires consent. It should be noted that the setting of an historic building is considered of great importance and an essential feature of its interest and character. Consent is not normally required for works of repair that are on the basis of like-for-like materials and exact matching original details. However, this is a grey area.

Application for listed building consent

Applications for listed building consent should be made to the local planning authority.

Listed building consent decisions

The local planning authority has eight weeks in which to consider an application. This can be extended by agreement with the applicant or revision of proposals, etc.

The legislation requires all listed building consents to have conditions, even if only time/recording conditions.

Listed building consent for works already executed

Listed building consent may be sought even though the works have already been completed. If consent is granted this is not retrospective; the works are authorised only from the date of consent.

Conservation areas

Local authorities have a duty imposed by section 71 of the *Listed Buildings Act* 1990 and equivalent sections of the *Scotland Act* of 1997, that they must regularly formulate and publish proposals for the preservation and enhancement of conservation areas, after consultation with local people at a public meeting. The advice insists that simply designating a conservation area will not ensure its protection and that planning authorities should analyse what makes an area special and develop policies to protect it, in consultation with local residents and businesses.

Other powers

The guidance gives powers to councils to control some minor developments in conservation areas including alterations to roofs, doors and windows, so as to prevent damage to the area's special character and to avoid councils having to pursue individual article 4 directions. From October 1994 many churches, previously exempt, were brought within conservation controls although Christian churches in active use still have ecclesiastical exemption.

Following publicity for the English, Welsh, Northern Irish and Scottish Heritage list of battlefields, PPG15 reminds developers and councils to also protect wider features of the historic environment such as important gardens and parks, which are now separately listed and graded. World Heritage Sites have separate high measures of protection.

Preservation presumption

PPG 15 reaffirms the presumption in favour of preserving listed buildings of special architectural or historic interest and a presumption in favour of retaining unlisted buildings which make a positive contribution to the character or appearance of a conservation area.

Environmental impact assessments

Environmental Impact Assessment (EIA) is the process for identifying the environmental impact of proposed developments. The legal requirements derive from the *Town and Country Planning (Environmental Impact Assessment) Regulations* 1999 as amended by the *Town and Country Planning (Environmental Impact Assessment) (England and Wales) (Amendment) Regulations* 2000.

The requirement for an EIA to be undertaken is mandatory for certain development projects. These projects are referred to as 'Schedule 1' developments and are defined in the Regulations. For other developments, which are defined in the Regulations and referred to as 'Schedule 2' developments, the decision as to whether an Environmental Statement is required to support the planning application is contingent on:

* whether any part of the development is located within a defined sensitive area;
* whether the development exceeds an applicable development threshold or criterion; and
* whether the development is likely to have significant environmental effects.

A procedure is set out in the Regulations which allows the need for an EIA to be subject to a screening opinion obtainable on application to the local planning authority. The decision of the local planning authority in response to the request for a screening opinion must be made within three weeks from receipt of the request, although there is provision for the local planning authority to request an extension. There is further provision within the Regulations for an applicant who disagrees with the local planning authority's screening decision to 'appeal' to the Secretary of State.

The Regulations also provide for a 'scoping opinion' to be obtained from the local planning authority. This provides guidance on the content and extent of matters that the authority considers should be covered by the EIA.

Further guidance on the EIA process can be found in the following:

- ❖ *Environmental Impact Assessment: A guide to procedures* produced by the Office of the Deputy Prime Minister, 2000;
- ❖ *Preparation of Environmental Statements for Planning Projects that Require Environmental Assessment: A good practice guide* produced by the Department of the Environment, 1995; and
- ❖ *Evaluation of Environmental Information for Planning Projects – A good practice guide* produced by the Department of the Environment, 1994.

European Community Directives, UK case law and European Court of Justice judgements have also aided the interpretation of the EIA Regulations. To clarify the requirements the then ODPM issued a *Note on Environmental Impact Assessment Directive for Local Planning Authorities in April 2004* and this provides a further useful guidance note on the process. The DCLG also issued a letter to all local planning authorities in June 2006 providing further guidance in response to recent ECJ judgements.

A revised Circular and Practice Guide has been published for consultation purposes and will, when finalised, provide an updated policy and practice context for EIAs reflecting the changes brought about by UK and European case law.

Dilapidations

The principle

'Dilapidations' refers to breaches of obligations either express or implied within a lease relating to: reinstatement of alterations; repair; decoration; breaches of statute, other specific requirements; and associated costs.

The fundamental purpose of a 'Schedule of Dilapidations' is to identify these breaches of covenant. The allegation of a breach of contract is the first step in the legal process. Consequently, for a Schedule of Dilapidations to have worth and perform the function for which it is drafted, it is necessary that the schedule is enforceable in a court of law. The legal remedy for breach of dilapidations obligations is normally a claim for damages. The Schedule of Dilapidations is usually prepared as part of a claim which itself should represent the damage actually suffered by the landlord. This might not equate to the cost of the works set out in the Schedule of Dilapidations as a consequence of section 18(1) of the *Landlord and Tenant Act* 1927 and common law principles. (See Section 18(1) of the *Landlord and Tenant Act* 1927 on page 117.)

Schedules can be prepared on behalf of a tenant, where there are alleged breaches by the landlord of its obligations to the tenant. However, the more common approach is for the document to be prepared on behalf of a landlord in relation to tenants' alleged breaches.

There are three types of landlords' Schedule of Dilapidations: Interim, Terminal and Final. An Interim Schedule relates to breaches during the lease term; the Terminal Schedule to breaches identified towards the end of the term; and the Final Schedule is one published after the end of the term. By far the most common is the Terminal Schedule of Dilapidations and it is this document that we focus on here. By virtue of its pre-eminence, guidance on practice and procedure associated with Terminal Schedules has been published by the Property Litigation Association, in the form of a Protocol.

Reform and the Dilapidations Protocol

In September 2006, the Property Litigation Association published a revised version of their Dilapidations Protocol. The revised document has made some minor changes to the original version including:

❖ a formal diminution valuation is not now required at an early stage (if the landlord has not yet or does not intend to carry out the works) but it is still required prior to legal proceedings being issued. Instead, the landlord's claim should now contain a written endorsement that the overall figure claimed is a fair assessment of the loss;

❖ the importance of considering Alternative Dispute Resolution methods is reinforced;

❖ the distinction between the Schedule of Dilapidations and the landlord's Claim is clarified;

❖ a requirement for the landlord to confirm to the tenant whether an earlier Schedule before the lease end date is introduced; and

❖ the anticipated timescales for actions by the parties are slightly revised.

Although the Lord Chancellor's department has not yet approved the Protocol, the courts may treat it as the normal and reasonable approach to pre-action conduct, and non-compliance might bring sanctions against the party concerned. Indeed, the RICS appended a copy of the previous Protocol to its own guidance note on dilapidations (4th edition), and it is probable that the revised version will be endorsed in similar fashion when the guidance note is next updated.

The underlying intention of the *Civil Procedure Rules* (CPR) is to increase the number of pre-action settlements, and to reduce court time, expense and ultimately the extent of litigation. The CPR have made a number of changes, including:

- ❖ pre-action offers – these can be made by either party pursuant to Part 36 of the *Civil Procedure Rules*;
- ❖ all claims must be accompanied by a statement of truth signed by the claimant; and
- ❖ the expert witness role has fundamentally changed under the CPR. The expert's function is to give an independent expert view; he or she owes a duty to one body only, and that is the tribunal before whom he or she appears. The expert witness is not there to create an argument in support of the party that appointed him or her.

Stages in the dilapidations process
Terminal dilapidation claims

Stage 1 – preparation
Obtain and appraise all relevant documentation including:

- ❖ leases;
- ❖ licences to alter;
- ❖ schedules of condition;
- ❖ side letters;
- ❖ photographs;
- ❖ fit out specifications;
- ❖ agent's letting brochures;
- ❖ any statutory notices served;
- ❖ deeds of variation;
- ❖ schedules of landlord and tenant's fixtures and fittings;
- ❖ details of outstanding service charges; and
- ❖ any rent deposit agreements.

This list is by no means exhaustive.

Stage 2 – the inspection
This must be comprehensive and thorough and include specialist professions if deemed necessary, such as a structural engineer or mechanical or electrical consultant.

Establish the original condition at the beginning of the term and the standard of repair that the tenant has covenanted to undertake, and identify the remedial work. Take into account the age, character and locality of the premises when let (*Proudfoot v Hart* 1890).

Include all measurements to aid calculation of the cost of the remedial works and use as proof as required at a later date.

Stage 3 – preparation of the Schedule of Dilapidations and claim
The Schedule should contain the information shown in the first five columns below. The additional columns relating to the tenant's and landlord's comments turn the Schedule of Dilapidations into a Scott Schedule, used as a negotiating tool between respective surveyors.

ITEM	CLAUSE No.	BREACH	REMEDIAL WORK REQUIRED	LANDLORD COST (£)	TENANT'S COMMENTS ON		LANDLORD'S COMMENTS ON	
					BREACH & REMEDY	COST (£)	BREACH & REMEDY	COST (£)

The Schedule of Dilapidations should be accompanied by a claim letter, which must include:

- ❖ landlord's and tenant's names and addresses;
- ❖ a clear summary of the facts on which the claim is based;
- ❖ the Schedule of Dilapidations (a separate document);
- ❖ any documents relied upon, such as invoices and evidence of costs and losses;
- ❖ confirmation that the landlord and advisors will attend meetings;
- ❖ a date by which the tenant should respond; and
- ❖ a summary of the claim including:
  - – cost of works,
  - – preliminaries,
  - – overheads and loss of profit,
  - – surveyors' fees for preparing the Schedule (quantified and substantiated),
  - – loss of rent,
  - – loss of service charge,
  - – surveyors' fees for negotiating a settlement (projected), and
  - – any sums paid to a superior landlord.

The Schedule of Dilapidations should be served within a reasonable time before the termination of the tenancy and typically not more than 56 days afterwards.

If a notice from the landlord has to be given to the tenant for reinstatement of alterations then this must be served within a reasonable period before the end of the tenancy so that the tenant is still able to start these works in time.

Electronic copies of the Schedule of Dilapidations should be provided to facilitate easier negotiation, preferably in a Scott Schedule format as shown in the diagram above.

Stage 4 – the response and negotiations

Following submission of the claim, the tenant must respond within a reasonable period, usually 56 days.

Surveyors should meet before the tennt is required to respond to the Claim on a without prejudice basis, preferably on site, to establish the facts. If further meetings are necessary a strict timetable should be adopted. In any case it is expected that experts of the respective parties in their like disciplines should also meet within 28 days of the tenant's response.

Final dilapidations claims

The approach to a Final Schedule of Dilapidations will be similar to that adopted for a Terminal Schedule. However, the Final Schedule is served after the end of the term, so care should be taken to ensure that a suitable notice requiring the tenant to reinstate alterations is served before the term date, if so required.

Interim dilapidations claims

These claims are made during the continuance of the lease term and are typically as a consequence of more significant breaches of obligations. This is a complicated area of law so legal advice should always be taken on the appropriate service of notices and counter-notices. Interim dilapidations claims are in pursuance of one, or a combination of more than one, of three remedies: determination of the lease; damages; or specific performance.

To be successful, a landlord would need to satisfy one or more of five grounds (summarised below):

- ❖ that immediate remedying is necessary to protect the value of the landlord's interest in the property, or that the value has already been affected;
- ❖ the work is necessary to comply with legislation;
- ❖ that where the tenant does not occupy the whole building, the work is necessary in the interests of other occupiers;
- ❖ that immediate remedying of the defect will be substantially cheaper than would be the case if the work was delayed; or
- ❖ special circumstances exist.

Jervis v Harris Notices (Repairs Notices)

Where the lease allows, landlords do have the option of entering the tenant's demise and completing the works themselves, at the cost of the tenant. This cost to the tenant is calculated as a debt, rather than as damages, so avoids the complications of capped damages claims as a consequence of section 18(1) of the *Landlord and Tenant Act* 1927 and common law. However, the lease will set out a series of events that the landlord must comply with before this opportunity is available to him or her. Typically these are:

- ❖ that a notice must be served on the tenant setting out exactly the alleged breaches;
- ❖ the tenant is given a reasonable time to comply with the notice; and
- ❖ only then can the landlord enter and carry out the works.

However, carrying out work within a tenant's demise is complicated. Significant problems could be encountered such as: trespass by the contractor, access to power and water, disruption of the tenant's business and the effect on the relationships between the parties. For these reasons this is a little-used remedy and it is most commonly employed for external works only.

Break clauses

Sometimes, covenants within a lease give the option for the landlord or the tenant to bring the lease to an end before the contractual expiry date. It is important to establish whether the break clause is 'condition precedent' or not.

Where the clause is conditional, the party exercising the break may be required to comply with a variety of conditions before the break can be deemed effective. At its most severe this may include absolute compliance with all obligations within the lease, or may just require that vacant possession is provided at the break date.

The risk of non-compliance with a conditional break clause is often substantially greater than the cost of the works necessary to comply. It is therefore essential to commence planning of these works in advance to avoid the possibility of the lease continuing for the remainder of the contractual term.

A recent case has assisted practitioners in understanding the extent of work that may be necessary to comply with a break clause that required the tenant to comply 'materially' with its obligations *(Fitzroy House Epworth Street (No 1) Ltd v The Financial Times Ltd)*. The tenant undertook approximately £900,000 worth of works, but approximately £20,000 worth of works remained incomplete at the relevant date. The court held that, because there had been no consequential delay to the landlord in reletting or selling the property, the tenant had indeed complied materially. However, a consequence of the Appeal Court ruling is that there was no disadvantage to the landlord's case as a consequence of the landlord and its advisors declining to assist the tenant in determining the extent of works that would be required to comply with the obligations.

Dilapidations and the Disability Discrimination Act 1995 (DDA)

The tenant is free to decide, as a Service Provider and Employer, how to comply with its obligations and duties under the DDA. It is the Service Provider or Employer who has the obligations to take reasonable steps to ensure that they are complying with their duties under the DDA. Subsequently, it follows that a landlord is unable to require a tenant to undertake works to comply with the duties imposed by the DDA during the term of a lease. Neither can it impose this as a part of a dilapidations claim at the end of, or during, a lease.

Under the terms of a lease it is likely that the tenant will be obliged to comply with statutory requirements. Under the DDA, the Service Provider or Employer has a duty to disabled people, not a statutory requirement to the landlord. At the end of the lease term the demised premises are vacated and subsequently there is no longer a Service Provider or Employer of any disabled people. It follows then that the demise at the end of the lease would not, at this point in time, be in breach of any duty imposed by the DDA.

If a tenant, either in a single let building or a multi-let building, provides a service to the public, the duties fall on the tenant.

If a landlord provides a service to the public, then the landlord is responsible under the Act for any common parts of the building, whether it is a multi-occupied office building or a shopping centre. However, it is not clear who is responsible under the Act in the case where the public only visit the common parts of a building at the invitation of the tenant. It is probable that the landlord could not unreasonably refuse consent for a tenant to make appropriate alterations outside the tenant's demise.

Where a tenant has undertaken works to comply, there are implications under the *Disability Discrimination (Providers of Services) (Adjustments of Premises) Regulations* 2001. If a landlord wishes to remove the alteration, there is nothing to prevent him or her doing this after the outgoing tenant has vacated, but all reinstatement of these elements must be at the landlord's own cost. Any requirement on the outgoing tenant to remove these alterations may be considered unreasonable and could be challenged in the courts. This is as yet untested, and it remains to be seen whether a tenant will be able to use this in defence against a reinstatement claim.

VAT and dilapidations

The Protocol, Clause 4.5, requires that the VAT status of the landlord should be stated. VAT in respect of dilapidations is a complex subject with its own set of rules, regulations and case law. Opinions are usually divided and much will depend on the circumstances. Where a tenant is making a payment to a landlord in full and final settlement of its dilapidation liabilities, under HM Revenue and Customs rules, the payment is not a 'taxable supply' for the purposes of VAT. This is because HM Revenue and Customs deem the payment to be one of damages and not a supply of something. VAT may be payable if the landlord passes the payment on to an incoming VAT registered tenant.

Complying with European Community Law, the *Finance Act* 1989 introduced major changes that included giving UK payers of VAT the option to pay VAT on supplies relating to an interest in commercial land. Where a person or company is registered for VAT there is a special statutory exemption to the charging of VAT on such supplies. Taxpayers can waive this exemption if they desire. To do this they must notify HM Revenue and Customs. For clarity, if a landlord has elected to waive its exemption on a building, it must charge VAT on such items as rent received. In this instance, it will not be appropriate to include VAT as part of a dilapidations claim. If the VAT exemption has not been waived then VAT need not be charged by the landlord on supplies, and VAT may form part of a dilapidations claim.

So the first issue to establish is whether the landlord is registered for VAT, i.e. is the landlord required by VAT law to charge VAT on its normal business transactions, such as rent receipts? If so, has it elected to waive its exemption to VAT on the specific building that is subject to the dilapidations claim? Once this has been established, a simplified VAT analysis might follow the steps shown in the diagram below. The Protocol requires that the claim establishes what the landlord's intentions are and states the landlord's and/or the demised property's VAT status. A basic understanding of the VAT issues is therefore necessary for the requirements under the Protocol to be met.

Dilapidations VAT Analysis

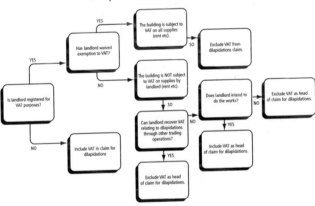

Valuation – diminution in value

See Section 18(1) of the *Landlord and Tenant Act* 1927 on page 117.

Summary of important statutes

Landlord and Tenant Act 1927, section 18(1)
Limits the cost of a claim for breach of covenant.

Law of Property Act 1925, section 146
Prescribes the form of notice for re-entry for forfeiture.

Law of Property Act 1925, section 147

Provides relief for tenants on long leases in respect of internal redecorations.

Leasehold Property (Repairs) Act 1938

Gives protection to certain tenants in respect of section 146 notice (ii) above.

Defective Premises Act 1972

Provides that a landlord shall be liable for lack of repair in cases where he or she knew or ought to have known of the defect.

The Civil Procedure Rules 1998

Introduced by Lord Woolf, they provide rules and practice directions for dispute procedures.

Summary of important case law

There have been a number of leading decisions relating to dilapidations law in the last few years. The following cases give an indication of developing areas of law.

Scottish and Mutual Assurance Society Limited v British Telecommunications plc (1999) (EGCS 43)

Section 18(1) of the *Landlord and Tenant Act* 1927 Part II.

Loss of rent.

Notice for reinstatement of alterations.

Shortlands Investments Limited v Cargill plc (1995) (EGLR 51)

Section 18(1) of the *Landlord and Tenant Act* 1927 Part II.

Trane (UK) Limited v Provident Mutual Life Assurance Co Limited (1995) (WGLR 78)

Compliance with conditions of break clauses.

Jervis v Harris (1996) (EGLR 78)

Use of provision for landlord's re-entry.

Extent of recovery of expenditure.

Mannai Investments Co. Limited v Eagle Star Life Assurance Co Limited (1997) (EGLR 69)

Accuracy of notice showing intent to break tenancy.

Credit Suisse v Beegas Nominees Limited (1994) (4 All ER 803)

Establishing the interpretation of the repairing covenants and the different types of obligation placed on the tenant.

Fitzroy House Epworth Street (No 1) Ltd and Fitzroy House Epworth Street (No 2) Ltd v The Financial Times Ltd (2006) (CA1 2207)

Test of 'material compliance' of a conditional break clause.

Requirements of landlords and their advisors to assist tenants under conditional break clause circumstances.

Section 18(1) of the Landlord and Tenant Act 1927

Section 18(1) of the *Landlord and Tenant Act* 1927 is divided into two limbs.

> **Limb 1** *provides that damages for a breach of covenant ..... to put or keep premises in repair ..... shall in no case exceed the amount ...... by which the value ..... of the premises is diminished owing to the breach.*

Limb 1 of section 18(1) applies in all dilapidations cases. The common law claim in dilapidations, usually comprises the following components:

1. Cost of works.
2. Fees for preparation and service of the Schedule.
3. Fees for carrying out of the works.
4. Fees for negotiating the claim.
5. Loss of rent, loss of empty rates and service charge.
6. Loss of insurance.
7. VAT.

Limb 1 of section 18(1) provides that whatever the amount of the common law claim, the landlord's entitlement in damages is limited to the amount by which the value of his or her interest has been diminished owing to the breach of the covenant to repair. (This is not the same as the covenant to redecorate or to reinstate.)

The operation of the Act requires comparison to be made between two valuations:

Valuation A – Assuming compliance.
Valuation B – Assuming actual condition.

The difference between Valuation A and Valuation B assesses the statutory cap on the amount of damages payable.

It has been held that where Valuation A is a negative figure and Valuation B is a greater negative figure the difference, amounting to the landlord's loss, is payable (*Shortlands Investments Plc v Cargill Plc*).

> **Limb 2** *of section 18(1) further provides, ... no damages shall be recovered ..... if it is shown that the premises, in whatever state of repair they might be or that shortly after the termination of the tenancy have been or be pulled down or such structural alterations made therein as would render valueless the repairs .....*

Limb 2 of section 18(1) would operate, for example, where it could be demonstrated that the landlord of an unmodernised 1960s office building intended, as at the expiry of the lease, to carry out refurbishment works to install a suspended ceiling, a raised floor and air conditioning.

In such a case, the landlord's proposals would significantly impact upon the repairs required to the interior of the building, rendering the benefit of the required repair valueless. As a consequence, to the extent that this work is rendered valueless, it will fall out of the claim.

However, unless the landlord intends to carry out works to the exterior of the building that will render valueless the exterior disrepair, the repairs required will remain a valid part of the claim.

The critical date upon which to establish the landlord's intention is at the expiry of the lease (see *Salisbury v Gilmore* (1948) and *Cunliffe v Goodman* (1950)).

The fact that the landlord is contemplating a number of options, including a potential refurbishment as at the expiry of the lease is not a sufficient basis itself to render the value of the repairs nugatory. A clear and fixed intention must be demonstrated.

Section 18(1) relates to repair only. It does not relate to the reinstatement or decoration content of the claim. However, these elements of the claim are governed by common law principles under which the landlord's entitlement is to be reimbursed for his or her financial loss, and the same principles apply. It will be relevant however, in assessing the loss, whether the landlord truly intends to reinstate tenant's alterations, for example, a mezzanine floor in a warehouse.

The introduction of the Pre-Action Protocol for Dilapidations, a second edition of which was published in 2006, has confirmed that valuations under section 18(1) are required when a claim is made in virtually all cases. The exceptions to this rule are when the landlord has either carried out the works or can demonstrate intention to do the works.

As a consequence, both landlords and tenants should obtain advice as to the likely impact of section 18(1) on their claim at an early stage.

Tenant fit out and licences to alter

The following comments are intended as an overview as to how licences for alteration are addressed in property and construction matters generally. These comments offer an overview only and professional advice should be sought to ensure any application for landlord approval is administered correctly.

What are they and how are they used?

A licence is a form of permission, a legally enforceable document, which is granted by a landlord to a tenant enabling the latter to exercise a right within a formal lease agreement.

There are many forms and types of licence relating to property such as change of use, assignment of a lease or subletting for example, but this section refers specifically to licences for alteration. These are most often used where a tenant seeks the landlord's formal approval to carry out alterations, fitting-out works and similar within the demised premises.

An application for formal approval is normally prepared when a tenant wishes to make significant changes, structural or otherwise, to a premises. Typically this may include subdivision works, provision of mezzanine floors, changing shop fronts, extending or other alterations.

It is important to review the lease obligations with regard to proposed alterations. The lease may prevent any changes or activities being undertaken at all. Such prohibitions may take the form of two types:

- ❖ **absolute**, where the landlord is not obliged to grant any consent or approval to an application; and
- ❖ **qualified**, where the landlord's approval is required but such approval should not be unreasonably withheld.

Whilst the lease may already permit the tenant to carry out minor or internal cosmetic works, the licence affords the landlord the opportunity of retaining a degree of control as to how more substantial work is carried out, mainly to ensure the landlord's interests and objectives for the premises are not compromised or reduced. For example, the licence may require that noisy work is done out of hours, to reduce the likelihood of other tenants alleging a breach of their right to quiet enjoyment of their own demise.

Licences for alteration are also used in some dilapidations claims. If there is no licence in place for works undertaken the landlord would probably have the right to insist on removal and reinstatement to the former condition and layout. However, if the licence is worded to avoid any form of reinstatement the changes made may be left in situ at the expiration of the tenure period. There are some exceptions to this, and the issue of reinstatement is considered elsewhere in this handbook.

There are occasions when an application may be required to satisfy certain legal and statutory requirements, for example to comply with the *Disability Discrimination Act*. In such situations the landlord's consent must not be unreasonably withheld.

The application and appraisal process

There are occasions where a tenant may have already formally agreed with the landlord that works can commence to an agreed scope. In such situations an application for formal approval may not necessarily be required, but the lease terms should clarify this. If an application is not considered necessary, the tenant should offer the professional courtesy of notifying the landlord when the work is to be carried out.

If the landlord is itself a tenant, then additional superior landlord approvals may be necessary. Be wary, however, that the superior landlord's interests may not necessarily be the same as the tenant-landlord's. All respective interests and requirements should be contained in the licence for alteration.

On the assumption, however, that the landlord is indeed the freeholder and the application is a straightforward procedure this should be acknowledged by the landlord and/or the landlord's adviser promptly. More often than not, tenants seek approval in order to improve their premises to improve business performance, and this should be considered in a pragmatic manner by the landlord.

There is no benchmark or minimum requirement governing the information to be submitted as part of the application. Clearly, it is advisable for the landlord (or the landlord's property adviser) and the tenant to discuss the extent of works to establish what information is expected as early as possible in the process, to avoid any delays in the application. Indeed, the parties may establish or agree that an application may not even be necessary.

In all application procedures the landlord should behave reasonably as to turnaround time, the level of information and detail needed, and whether any amendments or conditions would be necessary. It can be prudent to make use of a standard template checklist to ensure the basic and critical information is provided, thus allowing for further communication if more detail is needed.

In order for an efficient and prompt appraisal and response from the landlord, the tenant should ensure full details of the proposals are forwarded to the landlord. Unless the lease comments, there is no hard and fast rule to what level of information is deemed necessary. However, it is not unreasonable for an application to include the following technical information:

❖ complete set of architectural, structural and building services plans, specifications and scope of work;

❖ typical programme with commencement and completion dates;

❖ details of tenant project team for ease of communication; and

❖ copy of applications for statutory consents, and subsequent consent/discharge confirmation.

The landlord and/or the landlord's adviser would usually be able to form an opinion on the proposals fairly quickly and advise if any further information is needed. Similarly, advice can be obtained as to whether any ongoing inspection of the works is needed, and the procedure for final inspection and sign off.

Factors to consider

Clearly, there are a number of factors which may need to be determined when a landlord assesses an application. This may be reported on by external advisers from various professional disciplines depending on the scope, magnitude and complexity of the proposals.

Examples of factors to be considered may include the following:

❖ Is the applicant the current tenant, are they the sole occupier of the property, or will other tenants be disturbed or inconvenienced by the works?

❖ Are the proposals sensible for the property and the tenant's business objectives?

❖ If the proposals increase the rental value, the landlord should consider financing the works pursuant to the *Landlord and Tenant Act 1927*, in exchange for additional rent.

❖ Will the proposals have any bearing on changes to floor areas, service charge agreements, rateable values and similar?

❖ How will the work be carried out – in a single contract, or phased over time?

❖ Will building services installations be affected temporarily or permanently?

❖ Will the structural integrity of the property be compromised temporarily or permanently? Is phasing of the works needed which may affect third parties?

❖ Will the building work or the completed alterations affect the landlord's building insurance cover?

❖ Will any fire precautions be affected during or after the work? How will fire security be maintained?

❖ Who will be responsible for settling the landlord's costs and professional fees?

❖ Identify the need for any additional enabling or remedial work after the proposals are complete.

❖ Consider responsibility and liability for all design, construction work and the securing of all appropriate consents.

❖ Consider any landlord's obligation to provide additional parking areas, refuse collection point and similar.

❖ Consider the need and frequency for landlord work inspections, to ensure compliance with the agreed documents.

Form of consent

In many commercial property situations, the landlord's solicitor will draft a licence for alteration and agree this with the applicant's solicitor. It is usually the case that each party will have technical consultants and their agreed version of the plans and proposals would be appended to the main licence. Similarly, if the landlord wishes to insert specific conditions, such as sequencing of work to prevent disconnection in working hours, then these can be agreed and incorporated into the licence.

A signed and certified copy of the agreed licence is normally held with the lease for cross reference purposes.

It is normal practice that once the work has been completed, the tenant submits final copies of all statutory consents secured for the works, and permits the landlord to inspect the completed activity to ensure these are fully signed off and agreed, to complete the licence conditions. This should always be formalised in written form promptly.

Occasionally, some tenants carry out alterations without any form of approval or licence in place. Normally, the landlord could insist on reinstatement of an unlicensed alteration. However, the landlord's position may be reduced if the alterations are left unchallenged for a period of time. Similarly, if an unlicensed alteration has been undertaken but not discovered within 12 years (England and Wales), then it is possible the *Limitation Act* 1980 may apply.

Further information

Further reading on licence for alterations can be found in the RICS guidance note *Handling Tenant's Applications for Approval to Alterations.*

There is also extensive case law on this matter.

Latent Damage Act 1986

The *Latent Damage Act* 1986 enhances case law relating to certain cases of negligence, by imposing statutory limits in relation to the time in which cases may be brought to court if a defect is found.

The Act applies specifically to those cases of negligence that relate to latent damage and not to personal injury. In addition, recent case law suggests that in the meaning of the Act, negligence covers only a breach of a tortious duty of care and not a contractual duty of care.

Previous statute exists indicating time limits in which legal action must commence; section 14 of the *Limitation Act* 1980. The 1986 Act enhances section 14 by limiting any claims to six years after the damage occurred. This, however, can be extended under section 14A by a further three years from the date when the defect is discovered. In all cases however, a 15-year time limit is placed under section 14B of the Act. When considering claims for latent defects, the most important points to establish are the dates from when the negligence occurred and the cause of the negligence. For example, the negligence may have been caused by defective construction, design, or a combination of both. The date on which the defect technically arises may be confused by the ongoing contractual state of the project, i.e. whether a final certificate has been issued or a defect liability period is still active. In certain cases proceedings may be delayed on the basis that the damage has not yet occurred, but is in fact imminent.

Discovery of building defects – statutory time limits

The *Limitation Act* 1980 ('the 1980 Act') as modified by the *Latent Damage Act* 1986 (see above) lays down the periods within which proceedings to enforce a right must be brought. Upon the discovery of a defect in a building or structure, possible claims against the designers and constructors of that building or structure could arise in contract, in tort or under statute.

Contract

To bring an action for breach of a simple contract, court proceedings must be commenced within six years of the date on which the breach of contract occurred. If the contract has been completed under seal, rather than under hand, then the time limit prescribed by the 1980 Act is 12 years. Under the *Companies Act* 1985 (as amended) the 12-year limitation period also applies to companies when a contract is signed as a deed by two directors or a director and a company secretary.

Tort

The general time limit for actions in tort is six years from the date when the damage was suffered, with the exception that a time limit of three years applies to personal injury actions involving negligence. This period runs from the date of the accident concerned, although special rules apply for illnesses, which may not manifest themselves for many years after exposure to their cause, for example, asbestos.

Also, for negligence claims involving latent damage, the time limit laid down by the *Latent Damage Act* 1986 for commencing proceedings is six years from the date the damage was suffered. However this period can be extended for a further three years from the 'starting date'. The starting date is defined by the *Latent Damage Act* 1986 as the date on which the plaintiff first had both the required knowledge and the right to bring an action. The *Latent Damage Act* also includes a 'long-stop' provision preventing the instigation of any proceedings after the expiry of 15 years from the date of the negligence concerned.

Statute

Where a right derives from a breach of statutory duty, reference should, in the first instance, be made to the particular statute concerned, which may specify a time limit for the commencement of proceedings. The *Defective Premises Act* 1972 provides a particularly germane example. If the statute concerned is silent as to the time limit, then a period of six years will generally apply. If an action is brought in respect of a defective product, under the *Consumer Protection Act* 1987 there is a cut-off point of ten years from the 'relevant time' (usually the date of a supply).

It should be noted that the time limits for both tortious and contractual claims might be postponed where there is concealment, mistake or fraud.

Collateral warranties and reliance letters

Collateral warranties

Introduction

The doctrine of 'privity of contract' has for many years prevented someone who is not a party to a contract from enforcing that contract. As a consequence, third party reliance documents have been a feature of the property and construction industry for over 20 years and there is little sign of them dying out. Such documents commonly take the form of collateral warranties. These documents are also sometimes called 'duty of care deeds'.

What do they do?

Collateral warranties create a contract between two parties. The main purpose of the contract is to allow the recipient ('**beneficiary**') of the collateral warranty to rely on the proper and competent performance of services by the giver ('**warrantor**') of the collateral warranty when the services concerned have actually been provided originally to another party and not to the recipient.

Should the beneficiary discover that the services have not been provided properly and competently by the warrantor, the beneficiary has a contractual route of redress through the collateral warranty.

Who gives collateral warranties?

There is no general restriction in the UK property and construction industry on who can give collateral warranties. Literally any person providing professional services or supplying goods can give collateral warranties, but they are used more particularly by those responsible for design services, or responsible for construction activities, such as:

❖ project managers;

❖ architects (building, landscape);

❖ engineers (mechanical, electrical, structural, acoustic, geotechnical);

❖ cost consultants or quantity surveyors;

❖ main contractors; and

❖ specialist contractors with design obligations (lifts, cladding, steelwork, roofing).

The diagram below identifies, in simple form, how collateral warranties might come about.

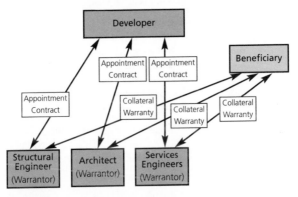

Who receives collateral warranties?

In the property and construction industry there are four basic parties who seek collateral warranties, namely:

❖ purchasers of freehold property (whether for investment of occupation);

❖ tenants of leasehold property (whether for investment of occupation);

❖ funders advancing loans for property acquisition and development; and

❖ employers under building contracts.

Are all warranties the same?

There is no single form of warranty wording adopted by the industry as a whole. Solicitors will have their own precedents as might property owners and developers. Certain industry bodies have developed their own precedents for use, for example:

❖ British Property Federation;

❖ Joint Contracts Tribunal (new suite from 2005) published by Sweet & Maxwell; and

❖ Construction Industry Council.

What are their common features?

Apart from identifying the beneficiary and the warrantor, warranties will normally contain clauses dealing with (1) the warrantor's Primary Obligation to the beneficiary and (2) limits to the warrantor's liability.

(1) Primary Obligation: This will normally be expressed in terms of use of reasonable skill and care and the warrantor will acknowledge that it owes the beneficiary the same obligations as are owed to the warrantor's client/employer in return for consideration on the part of the beneficiary. The payment is nearly always a nominal sum (such as £1 or £10), but there is no reason why the sum should not be more substantial.

(2) Limits on liability: Potential liabilities arising under the collateral warranty may be limited in terms of:

- ❖ type of loss for which the warrantor is to be liable;
- ❖ net contribution when other parties also giving warranties are considered equally or jointly liable for the loss;
- ❖ equivalent rights to defence allowing the warrantor to raise in defence rights equivalent to those available in respect of claims from the client or employer;
- ❖ prohibited (deleterious) materials;
- ❖ professional indemnity insurance required;
- ❖ copyright and use of documents by the beneficiary;
- ❖ assignment rights and restrictions;
- ❖ limitation periods for the bringing of an action; or
- ❖ exclusion of *Contracts (Rights of Third Parties) Act* 1999.

Collateral warranties given to purchasers and tenants are normally almost identical.

Collateral warranties given to funders contain many of the same provisions as purchaser or tenant warranties but they might also include 'step-in rights'. These are rights permitting a funder to replace the warrantor's client or employer, in order to ensure that a scheme or transaction being funded is completed in the event that the client or employer becomes insolvent or otherwise fails to properly discharge their obligations to the warrantor.

Collateral warranties will normally be completed as deeds rather than as simple contracts. This means that the limitation period (the period within which legal proceedings for breach of the terms of the warranty must be commenced) is 12 years. A warranty completed as a simple contract would impose a limitation period of 6 years only on the beneficiary (*Limitation Act* 1980).

What do collateral warranties cost?

It is common for warranties to be provided at little or no cost. However, there is no reason why a more substantial fee should not be charged for a warranty by the warrantor, if the circumstances merit the levying of such a charge. The beneficiary will normally be expected to pay the fee for the warranty. There is no industry-recognised scale for fees associated with the provision of a warranty. Reasonableness, the perceived commercial value of the warranty, and the bargaining positions of the parties are the drivers in respect of the fee sought and paid.

What about the *Contracts (Rights of Third Parties) Act* 1999?

In the late 1990s, in a move to offer an alternative to collateral warranties, parliament enacted the *Contracts (Rights of Third Parties) Act* 1999. This Act came into full force and effect on 11 May 2000. It allows one party entering into an agreement with another party to contract on behalf of a third party, which might be a specific person or a class of person. The Act has not abolished the doctrine of privity of contract – it still exists – but the

1999 Act provides parties with a means to modify the doctrine, for the purposes of individual contracts, if they so decide.

With the arrival of the *Contracts (Rights of Third Parties) Act* 1999, collateral warranties were expected to decline in importance and wither away. Collateral warranties were (and perhaps still are) viewed as difficult and costly to procure. The provisions of the 1999 Act have not fallen into common usage however, and remain largely untested in law. Collateral warranties still have the upper hand when it comes to extending the benefit of contractual obligations and rights to third parties and the operation of the *Contracts (Rights of Third Parties) Act* 1999 is usually expressly excluded from agreements, including collateral warranties.

Reliance letters

Introduction

These are generally simpler documents than collateral warranties and, as the name suggests, they take the form of letters rather than more formal deeds or agreements. They are a recent appearance on the property and construction scene and tend to be encountered more frequently in relation to professional advisers' reports on properties as opposed to construction works.

Reliance letters tend to arise more commonly in relation to property transactions, as opposed to development work.

What do they do?

Reliance letters enable a third party to rely, for some purposes, on professional advice and opinion expressed in a report produced (normally) by a consultant for another party at an earlier point in time. This is particularly beneficial, for example, if the third party is seeking to purchase a property and wishes to rely on a report (or reports) produced in the recent past for the vendor.

Reliance letters can, but do not normally, result in the formation of a contractual relationship between the relying party and the party issuing the letter. The relying parties redress is in the law of tort, specifically negligent misrepresentation following the House of Lords decision of *Hedley Byrne & Co Ltd v Heller and Partners Ltd* 1964.

❖ Hedley were advertising agents who had provided substantial amounts of advertising on credit for Easipower. If Easipower did not pay for the advertising then Hedley would be responsible for such amounts. Hedley became concerned that Easipower would not be in a financial position to pay the debt and sought assurances from Easipower's bank (Heller and Partners Ltd) that Easipower could pay for the additional advertising which Hedley was proposing to give them on credit.

❖ Heller, gave a favourable report of Easipower's financial position, but stipulated that the report was given 'without responsibility'. On the strength of the report given by Heller, Hedley placed additional orders for Easipower. Easipower went into liquidation. Hedley lost £17,000 and commenced an action against Heller for damages under the tort of negligence.

❖ The House of Lords held that a negligent, although honest, misrepresentation, may give rise to an action for damages for financial loss, even if there was **no contract** between the advisor and the advisee, and no fiduciary relationship. The law would imply a duty of care when the advisee seeks information from an advisor who has special skill and where the advisee trusts the advisor to exercise due care, and that the advisor knew or ought to have known that reliance was being placed upon his or her skill and judgement.

❖ Fortunately for Heller, in this case, they expressly disclaimed responsibility and there was therefore no liability, as this effectively barred the claim. However, the decision established the doctrine of negligent misrepresentation.

Who gives reliance letters?

There is no general restriction in the UK property and construction industry on who can issue reliance letters. Literally, any professional person providing advice in the form of a report can allow a third party to rely on the report that he or she produces. There is no obligation in law on a professional to extend their liability in this manner: it is a commercial decision for the professional concerned and might well attract a fee.

Who seeks reliance letters?

Reliance letters are most commonly given to:

❖ purchasers of freehold property (whether for investment of occupation); or

❖ funders such as the banks.

There is no reason why a prospective tenant of property (whether for investment or occupation) could not seek a reliance letter, but this is less common.

It is for the party seeking reliance to determine whether they properly understand the context of the report and the circumstances surrounding its preparation. This might necessitate confirmation of the terms of reference and brief given to the professional originally in order to be sure that the advice and opinions in the report itself are not taken out of context. The professional will not warrant that the report concerned is fit for the purposes of the relying party.

Are all reliance letters the same?

No – reliance letters vary widely in content. There is no single form of wording for such letters adopted by the industry as a whole. Solicitors will have their own precedents as might professionals who issue reliance letters regularly.

What are the common features of a reliance letter?

Reliance letters are generally shorter than collateral warranties. For a reliance letter to be effectual, it is not necessary for it to record or evince the payment of a sum of money by the relying party to the professional. Reliance letters are addressed to the party seeking reliance. The letter should:

❖ state the reason why reliance is being sought – this will often, but not always, be linked to the purchase of a property, or funding of such a purchase;

❖ identify the document(s) on which reliance is being placed and expressly acknowledge that the relying party is entitled to and will rely on the documents;

❖ identify the specific instructions and brief pursuant to which the documents were originally produced; and

❖ set out any restrictions placed on the reliance including:

• the financial limit of any liability that the professional is willing to assume;

• a limit on the period of time over which the professional is willing to extend their liability (typically 6 or 12 years but sometimes less or more depending on the circumstances);

• whether or not the benefit of the reliance can be assigned to any third party; and

• confirmation that the advice in the document(s) concerned has not been updated.

What do reliance letters cost?

There are no recognised scales or rates in the property or construction industry relating to the provision of reliance letters.

It is more common to charge for reliance letters than for collateral warranties, as why should a professional extend their liability to others for nothing. A fee for each report relied upon is a reasonable starting point, as each report could give rise to liability. The number of different parties to whom the letter is addressed is also a relevant consideration.

Reasonableness, the perceived commercial value of the letter, and the bargaining positions of the parties are factors to consider in the final agreement of a fee.

Conclusion

Depending on the precise manner of drafting, it can be possible for a reliance letter to comprise a collateral warranty. For this to be the case the letter needs to contain evidence of a payment by the relying party to the vendor and it needs to be signed and delivered as a deed rather than simply signed like a letter.

Expert witness

Expert evidence in court proceedings is dealt with by Part 35 of the *Civil Procedure Rules* (CPR) and accompanying practice direction which came into force on 26 April 1999. This has been supplemented by the Civil Justice Council's Protocol for the Instruction of Experts to give Evidence in Civil Claims ('the Protocol') which took effect from 5 September 2005. The Protocol is intended to assist in the interpretation of the provisions of CPR Part 35.

The CPR states that it is the duty of an expert to help the courts on matters within his or her expertise. This duty overrides any obligation to the person from whom he or she has received instructions or by whom he or she is paid. The expert should therefore:

- ❖ be independent/impartial; the Protocol sets out a useful test of 'independence' namely, whether the expert will 'express the same opinion if given the same instructions by the opposing party';
- ❖ state any reservations about the case he or she is instructed upon;
- ❖ identify areas outside his or her expertise;
- ❖ consider all material facts in his or her report and state all facts and assumptions, upon which his or her opinion is based;
- ❖ state where necessary that it is only a provisional report, because only limited information/data was available when it was compiled;
- ❖ advise instructing solicitors if further information, i.e. the other expert's report, changes his or her opinion;
- ❖ make available all documents referred to in the report (i.e. survey reports, plans, calculations, photographs, etc.); and
- ❖ keep the report as brief as possible, but without losing the reasoning and conclusions, upon which his or her opinion is based.

The written report

There needs to be a statement setting out the brief and instructions given.

The report is to be written in the first person and it must be an individual who prepares the report and not the company or firm.

The report should be addressed to the court.

Although the report should be as brief as possible, accuracy should not be sacrificed to brevity.

The expert witness must be able to substantiate each and every sentence of the report and highlight any areas where his opinions are based on inadequate factual information. It is not the expert's role to make or advance legal arguments.

The report should contain the expert witness's curriculum vitae (CV).

It is compulsory to include a declaration in the report that the expert understands that his duty is to the court and that he has complied with that duty. A statement of truth must also verify the report. The wording to be included within the expert's report immediately before the signature is as follows:

I believe the facts as stated in this report are true and that the opinions I have expressed are correct.

The Protocol emphasises that this wording is mandatory and must not be modified.

Under the CPR, each party has 28 days after receipt of the opposing expert's report to put written questions. Unless the court gives permission for more general questions, these can only be for the purpose of clarifying the report.

Without prejudice meetings

Without prejudice meetings between experts are necessary and important. The court, under the CPR, may, and normally does, require the experts to produce a joint statement from 'without prejudice' meetings setting out what has and has not been agreed. Reflecting the provisions of CPR 35, the Protocol states that agreements between experts during discussions 'shall not bind the parties unless the parties expressly agree to be bound by the agreement'. However the Protocol adds a strong caveat that in view of the overriding objective of the CPR which encourages that cases are dealt with expeditiously and fairly, 'parties should give careful consideration before refusing to be bound by such an agreement, and be able to explain their refusal should it become relevant to the issue of costs'.

Giving evidence in court

If the case gets to a hearing, then the expert witness will be required to give evidence. The stages of examination of the evidence will be:

- ❖ examination in chief;
- ❖ cross-examination;
- ❖ re-examination; and
- ❖ questions from the judge.

A few helpful hints in giving evidence are listed below:

- ❖ Take time, don't rush.
- ❖ Succinctly answer only the questions that are asked. Use plain language.
- ❖ Do not digress from the question asked.
- ❖ Do not act as advocate.
- ❖ If the question is not understood nor heard – say so.
- ❖ Know the report 'inside out'.

Cross-examination will challenge credibility; so consider the following:

- ❖ Do not feel obliged to fill a silence.
- ❖ Do not be afraid to answer repeated or different questions with the same answer again and again.
- ❖ If asked a closed question, if appropriate state that there may not be a yes or no answer.

❖ Do not be rattled by a number of quick fire questions.

❖ Do not argue with counsel.

❖ If he or she becomes aggressive, stay cool.

❖ Beware of the important question slipped in among a number of trivial questions.

The above notes only deal briefly with the CPR and Protocol. These notes should not be considered as comprehensive text. The role of the expert is evolving through the interpretation of the CPR in case law and any expert should ensure that he or she fully understands that role in the light of the current law.

Dispute resolution

Disputants and their advisors have a variety of dispute resolution mechanisms that they can select to resolve their disputes.

The principal dispute resolution procedures are:

Adjudication

This process is enshrined in the *Housing Grants, Construction and Regeneration Act* 1996. A wide variety of the disputes arising under construction contracts can be referred to adjudication. The Act does not deal with disputes with residential occupiers unless the parties agree that adjudication will apply. Adjudication is popular not least because an adjudication award has to be made within 28 days of the case being referred to an adjudicator unless the parties agree otherwise.

Arbitration

Arbitration is based on the contractual provisions agreed by the parties. Procedures under the 1996 Arbitration Act have given the arbitrator wide powers to resolve disputes without unnecessary cost or delay, and in a fair manner without undue interference from the courts. The right of appeal is limited.

Early Neutral Evaluation (ENN)

Technology and Construction Court judges are prepared to arrange a short hearing of a case, on specific issues, on a without prejudice basis and give preliminary views on the merits, as an aid to settlement discussions between the parties. If a judge determines a particular issue by ENN the parties are free to agree whether or not they will be bound by it. If the ENN does not result in settlement, the case can proceed to trial but will be heard by another judge with no knowledge of the outcome of the ENN.

Independent expert

This forms a valuable means for the speedy resolution of technical disputes. The procedure is generally straightforward and flexible. Issues in dispute are referred to an expert to decide using his or her own professional expertise or judgement. It has been successfully used for many years in rent review matters, but has much wider application to technical disputes. If the parties agree to be bound by the expert's decision it cannot be appealed unless there is misconduct on the part of the expert.

Litigation

The *Civil Procedure Rules* 1998 have led to more efficient running of cases both in terms of costs and time. The Technology and Construction Court in the High Court deals with construction disputes and has considerable experience of doing so. Before court proceedings are commenced, the parties should comply with the Pre-Action Protocol for Construction and Engineering disputes. This requires the parties to set out their respective cases in correspondence and to meet on a without prejudice basis to seek to settle the dispute or narrow the issues involved, prior to the issue of court proceedings.

Mediation

Mediation is a voluntary and non-binding procedure. It is a private process in which an independent neutral person helps the parties reach a negotiated settlement. The Mediator usually does not make a determination on the dispute but may do so if the parties agree and he or she considers that it will assist in reaching a settlement.

The Provisions of Part II of the Housing Grants, Construction and Regeneration Act 1996

The following aims to set out a brief outline of the issues which need to be considered when determining whether contractual terms are compliant with Part II of the *Housing Grants, Construction and Regulation Act* 1996 or whether certain provisions will be incorporated into the contract by the Scheme for Construction Contracts (Scheme).

Parties to a construction contract are free to negotiate and agree the terms and conditions under which the works and services are to be carried out. However, there are times where a contract fails to comply with the minimum requirements relating to adjudication and payment laid down by the Act. Consequently, certain provisions will automatically be incorporated into the contract by the Scheme for Construction Contracts.

When does the Act apply? (S104 – 107)

The Act applies to:

❖ Contracts entered into on or after **1 May 1998.**

❖ **Contracts in writing.** It is sufficient if the contract is evidenced in writing.

❖ Contracts for **construction operations** which include the construction, alteration, repair, maintenance, decoration, demolition and installation in buildings forming or to form part of the land and also architectural, design, surveying or engineering advice.

❖ The carrying out of construction operations in England, Wales or Scotland whatever the applicable law of the contract.

The Act does not apply to:

❖ Contracts with **residential occupiers** for work on their property where they intend to occupy the property as their residence.

❖ Certain mining, drilling and extraction operations.

❖ Installation or demolition of plant or machinery or steelwork to support or provide access to plant or machinery on a site where the primary activity is nuclear processing, power generation, water or effluent treatment, or the production processing of chemicals pharmaceuticals, oil, gas, steel, food or drink.

❖ Manufacture and delivery of materials not involving installation.

❖ Artistic works.

Letters of intent may be subject to the Act where they are sufficient to amount to a legally binding contract in their own right.

Adjudication (S108)

The contract must:

- ❖ Allow either party to refer a dispute to adjudication at any time.

- ❖ Provide for the appointment of an adjudicator within seven days.

- ❖ Require the adjudicator to reach a decision within 28 days **after** the dispute has been referred to the adjudicator (or a longer period if agreed by the parties).

- ❖ Allow the adjudicator and the party who referred the dispute to the adjudicator to extend the period for the decision by up to 14 days.

- ❖ Impose a duty on the adjudicator to act impartially.

- ❖ Enable the adjudicator to take the initiative in ascertaining the facts and the law surrounding the dispute.

- ❖ Provide for the decision of the adjudicator to be binding on the parties until the dispute is taken to arbitration or the courts.

- ❖ Provide that the adjudicator is not liable for anything he or she does unless he or she acts in bad faith.

If the contract does not comply with all eight elements in full, all the adjudication provisions of the contract will be set aside and the adjudication procedures under the Scheme for Construction Contracts will apply. The procedures under the Scheme cover the eight points listed above and introduce time limits.

Payment

The Act and the Scheme for Construction Contracts provide a 'menu' of payment provisions covering:

- ❖ payment by instalments;
- ❖ final payment;
- ❖ withholding payment; and
- ❖ conditional payment.

If a contract fails to comply with any one of the provisions from the 'menu' the relevant provisions from the Scheme will apply. The remainder of the contractual provisions that do comply with the Act will remain intact. It is therefore possible to end up with a contract where the payment provisions are a mixture of express terms agreed between the parties and implied terms from the Scheme.

Payment by instalments (S109 – 110)

A party to a construction contract is entitled to payment by instalments, stage payments or other periodic payments unless:

- ❖ the contract specifies that the duration of the work is less than 45 days; or

- ❖ the parties agree that the work is estimated to take less than 45 days.

Where the work falls within the 45 day limit, the right to instalment payments is excluded but all other payment provisions (notice of withholding payment, set-off, etc.) will apply as will the adjudication provisions outlined above.

Where a contract falls below the 45 day limit, payment of the contract price falls due 30 days after completion of the work (or 30 days after the contractor's claim if later) and payment must be made within 17 days.

In all other cases, the parties can agree between themselves:

- ❖ the amounts of each payment;
- ❖ the intervals between each payment;
- ❖ the date each payment becomes due; and
- ❖ the final date by which each payment must be made.

If the contract does not contain a clear mechanism for determining each of these four elements they will be determined by the Scheme for Construction Contracts, namely:

- ❖ The amount of each payment will be based on the value of the work and other costs to which the contractor is entitled during the payment interval.
- ❖ There will be 28 day payment cycles.
- ❖ Payment is due seven days after each 28 day period (or seven days after the contractor's claim for payment if later).
- ❖ The final date for each payment is 24 days after each 28 day period (or 24 days after the contractor's claim for payment if later).

The contract must provide for the paying party to give notice within five days of the date on which each instalment becomes due, specifying the amount proposed to be paid and the basis on which it is calculated. Any attempt in the contract to vary or exclude this requirement will be ineffective and this provision will be implied by the Scheme for Construction Contracts.

Final payment

The contract must contain a clear mechanism for determining when the final payment due under the contract becomes payable and the final date by which that payment must be made.

The parties are free to agree the dates or periods within which the final payment is due and is payable but if there is no such mechanism, in accordance with the Scheme the final payment:

- ❖ is due 30 days after completion of the work (or 30 days after the contractor's claim for payment if later); and
- ❖ the final date for making the final payment is 47 days after completion of the work (or 47 days after the contractor's claim for payment if later).

Withholding payment (S111)

- ❖ No payment can be withheld unless a 'notice of intention to withhold payment' has been given, specifying the amount to be withheld and the grounds for withholding payment.
- ❖ The notice must be given before the final date for payment.
- ❖ The contract can specify how long before the final date of payment, the notice must be given (even if it is just one day) but if this notice period is not specified, the Scheme applies and at least seven days notice must be given.

Conditional payment (S113)

Any provision in a contract which makes payment conditional upon the paying party receiving payment from someone else is ineffective and the payment provisions of the Scheme outlined above will apply.

The only exception is where the contract provides that payment may be withheld if the reason for non-payment is the insolvency of someone else in the payment chain.

Suspending performance (S112)

If any payment is not received by the final date for payment and a notice of withholding payment has not been served, the contractor may suspend work after giving seven days notice of his intention. The right to suspend performance ceases when the relevant payment is received. The period in which to complete the works is automatically extended by the number of days of the suspension.

This brief summary of the provisions of Part II of the *Housing Grants, Construction and Regeneration Act* 1996 is not intended to be a detailed explanation of the provisions of the Act and we recommend that legal advice is sought on any specific issues.

Adjudication under the Scheme for Construction Contracts – how to get started

Adjudication under the *Housing Grants, Construction and Regeneration Act* 1996 (the Act) allows for a quick fix method of dispute resolution. The right to refer a dispute to adjudication is available to a party to a construction contract within the meaning of the Act at any time.

Below is a brief explanation of the steps required to commence an adjudication under the Scheme for Construction Contracts, i.e. **where there are no contractual adjudication provisions.**

Where adjudication is your chosen method of dispute resolution, it is essential that you comply with the strict time limits laid down by the scheme and any timetable imposed by the adjudicator. The adjudicator is under an obligation to reach a decision within 28 days of referral unless the parties agree otherwise.

It is not possible to contract out of the time constraints laid down for adjudication by the Act.

Procedure

To commence adjudication you must take three steps:

❖ give notice of adjudication;
❖ request an adjudicator to act; and
❖ serve a Referral Notice.

Notice of Adjudication

This must be in writing, be given to every other party to the contract and contain:

❖ details of the parties involved;
❖ a brief description of the dispute;
❖ details of when and where the dispute arose;
❖ what you are seeking from the adjudicator, for example, an award for a specific sum; and
❖ names and addresses of the parties to the contract (including the addresses which the parties have specified for the giving of notices, if any).

Note: In view of the very tight timescale for adjudication you should ensure that your claim is fully prepared before issuing the Notice of Adjudication.

Appointing an adjudicator

After giving notice of adjudication you must make a request for an adjudicator to act. The timescale for the appointment of an adjudicator is extremely tight and a request for the appointment of an adjudicator should be made at the same time as giving the Notice of Adjudication. In order to determine who to appoint you should consider the following:

If your contract names an adjudicator, contact that person to ensure that he or she is ready and willing to act.

If an Adjudicator Nominating Body (ANB) is named in your contract, contact that body and ask for an appointment to be made.

If no adjudicator or ANB has been named in your contract you can contact any ANB such as:

- ❖ The Association of Independent Construction Adjudicators, 0870 429 6353.
- ❖ The Royal Institution of Chartered Surveyors, Dispute Resolution Service, 020 7334 3806.
- ❖ The Chartered Institute of Arbitrators, 020 7421 7444.
- ❖ The Royal Institute of British Architects, 020 7580 5533.
- ❖ The Technology and Construction Solicitors Association, 020 7367 2000.
- ❖ The Construction Industry Council, 020 7637 8692.

Contact the most appropriate ANB depending upon the nature of the dispute and the issues involved. Some ANBs will be able to offer a greater diversity and breadth of experience.

If an ANB is used: The ANB has five days to inform you of the nominated Adjudicator. The nominated adjudicator then has up to two days to confirm his or her appointment.

Caution: If a named or nominated adjudicator refuses to act, another adjudicator can be agreed or nominated by any ANB, but beware the time limit for issuing the Referral Notice. If an alternative adjudicator cannot be appointed within seven days of the Notice of Adjudication the safest course is to issue a fresh Notice of Adjudication.

Referral Notice

Within seven days of the Notice of Adjudication you must send the Referral Notice to the adjudicator formally referring the dispute to him or her. The Referral Notice must be in writing, be given to the adjudicator and every other party to the dispute and:

- ❖ contain the basis of your claim, including an explanation of how the dispute arose and identifying the issues in dispute;
- ❖ be accompanied by copies of (or relevant extracts from) your contract (whether this is a standard printed form or evidenced in correspondence);
- ❖ include any documents upon which you wish to rely in support of your case;
- ❖ contain the remedies and award you are seeking; and
- ❖ give the adjudicator wide jurisdiction by giving him or her an alternative, for example, 'such other sum as the adjudicator may determine'.

It is important that the Referral Notice clearly sets out the issues in dispute which the adjudicator is being asked to determine including the history of the case and any arguments raised by the other party as well as identifying the remedies sought. Claims not identified in the Notice of Adjudication cannot be introduced later in the same adjudication.

Following service of the Referral Notice the adjudicator should set a timetable for dealing with the adjudication including a response from the opposing party and request any further information or evidence in order to reach his or her decision.

Neighbourly matters

Legislation

Rights to light

The subject of rights to light usually concerns the assessment of whether proposed obstructions (for example, new developments) are likely to interfere materially with neighbours' easements of light. Interpretation of whether a material right to light issue is likely to arise requires knowledge of the law, particularly easements and nuisance, and an understanding of the technical measurements of skylight entering a room. It is then possible to assess the risk of injunction and, where appropriate, the likely level of damages that could be awarded. It is also possible to determine how to modify a proposed scheme in order to reduce or overcome potential problems.

Legal background

Rights to light problems bring together two distinct but different areas of English law namely private nuisance – a subdivision of the law of torts; and easements – a subdivision of land law.

Private nuisance

The tort of private nuisance, like the tort of public nuisance, regulates activities affecting individual rights in or rights over real property (land).

A private nuisance may be defined as:

> An unreasonable interference with a person's use or enjoyment of land itself, or some right over or in connection with land (i.e. a right to light).

The law of nuisance tries to balance the legitimate activities of neighbours – a give and take approach. Interference with a right to light must be objectively unreasonable in its extent and severity if it is to be sufficient to constitute a nuisance in the eyes of the courts. Only when the courts are satisfied that the interference is unreasonable will they remedy the situation by awarding an injunction and/or damages. It should be appreciated that levels of natural light can often be interfered with to a marginal extent and this will not necessarily constitute an infringement of a proprietary right that will be recognised as a nuisance.

Easements

An easement may be defined as a right annexed to land to use or to restrict use of neighbouring land in some way. For an easement to be valid, four essential characteristics must be satisfied:

- ❖ There must be a dominant tenement and a servient tenement.
- ❖ The right must accommodate (benefit) the dominant tenement.
- ❖ The dominant tenement and the servient tenement must be owned or occupied by different persons.
- ❖ The right concerned must be capable of forming the subject matter of a grant.

Rights to light have been recognised as a valid easement for centuries. The general rights to light principles set out below have been distilled from the large body of case law that exists.

A right to light can be defined generally as:

> A negative easement providing a right for a building to receive sufficient natural light through a defined aperture (usually a window), over the land of another, in perpetuity or for a term of years.

Nature of a right to light

A right to light is not personal – it runs with property/buildings.

A right benefits the dominant tenement and burdens the servient tenement. A right to light is for 'sufficient' natural light only and this is taken to mean enough light, 'according to the ordinary notions of mankind' for:

❖ comfortable use and enjoyment of a dwelling house; or

❖ beneficial use of and occupation of a warehouse, shop or other place (office, etc.).

The test for 'sufficiency' is whether or not the dominant tenement will be left with enough light according to the ordinary requirements of mankind. Sufficiency is not based on the measure of light lost. See *Colls v Home & Colonial Stores* [l904] AC 179.

Actionable injury and measurement of light

No specific rule has been developed by the courts to define exactly when a reduction in natural light becomes actionable. The test for injury is uncertain but flexible. The court will have regard, in all cases, to the specific facts and circumstances and it will usually hear objective technical evidence from a rights to light expert, as well as more subjective evidence from the injured party.

A form of technical evidence has evolved that entails analysis of the amount of the notional sky dome that can be seen from a series of points in an affected room at table level. At any given point on the working plane there is a minimum amount of sky area below which the level of daylight at that point will be inadequate. Adequacy is considered to be just enough for undertaking work that requires visual discrimination, such as reading, drawing or sewing. In technical terms this is one lumen or 1/500th of a standard uniform dome of overcast sky in December (i.e. 0.2% sky factor).

It is possible to plot the 0.2% sky factor contour in the subject room and measure the area of the room that will receive more than adequate light both before and after development. Today, leading rights to light experts tend to do this with the aid of 3D computer modelling and specialist software, which is more accurate and efficient than the laborious manual Waldram method.

Having measured the area that will be adequately illuminated, it is possible to assess whether an actionable injury will arise. Very generally, for day-to-day practical purposes, light specialists have adopted the general conventions that:

❖ A commercial property may be considered actionably damaged when less than 50% of an office floor area is lit to the critical one lumen (0.2% sky factor) level i.e. the so-called 50/50 rule.

❖ A residential/domestic property should be considered actionably damaged when less than 55% of a room area is lit to the critical one lumen (0.2% sky factor) level.

It must be understood that the percentages mentioned above are not strongly founded in specific legal authority, although courts will make reference to previously decided cases where the facts are similar. The courts regard the so-called 50/50 rule as a 'convenient rule of thumb'.

Acquisition of a right to light

A right to light may be created by:

❖ express grant or reservation (sometimes encountered);

❖ implied grant or reservation (rarely encountered); or

❖ prescription (very common and often called 'ancient lights').

Prescription means the procuring of a right on the basis of a long established custom and three methods of prescription exist, namely:

- ❖ time immemorial (right enjoyed since before 1189);
- ❖ doctrine of lost modern grant (right enjoyed continuously for minimum 20 years); and
- ❖ *Prescription Act* 1832: sections 3 and 4 (right enjoyed continuously for 20 years).

(Note: In the City of London, because of the 'Custom of London', the acquisition of a right by the doctrine of lost modern grant is not available – see *Bowring Services Ltd v Scottish Widows* 1995.)

Defeating a right to light

Prescription through the doctrines of lost modern grant or time immemorial can be defeated if it can be shown that the easement has not been enjoyed, 'as of right', i.e. through force, secrecy or with permission.

Statutory prescription, under the *Prescription Act* 1832, may be defeated if the servient party can show that:

- ❖ at some time within the last 19 years, they have prevented the entry of natural daylight through the subject apertures by erecting an opaque physical obstruction for a continuous period of at least one year;
- ❖ at some time in the last 19 years, they registered a light obstruction notice under the *Rights of Light Act* 1959 for a whole year (see below); or
- ❖ the right has been enjoyed under some consent or agreement expressly given for that purpose by deed or in writing.

Defending your right to light

A prescriptive right to light may be lost if it is not defended in the face of development. A neighbour who acquiesces in or submits to an interruption of light for one year or more will lose a claim to a prescriptive right under section 4 of the *Prescription Act* 1832. See *Dance v Triplow and Another* [1992] 17 EG 103.

Successful defence of a prescriptive right to light relies much on eternal vigilance and prompt protestation in writing to the obstructor. The protestations should also be repeated at regular intervals. Ultimately legal proceedings will need to be brought against a developer who ignores the objections and the timing of this may considerably affect the chances of obtaining an injunction.

Remedies

The current legal system permits the awarding of:

- ❖ prohibitory or mandatory injunctions; and/or
- ❖ common law damages.

Injunctions

The courts are reluctant to sanction a wrong doing by a servient party in allowing that party to purchase his or her neighbour's rights. Generally, an injunction is regarded as the normal remedy, with damages the exception.

The court may award damages in lieu of an injunction if all the four requirements below can be answered in the affirmative:

- ❖ Is the injury small?
- ❖ Would a small money payment be an adequate remedy?
- ❖ Would it be oppressive to the defendant to grant an injunction?

❖   Is the injury one that can be estimated in money terms?

These requirements are derived from *Shelfer v City of London Electric Lighting Co* [1895] 1 Ch 287 31, however, the courts have departed from a strict application of the test and it is not necessarily applicable to every rights to light situation.

The conduct of parties will also have a significant bearing on the matter. If a developer ignores the communicated protestations from his or her neighbour and continues developing regardless then once a nuisance is proved an injunction should be the default remedy.

Damages (compensation)

Compensation for injury to a right to light may be assessed using one of two methods:

❖   the traditional valuation approach; or

❖   the developer's profit approach.

For commercial property, the valuation approach is based on a freeholder in possession. A 'base book value' is calculated for the light loss, which may then be enhanced by a multiplier of up to three or four times, having regard to the case of *Carr Saunders v Dick McNeil Associates Ltd and Others* [1986]. Any compensation will be appropriately apportioned between the various interests in the dominant tenement. For leases, this is generally dependent upon the number of years remaining until the next rent review. For residential property, however, the assessment of compensation is more subjective.

For very serious rights to light injuries, it may be more appropriate to adopt the developer's profit approach, when assessing compensation. This approach considers the possibility of sharing the profit that a developer will make from the extra floor space that could be prevented from being built if the adjoining owner obtained an injunction. The profit share can be up to 50/50 in very severe cases.

Dos and don'ts

❖   Do establish whether surrounding properties enjoy rights to light, including other tenanted parts of the client's property, and identify all parties with an interest.

❖   Do establish whether development proposals are likely to leave the surrounding buildings with inadequate light.

❖   Do take specialist advice from a rights to light consultant at an early stage.

❖   Do obtain copies of all leases, deeds, transfers, restrictive covenants, and so on, that could have a bearing on the legal position.

❖   Don't be fooled by buildings that look less than 20 years old or have blocked-up windows: case law is complex and there could still be a right to light!

❖   Do consider whether the Crown has ever had an interest in the development site: the surrounding buildings may not be entitled to rights to light.

❖   Do consider whether the development site has ever been acquired or appropriated by the local authority for planning purposes under section 237 of the *Town and Country Planning Act* 1990, as this affects the potential for injunctions.

❖   Do obtain copies (if available) showing the massing and profile of the existing building on the development site, and the proposed building or extension, and also up-to-date floor layout plans for the surrounding buildings.

- ❖ Do establish the extent of a right (i.e. the number, size and location of apertures).
- ❖ Do consider whether transferred or 'incorporated' rights to light exist.
- ❖ Do seek the advice of lawyers if the legal position is complicated beyond your experience by any controlling deeds or similar documents.
- ❖ Do ensure that your client understands that the law relating to rights to light, and the valuation techniques, are not an exact science.
- ❖ Do remember that you cannot rely on a neighbour, particularly a residential owner, settling for compensation.
- ❖ Do explain to your client that there are no general statutory procedures for dealing with rights to light issues and that there are no prescribed periods and deadlines during or by which parties are obliged to settle issues.
- ❖ Don't allow a 'dominant' party to be pressured into early agreement of compensation.

Light obstruction notices

Light obstruction notices can be used to either defeat an existing right to light that has been acquired by statutory prescription or prevent such a right from being acquired. They are a useful tool for preserving the development potential of a site and can also be used to 'flush out' potential claims.

Under Section 2(1) of the *Rights of Light Act* 1959 a light obstruction notice can be registered with the local authority as a local land charge for a period of one year.

Further information

The two main statutes that are relevant to rights to light are:

- ❖ the *Prescription Act* 1832; and
- ❖ the *Rights of Light Act* 1959.

There exists a large body of rights to light case law. The selection of case reports listed below includes the more recent and more important decisions.

- ❖ *Allen and Another v Greenwood and Another* [1975] 1 All ER 819 6, 35-6
- ❖ *Bowring Services Ltd v Scottish Widows Fund & Life Assurance Society* [1995] 16 EG 206
- ❖ *Carr Saunders v Dick McNeil Associates Ltd and Others* [1986] 1 WLR 992 37, 43
- ❖ *Charles Semon & Co v Bradford Corporation* [1922] 2 Ch 737
- ❖ *Colls v Home & Colonial Stores* [1904] AC 179 4, 9, 10, 29, 31-2, 34
- ❖ *Dance v Triplow and Another* [1992] 17 EG 103
- ❖ *Deakins v Hookings* [1994] 14 EG 133
- ❖ *Ecclesiastical Commissioners for England v Kino* [1880] 14 ChD 213 40
- ❖ *Fishenden v Higgs and Hill Ltd* [1935] 153 LT 128 33
- ❖ *Lyme Valley Squash Club Ltd v Newcastle under Lyme Borough Council and Another* [1985] 2 All ER 405 28-9
- ❖ *Marine and General Mutual Life Assurance Society v St. James Real Estate Co Limited* [1991] 2 EGLR 178
- ❖ *Midtown Ltd v City of London Real Property Co Ltd* [2005] 14 EG 130

- ❖ *Ough v King* [1967] 3 All ER 859 34
- ❖ *Price v Hilditch* [1930] I Ch 500 5, 37, 43
- ❖ *Pugh and Another v Howels and Another* [1984] 48 PCR 298 36-7
- ❖ *Scott v Pape* [1886] 31 ChD 554 6, 80
- ❖ *Sheffield Masonic Hall Co v Sheffield Corporation* [1932] 2 Ch 17 43
- ❖ *Shelfer v City of London Electric Lighting Co* [1895] 1 Ch 287 31
- ❖ *Wheeldon v Burrows* [1879] 12 ChD 31 78
- ❖ *Wrotham Park Estate Co v Parkside Homes Limited* [1973] ChD 321.

Daylight and sunlight amenity

As greater emphasis is placed on environmental issues, local planning authorities are increasingly concerning themselves with the effect of developments on the daylight and sunlight enjoyed by neighbouring properties. The local authority's Unitary Development Plan or Local Plan should always be consulted, as it will give an indication of what they expect in this regard.

The Building Research Establishment (BRE) published Report 209 in 1991 titled *Site layout planning for daylight and sunlight: A guide to good practice* written by P J Littlefair. It was intended to give guidance on how to ensure good daylight and sunlight to proposed new development through good design, while avoiding detrimentally affecting neighbours' daylight and sunlight amenity. It sets out various tests that can be undertaken to establish if a problem is likely to be created.

The BRE report was not intended to be mandatory. However, it is not uncommon for planning authorities to require a developer to submit a daylighting and sunlighting study in support of a planning application and some may expect compliance with the recommendations given in the guidelines.

It is important to note that even if a scheme is granted planning consent this will not override the private rights of individuals, and therefore, rights to light may still be an issue. See *Brewer and another v Secretary of State for the Environment and others* [1988] 2 PLR 13.

Daylight

The BRE report states that if any part of a new building or extension, measured in a vertical section perpendicular to a main window wall of an existing building, from the centre of the lowest window, subtends an angle of more than 25° to the horizontal, then the diffuse daylighting of the existing building may be adversely affected. This will be the case if either:

- ❖ the vertical sky component measured at the centre of an existing main window is less than 27%, and less than 0.8 times its former value; or
- ❖ the area of the working plane in a room which can receive direct skylight is reduced to less than 0.8 times its former value.

In such circumstances the occupants of the existing building will notice the reduction in the amount of skylight and more of the room will appear poorly lit.

Sunlight

The BRE report advises that new development should take care to safeguard access to sunlight for existing dwellings and any non-domestic buildings where there is a particular requirement for sunlight. If a living room of an existing dwelling has a main window facing within 90° of due south, and any part of a new development subtends an angle of more than 25° to the horizontal measured from a point 2 metres above ground in a vertical section, perpendicular to the window, then the sunlighting of the existing dwelling may be adversely affected.

The sunlight amenity of the existing dwelling will be considered to be adversely affected if the window reference point:

❖ receives less than one quarter of annual probable sunlight hours, and/or less than 5% of annual probable sunlight hours during the winter months between 21 September and 21 March, and the available sunlight hours in either period is reduced to less than 0.8 times its former value.

Analysis

The BRE report sets out the methods by which the effect of a development on existing neighbouring buildings may be calculated. If the local planning authority requires an assessment to be undertaken and submitted in support of a planning application, it is usual for the analysis to follow the tests in BRE Report 209.

The target values recommended in BRE Report 209 are quite demanding and can be difficult to achieve, particularly in dense urban environments. Care may need to be taken when applying the guidance and interpreting the results of analyses.

Further information

❖ BRE Report 209, *Site layout planning for daylight and sunlight: A guide to good practice*;

❖ BS 8206-2: 1992, *Lighting for buildings: Code of practice for daylighting*;

❖ *Brewer and another v Secretary of State for the Environment and others* [1988] 2 PLR 13;

❖ Planning appeal by St George Central London, decided 20 April 2004;

❖ *Malster v Ipswich Borough Council* [2001] EWHC ADMIN 711; and

❖ Planning appeal by West End Green (Properties) Limited, decided 10 October 2005.

High hedges

The current position

The *Anti-social Behaviour Act* 2003 came into operation in England on 1 June 2005. Part 8 of the Act provides Local Authorities with powers to deal with complaints about high hedges.

The legislation means that neighbours who are in dispute over a high hedge can now go to their Local Authority for resolution. Note that 'in dispute' does not mean one neighbour can simply bypass the other and expect a favourable response from the Local Authority. The legislation provides a vehicle for neighbours who have discussed the matter and have tried, but exhausted, all other possibilities for resolving their dispute.

Note also that the Local Authority is not expected, nor empowered, to mediate between the neighbours or to assist or progress negotiations. Its role is simply to adjudicate on whether 'the hedge is adversely affecting the complainant's reasonable enjoyment of their property'.

In its deliberations the Local Authority must consider all the relevant factors and must try to strike the right balance between the interests of the two neighbours. It may also consider the interests of the wider community if it considers this may be adversely affected.

Once it has considered all the relevant issues (not the neighbours' arguments), the Local Authority will either dismiss the matter and write to the neighbours telling them its reasons, or it will write to the hedge owner in a formal notice setting out what he or she must do (and by what date they must do it) to the hedge in order to remedy the problem.

A hedge owner who fails to comply with the notice or in any way fails to carry out the works which are required by the Local Authority will be guilty of an offence. Upon summary prosecution the failing hedge owner could receive a fine of up to £1,000 and continuing fines which will accumulate on a daily basis whilst the owner remains in breach of the order.

Tall stories and the truth of the matter

High hedges are all those which are over two metres tall.

Not true: The legislation does not apply to all hedges, only to those which are evergreen or 'semi-evergreen'. It does not cover single or deciduous trees. For clarification this means a hedge which has two or more consecutive trees or shrubs which are evergreen, or one which is predominantly evergreen. Furthermore, some hedges over two metres do not block light, do not cause a nuisance and do not prevent anyone from enjoying their own land. Therefore, they are not going to be the subject of a dispute and can safely be allowed to grow as high as they will.

You need permission to grow a garden hedge over two metres tall.

Not true: A hedge owner can grow a hedge as high as he or she likes in the first instance. Permission is not required and the Local Authority will take no automatic action unless a dispute is referred to it. If both neighbours want a tall hedge and are not in dispute over it then it is very unlikely that a Local Authority will become involved.

If the Local Authority receives a complaint it will order the hedge to be cut down to two metres.

Not true: If a Local Authority receives a complaint it will weigh up all the relevant matters and consider the merits of each case in isolation. It may order a reduction in height, either in one cut or in stages if a single cut could be drastic enough to kill the hedge. The Local Authority may stipulate a greater height than two metres if it considers that this height will abate the nuisance sufficiently. The confusion seems to stem from the fact that the Local Authority may not order a reduction to less than two metres. Additionally, the Local Authority cannot require the hedge to be removed completely.

The hedge will be a nuisance if it blocks light to a neighbouring property.

Not true: Whilst a hedge which is blocking a neighbouring owner's light may be interpreted as a nuisance this is not unequivocal. Each case will be considered individually and an appropriate order will be made, but the legislation does not guarantee an adjoining property access to uninterrupted light.

Anyone served with an order under Part 8 of the Anti-social Behaviour Act 2003 will be the subject of an ASBO.

Not true: There is no provision in the Act to serve an Anti-social Behaviour Order in respect of high hedge complaints.

Further information

There is, of course, a lot more to high hedges and their problems than has been outlined above. Much of the information is somewhat confusing and needs to be interpreted carefully.

Be aware, also, that a number of organisations exist purely to complain about high hedges. Some of these organisations can be really helpful, however they do not all consider the interests of fair play and some may offer confusing, if not misleading, information.

It is better, then, to get information from an official source.

The Department for Communities and Local Government (DCLG), formerly the Office of the Deputy Prime Minister, has more information, including guidance from the Building Research Establishment on calculating light loss and appropriate hedge height. Their website can be found at www.communities.gov.uk/index.asp?id=1127822

A review of guidance from DCLG can be found at www.communities.gov.uk/pub/857/Reviewofguidanceonhedgeheightandl ightlossPDF545Kb_id1127857.pdf

Although the Act applies in Wales, the situation is slightly different. Further information can be found on its application in Wales at:

- ❖ www.wales.gov.uk/subiplanning/content/highhedges/ highhedges-guide-final-e.pdf
- ❖ www.hmso.gov.uk/legislation/wales/wsi2004/20043238e.htm

Party wall procedure

The *Party Wall etc. Act* 1996 came into force throughout England and Wales on 1 July 1997. All previous local enactments, including the *London Building Acts (Amendment) Act* 1939 Part VI and the *Bristol Improvement Act* 1847, have now been repealed.

The general principle of the Act is to enable an owner to undertake certain specific works on, or adjacent to, adjoining properties while giving protection to potentially affected neighbours. As suggested by the word 'etc.' in its title, the Act relates not just to party walls.

The parties

The owner of the property where the work is to be undertaken is the 'building owner'. The owner of the adjoining property is the 'adjoining owner'. There can be many adjoining owners including freeholder, leaseholder and anyone with an interest greater than from year to year. Under the Act, the word 'owner' can also include people with a contract to purchase or an agreement for lease; this arrangement allows a prospective owner to serve notice, and even commence work, before completion of the contract.

Party structures

A party wall is one that stands on the land of two owners, by more than its footings, or one which separates buildings of different owners. In the first case, the whole wall is a party wall whereas in the second, it is only a party wall for the extent to which the two buildings are using it and the whole of the rest of the wall belongs to the person on whose land it stands. Other types of party structure are party fence walls (i.e. shared garden walls) and party floors (e.g. separating different flats).

In the case of a party wall, each owner owns the part of the wall that stands on their own land, but also has rights over the remainder of the wall. The Act allows owners to treat the whole of the party wall as if it were their own, and debars them from dealing with their half on its own without informing their neighbours.

Before exercising any of the rights bestowed upon them, owners must follow the procedures set down in the *Party Wall etc. Act* 1996. If an owner wishes to underpin, raise, cut into, thicken or demolish and rebuild a party wall, they must give notice of their intention to do so. In the event that the adjoining owner disagrees, each party must appoint a surveyor and a formal agreement known as a party wall award must be entered into.

An adjoining owner may respond to a party structure notice by serving a counter notice requiring certain specified works to be undertaken to the party wall for his future purposes. However the notice must be served within one month of the original notice and the adjoining owner will be responsible for the cost of the additional work.

Excavations adjacent to structures

The *Party Wall etc. Act* 1996 requires notice to be served on adjoining owners of certain intended excavations within 3 metres or 6 metres of adjacent buildings or structures.

Refer to figure below for details of these notifiable excavations.

3 metre notice

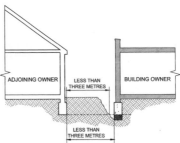

6 metre notice

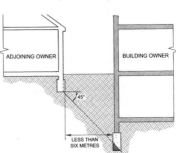

The excavations could be for any purpose, not just for a building or its foundations.

New walls at boundaries

Where it is proposed to build at the 'line of junction' (i.e. the boundary) notice may need to be given to the adjoining owners. This will be the case where the boundary is not already built upon, or is built upon only to the extent of a boundary wall (not being a party fence wall or external wall of a building). In return, a right to construct projecting mass concrete footings work may be claimed.

General rights and obligations

The *Party Wall etc. Act* 1996 grants various general rights and obligations in relation to work undertaken in pursuance of the Act. The key ones are as follows:

- ❖ obligation to serve notice on adjoining owners before undertaking the work;
- ❖ obligation to execute the work in compliance with other statutory requirements and in accordance with details agreed either by the parties or by appointed party wall surveyors in an Award;
- ❖ right of access to enter and remain on adjoining owners' land so far as is reasonably necessary to facilitate the work;
- ❖ duty not to cause unnecessary inconvenience;
- ❖ duty to compensate adjoining owners for loss or damage arising as a consequence of the work; and
- ❖ obligation to make good damage caused by work to party structures.

Agreeing the works

The building owner and adjoining owner may agree the details of the works between them. Where disagreements occur, either deemed or actual, the Act provides a mechanism for resolving them through the appointment of party wall surveyors. The appointed surveyors have a duty to settle the matter by making an award and they must act expediently and impartially, having regard to the interests and rights of both parties.

Dos and don'ts

- ❖ Do consider whether proposed excavations and building works require the serving of notices under the Act.
- ❖ Do allow adequate time in the project programme for identifying and resolving all party wall issues. Time periods stated in the Act are statutory minimums, and often longer periods should be allowed.
- ❖ Do establish which party will act as the 'building owner' and verify his or her legal interest in the property.
- ❖ Do remember that if the building owner parts with his or her interest in the property part-way through proceedings, matters will have to start afresh.
- ❖ Do remember that the interests of all relevant adjoining owners will have to be identified with certainty and each owner notified separately.
- ❖ Do remember that each adjoining owner has a right to disagree with the proposals and to appoint a surveyor.
- ❖ Don't let unreasonable or unresponsive adjoining owners or surveyors hinder progress: use the mechanisms in the Act to force matters along.
- ❖ Do make allowance within the cost plan for the reasonable fees of the adjoining owners' surveyors and any necessary subconsultants (typically structural engineers).

❖ Do ensure that the design team and contractors cooperate and produce all necessary drawings, method statements, calculations, etc. in good time.

❖ Do ensure that the proposed time and manner of carrying out the work is reasonable and that no unnecessary inconvenience will be caused.

❖ Do consider making provision within tender documents for restrictions on working hours and/or methods of working for noisy elements of work falling within the scope of the Act.

❖ Do ensure that the procedures required by the Act are followed meticulously; otherwise, notices and awards could be invalidated.

❖ Do remember that the party wall surveyors are administering the Act impartially and not representing clients.

❖ Do ensure that awards are agreed prior to starting the relevant work.

❖ Don't confuse common law and rights to light matters as being part of party wall procedures.

❖ Do establish a line of communication between adjoining owners and contractors for dealing with day-to-day issues of noise, dust, and so on.

❖ Do ensure that any variations in the agreed works are agreed between the parties, or by their appointed surveyors.

❖ Finally, do ensure that all parties fulfil their obligations.

References

Party Wall Legislation and Procedure, RICS guidance note (5th edition), RICS Books, 2002.

The Party Wall Act Explained – A Commentary on The Party Wall etc. Act 1996 (The Green Book), Pyramus and Thisbe Club, 2nd edition, 1997.

Party Walls – The New Law, S. Bickford-Smith and C. Sydenham, 2nd edition, Jordans, 2003.

A Practical Manual for Party Wall Surveyors, J. Anstey, RICS Books, 2000.

Anstey's Party Walls and What to Do with Them, G. North, 6th edition, RICS Books, 2005.

An Introduction to the Party Wall etc. Act 1996, J. Anstey and V. Vegoda, Lark Productions, 1997.

The Party Wall Casebook, P. Chynoweth, Blackwell Science, 2003.

Party Wall etc. Act 1996, audio cassette, Owlion.

Party Walls – Best Practice Roadshow, audio CD, Owlion, 2002.

Party Wall etc. Act, 1996: explanatory booklet, Office of the Deputy Prime Minister (ODPM).

Practical Neighbour Law Handbook, A. Redler, RICS Books, 2006.

Useful websites

Party Wall etc. Act 1996 – Office of Public Section Information:
www.opsi.gov.uk/acts/acts1996/1996040.htm

Royal Institution of Chartered Surveyors:
www.rics.org/property/propertymanagement/easements/partywallsurveying.htm

Pyramus and Thisbe Club:
www.partywalls.org.uk

Department for Communities and Local Government (DCLG):
www.communities.gov.uk

Party Wall and Rights to Light Discussion Forum:
www.partywallforum.co.uk

Access agreements

Access to Neighbouring Land Act 1992

Under the *Access to Neighbouring Land Act* 1992 a court may grant an order for access to land where such access is required to enable the execution of basic preservation works and where access has been refused by the neighbour. Such works include:

- ❖ maintenance, repair or renewal of any part of a building or structure;
- ❖ clearance, repair or renewal of drains, sewers, pipes and cables;
- ❖ cutting back or felling trees and hedges in certain circumstances; and
- ❖ filling in or clearing any ditch.

The Act contains provisions for the preparation of schedules of condition and for overseeing of the work by surveyors. Surveyors can also be called upon to provide evidence where claims for damage under the Act are made.

The access order made by the court may require the payment of consideration, having regard to the likely financial advantage to the applicant and the degree of inconvenience, except where the works are to residential land.

Often the knowledge that rights exist under the Act will prompt neighbours to be accommodating, but, even then, it is still sensible to enter into an informal access agreement in the form of a licence with accompanying schedule of condition.

The Act is available online at:
www.opsi.gov.uk/acts/acts1992 /ukpga 19920023 en 1.htm

Rights of way and fire escape agreements

More intense use of an existing right of way often requires re-negotiation of the right altogether. One type of right commonly encountered relates to fire escape routes benefiting properties that adjoin a development. The rights are often disrupted by large-scale redevelopment and negotiations for both temporary escape rights during the redevelopment and for revised escape rights over the new permanent development will be required.

Oversailing cranes and encroaching scaffolds

Most large developments necessitate the use of at least one crane. There are benefits to the developer or contractor of using fixed-jib tower cranes, as opposed to luffing-jib or folding-jib cranes, such as reduced cost and increased speed and load capacity. However, where the jib of a crane will oversail adjoining land, the agreement of the adjoining land owner, and any other party with an interest in the air space above it, will be needed.

Without such agreement the developer will be committing a trespass on every oversailing occasion.

The law on this matter comes from the tort of trespass. The position was clarified in the case of *Anchor Brewhouse Developments Ltd and others v Berkeley House (Docklands Developments) Ltd* [1987], in which the plaintiffs sought, and were granted, injunctive relief in relation to an unauthorised oversailing crane.

While some developers manage to place oversailing risks on their contractors, when work is abundant such contractors will often not accept such risks or, if they do, their tender prices are significantly enhanced.

Similar trespass issues often arise in relation to temporary independent scaffolding, although, wherever possible, rights granted by the *Party Wall etc. Act* 1996 and emanating from the *Access to Neighbouring Land Act* 1992 should be exercised.

Developers and/or their contractors should give consideration at an early stage to the issue of access onto or over adjoining land or the airspace above it. Neighbours should be approached in advance for consent and the terms of such consent will be the subject of negotiation by the parties. It is sensible to enter into an access agreement or licence and the developer may be expected to pay a sum of money in consideration or grant reciprocal oversailing rights. Typically such agreements will provide for indemnities, insurance arrangements, schedules of condition, payment of fees and costs and so on.

Construction noise and vibration

The law relating to construction noise and vibration is controlled by the common law of nuisance and a number of statutes, in particular the *Control of Pollution Act* 1974. A range of guidance is available, including BS 5228, Part 1 (1997), Part 2 (1997) and Part 4 (1992).

Nuisance

A private nuisance is 'an unreasonable interference with a person's use or enjoyment of the land'. If a neighbour can demonstrate that a nuisance exists and that he has suffered substantial damage as a result, then he may be successful in bringing an action against the parties creating the nuisance.

The remedies available are injunctions and/or damages. The courts have, however, traditionally regarded demolition and construction sites as a special case as far as noise is concerned. It would appear that as long as the works are carried out with proper skill and care, and all reasonable precautions are taken to minimise disturbance to neighbouring occupiers, no action in nuisance will arise.

Developers and contractors have to ensure that they take 'reasonable precautions'. They must be aware of the definition of 'best practicable means' in the *Environmental Protection Act* 1990. This includes considering local conditions and circumstances, the current state of technical knowledge and financial implications.

A leading case on construction noise and nuisance is *Andreae v Selfridge* [1938] 3 All ER 264 where the judge held that provided demolition and building operations are 'reasonably carried on, and all proper and reasonable steps are taken to ensure that no undue inconvenience is caused to neighbours, whether from noise, dust or other reasons, the neighbours must put up with it'.

Control of Pollution Act 1974

The *Control of Pollution Act* 1974 deals, in part, with the control of noise on construction sites. Section 60 empowers a local authority to serve notice imposing certain limitations. These limitations include specifying the hours of work, permitted noise levels and the particular plant and machinery that may be used. The recipient may appeal against the notice within 21 days. Contravention of the notice is an offence under the Act. Section 61 provides an opportunity for a developer or contractor to apply to the local authority in advance of the works and seek agreement to such matters as the method of carrying out the work and the steps that will be taken to minimise noise. The local authority is not obliged to give its consent and, even if it does, it may attach conditions to it. It may also change the conditions if it sees fit.

The local authority will often specify that 'best practicable means' are used. The developer/contractor will be expected to adopt the quietest viable method of working within reasonable cost limits. The local authority may also require continuous noise and vibration monitoring and regular liaison meetings with neighbours.

Architectural and design criteria

Basic design data

Internal circulation

Space allowances: (minimum areas per person)

Building type	m²	sq ft
Offices (excluding cores)	9.3	100
Retail	4.6–7.0	50–75
Factories	7.0	75
Restaurants	0.9–1.1	10–12

Lighting requirements

Circulation: 150 Lux
Casual work: 200 Lux
Routine work: 300 Lux
Offices: 350 Lux – 500 Lux
Drawing office: 750 Lux
Fine work: 1000 Lux
Very fine work: 1500 Lux
Minute work: 3500 Lux

Noise and acoustics requirements

Auditoria: 20–30 dB (A) Leq
Bedroom: 30–35 dB (A) Leq
Small office: 40–45 dB (A) Leq
Large office: 45–50 dB (A) Leq
Light industrial: 50 – 55 dB (A) Leq

Design values for internal environmental temperatures

Flats, residences and hotels
Living rooms — 21°C
Bedrooms — 18°C
Bathrooms — 22°C
Staircases and circulation — 16°C

Offices
General — 20°C
Private — 20°C
Circulation — 16°C

Retail
Small — 18°C
Large — 18°C
Department stores — 18°C
Fitting rooms — 21°C
Store rooms — 15°C

Restaurants — 18°C

Factories
Sedentary work — 19°C
Light work — 16°C
Heavy work — 13°C

Hotels
Bedrooms — 22°C
Public rooms — 21°C
Circulation — 18°C

External circulation

Car parking	Standard bay 2.4 x 4.8m	Allow 6.1m for head-on parking. Area per car 18.8m²
Ramps	Car parking garages	10%
	With transition ramps at half the ramp gradient for 2.4m at each end	15%
	Pedestrian	10%
Carriageway widths	One-way four lanes	14.6m
	One-way two lanes	7.3m
	Two-way two lanes	max. 7.3m, min. 6.0m
Vehicle sizes	Cars max. length	5.7m
	Cars min. length	3.05m
	Lorries max. length	18.0m
	Vans max. length	6.0m
	Standard refuse lorry length	7.4m
	Standard fire appliance length	8.0m

Building types

Housing

Typical approximate housing equivalent densities:

50 houses per acre = 124 houses per hectare
40 houses per acre = 99 houses per hectare
30 houses per acre = 74 houses per hectare
20 houses per acre = 49 houses per hectare
10 houses per acre = 25 houses per hectare

Recommended planning grid – 300mm
Recommended minimum floor to ceiling – 2300mm
Minimum floor to floor – 2600mm
Recommended areas for number of persons per dwelling (m²) are identified in the folllowing table.

Houses:	1	2	3	4	5	6	7
One storey	30	44.5	57	67	75.5	84	
Two storey				72	82	92.5	108
Three storey					94	98	112
Flats	30	44.5	57	70	79	86.5	
Maisonettes				72	82	92.5	

Parker Morris is the preferred standard for new buildings by local authorities and housing associations. Private housing is subject only to space requirements by the Public Health Acts.

Hotels

Types

- ❖ city centre hotels
- ❖ motor hotels
- ❖ airport hotels
- ❖ resort hotels
- ❖ motels

Space allocation

	(m²/room gross)
❖ city centre hotel	45–65
❖ motor hotel	35–45
❖ resort hotel	40–55

Hotels under 77–80 rooms only viable as family run businesses.

Fire precautions

Travel distances for escape are dealt with in BS 5588 Part 2, 1997 and also in Part B of the Building Regulations.

Car parking

- ❖ resident guests: one space/bedroom
- ❖ conference facilities: one space/five seats

Required provision must be agreed with the local authority.

Recreational

The dimensions of a number of particular sports facilities are identified in the following table.

Outdoor sport facilities

Olympic standard swimming pools	length width constant depth	50m 21m 1.8m
Running tracks	200m 300m 400m	86.79 x 61.78m 126.52 x 86.48m 170.91 x 133.00m
Association Football pitch size		100m–110m x 64m–75m
Rugby Union pitch size		144m x 69m (max.)
Hockey pitch size		90m x 55m
Tennis court size		10.97m x 23.77m

Indoor sport facilities

Netball court size		30.50m x 15.25m
Badminton court size		13.4m x 6.1m
Table tennis (international)		14.0m x 7.0m
Table size		2.743m x 1.524m
An indoor space 32m x 26m can contain the following sports:	Two badminton courts, karate, fencing, table tennis, basketball, archery, volleyball, soccer, hockey.	

Industrial

Site coverage and floor loading standards for industrial property are identified in the following table.

Site coverage:	Plot ratio normally maximum of 1:1 including office content. Site coverage should not exceed 75% (normally approx. 50–60%)	
Car parking in factories:	Staff:	1 car/50m² of gross floor area
	Visitors:	10% of staff parking
Car parking in warehouses:	Staff:	1 car/200m² of gross floor area
	Lorry parking: Minimum standards for loading bays:	70m² for every 100m² gross floor space
		140m² for every 250m² gross floor space
		170m² for every 500m² gross floor space
		200m² for every 1000m² gross floor space
		300m² for every 2000m² gross floor space
		50m² for every additional 1000m² gross floor space
Factory building types:	Light duty industrial:	Spans min. 9m max. 12m Ht. to eaves 4.5m Floor loading 16kN/m²
	Medium duty industrial:	Spans 12m–18m Ht. to eaves 6.5m Floor loading 25kN/m²
	Heavy duty industrial:	Spans 12m–20m Ht. to eaves 7m–12m Floor loading 15–30kN/m²
Warehouses:	General purpose:	Spans 12–18m Ht. to eaves 8m Floor loading 25kN/m²
	Intermediate high bay:	Spans 12–20m Ht. to eaves 14m Floor loading 50kN/m²
	High bay:	Ht. to eaves 30m Floor loading 60kN/m²

Offices

Methods of calculating areas
- ❖ For planning purposes, gross total area measured over external walls.
- ❖ For cost purposes, gross total area measured inside external walls.
- ❖ Nett areas are measured between inside walls and exclude core areas, ducts and staircases.

Definition of space
- ❖ very deep space: over 20m
- ❖ deep space: 11–19m
- ❖ medium deep space: 6–10m
- ❖ shallow space: 4–5m

Dimensional criteria
- ❖ planning grids: 900mm 1200mm 1500mm
- ❖ floor-to-floor heights: 2700mm–5100mm
- ❖ floor-to-ceiling heights: 2400mm–3000mm
- ❖ floor zone: 300mm–1200mm

Means of escape
- ❖ Maximum travel distance with escape in only one direction – 12.2m.
- ❖ Maximum travel distance with escape possible in alternative direction – 46m.
- ❖ Maximum distance between exits on a storey – 61m.

At least one fire fighting stair required with floor more than 18m above ground floor level.

Lavatory provision based on the *Offices, Shops and Railway Premises Act 1963*, sections 9 and 10.

Car parking
- ❖ Staff: one space for each 25m² of gross floor area.
- ❖ Visitors: 10% of parking provision required.

Required provision must be agreed with the local authority.

BCO best practice for new offices and fitting out works

It has long been recognised that good design can help improve the workplace environment and contribute to business performance. The British Council for Offices (BCO) research and develop best practice in the specification of commercial offices.

The BCO launched their first guide to the specification of offices in 1994 and their latest guide, *The British Council for Offices Guide 2005 Best Practice in the Specification of Offices* (the BCO Guide), sets out guidance on current best practice for shell and core developments.

The BCO Guide considers:

- ❖ **Site issues** – The location of the development and proximity to local amenities, the density of the development to the site (plot ratio), the orientation of the development to surrounding buildings and the design of landscaping.

- ❖ **Building form** – Design issues such as the plan shape and floor plate efficiency, the coordination of building elements and services (the planning grid), requirements for circulation space and the design of the building core, lifts and toilet accommodation.

❖ **Engineering design** – Design criteria and objectives for the structure and envelope, building services and security considerations.

Throughout the BCO Guide reference is made to good practice published by recognised organisations such as Centre for Window and Cladding Technology (CWCT), Building Research Establishment (BRE) and Chartered Institution of Building Services Engineers (CIBSE).

Recent legislative changes have focused designers' attention on environmental and sustainability issues and this is reflected in the latest edition of the BCO Guide.

Examples of BCO design criteria include:

❖ net floor area (per person) = $12m^2–17m^2$

❖ floor plan efficiency (net internal area / gross internal area) = 80–85%

❖ finished floor to underside of ceiling = 2600mm–3300mm

❖ plan depth (window to window or atrium, not core) = 13.5m–21.0m

❖ column grid = 7.5m–9m

❖ raised floor void = minimum 150mm (300mm for computer floors)

❖ live load (general) = minimum $2.5kN/m^2$ (for 95% of the lettable floor area)

❖ live load (high) = minimum $7.5kN/m^2$ (for 5% of the lettable floor area for filing and paper storage)

❖ office lighting = 300–500 Lux minimum average maintained illuminance

❖ comfort (summer air conditioned space) = 22°C +/– 2°C

❖ comfort (winter) = 20°C +/– 2°C

❖ fresh air standard = 12–16 litres per person per second

❖ noise criteria (open plan offices) = NR 38

❖ noise criteria (cellular offices and meeting rooms) = NR 35

The above specification data is based on data from the BCO Guide, and is reproduced with permission from the British Council for Offices.

The BCO also produce the *Office Fit-out Guide* which complements the BCO Guide. Last published in 2003, this describes the key decisions that face clients and their project team when undertaking a typical fit-out project. It recommends the use of management checklists and goes on to describe the processes that need to be considered at pre- and post project stage. It ends with a section on move management and operational issues.

Whilst every development will have its own set of requirements and objectives, the BCO guides provide a useful source of benchmark information and guidance on processes for successful execution.

Specifications

The specification is the hub around which the various documents forming a modern day building contract are assembled.

The specification will incorporate a complex array of information, which will include design, testing, procedural, visual and quality control information.

The parties will seek to have fully prescribed the product to which they are to sign up under a building contract. The standard forms of building contract generally recognise the specification as a contract document, but there are exceptions such as the JCT98 Standard Form with Quantities, which does not and care must be taken to ensure that the wording is amended to include the specification.

The specification as a building contract document will typically be supported by the preliminaries and either bills of quantities or contract sum analysis. It will schedule the drawings to which it refers, and which should form the contract drawings.

Different specifications for different contracts

Design specification

This form of specification will be used where the author wishes to prescribe the project in as much detail as possible, no imagination is required as to the clients' requirements. Products will be named and the assembly of the building will be described and supported with drawn information on a 'do as I say' basis.

The form of contract employed here will be a traditional one which will not carry a design responsibility for the contractor.

Performance specification

A performance specification sets out design parameters to which contractors are invited to submit their proposals. This can be a procurement route used where the design team have little idea as to products or visual requirements.

The client will not need to advance the design as far before inviting tenders from interested contractors. This is a more economic approach since pre-contract design costs are usually less at the early stages of procurement.

The specification for a design and build contract will initially form the employer's requirements latterly supported by the contractor's proposals once agreed with the selected contractor. This approach has the benefit of the contractor bringing the supply chain knowledge to the client at an early stage while still in competition.

The parameters of design so described in a performance specification can either be laid down loosely or brought in very tight according to the degree of control the client wishes to retain.

Specification writing

Construction consultants have established standardised data at their disposal to assist and form the basis to prepare their documents. Online specification writers are available, the most widely used is National Building Specification (NBS): www.nbsservices.co.uk. This is a subscription service.

The NBS system stores a fully comprehensive set of specifications for most conceivable products and materials which may be adapted, added to or modified according to a particular project.

The NBS has recently published *NBS Educator* which is designed to provide construction industry students, lecturers and professionals who need to understand contract documentation, such as specifications and schedules of work. The NBS Educator website includes a variety of functions to navigate which provides the user with suggestions and ideas as well a reference library for different aspects of specification writing.

Another specification tool that can be accessed online is Barbour Index which has recently launched its Specification Expert website which is at www.barbour-index.co.uk. The service is designed to create, edit and manage specification documents. The service makes writing specifications quick and easy, offering a comprehensive library of all major specification clauses. It is available in two versions: Building (Architectural and Building Surveying) and Building Services which incorporates the National Engineering Specification.

Site archaeology

While the British Government, including associated Scottish Parliament, Welsh Assembly and Northern Irish Authorities, are consulting on changes to Heritage, Scheduled Ancient Monuments and Archaeological Protection Legislation including the production of Unified Lists covering all categories, no final decisions have yet been made. Accordingly, the following procedures remain currently in place. There were indications that both White and Green papers in these subjects were to have been issued sometime in 2004 but no dates are yet confirmed as at the time of writing.

Traditional dictionary definitions focus on the study of history through excavation (usually implicitly below ground) and the analysis of the remains.

Not everyone will realise that in the construction world we have to deal with two types of archaeology:

❖ the traditional excavation of what lies hidden below ground; and

❖ the archaeology of standing buildings or above-ground archaeology.

How does archaeology affect construction?

Archaeology affects construction primarily through the way that the planning process limits and controls development. Both above and below ground archaeology can easily be applicable to the same site.

The present key government reference document is Planning Policy Guidance Document 16 published in November 1990 (PPG16). The government was consulting for the replacement for PPG16 with the first of the new Planning Policy Statements (PPS), in this case the Planning Policy Statement on *Planning for the Historic Environment*.

However PPG16 is still current and the ministerial statement (DCLG having replaced ODPM) of 5 May 2006 stated that the review and replacement of PPG16 (amongst others) will only take place as and when necessary.

PPG16 sets out the Secretary of State's policy on archaeological remains on land, and how they should be preserved or recorded both in an urban setting and in the countryside.

Planning permission is required for works of development – the carrying out of building, engineering, mining or other operations in, on, over or under land or the making of any material change in the use of any buildings or other land.

The first port of call for any planning application is the local planning office and the published documentation in either the Development Plan or the Unitary Development Plan.

If the Local Development Plan and/or the Local Planning Office identifies a site as one with scheduled ancient monuments or locations where archaeological remains are believed to exist then it is vital to engage in the earliest possible consultation with the county archaeologists or their equivalents at English Heritage, Historic Scotland, CADW (Welsh Heritage) and the Environment and Heritage Service in Northern Ireland.

This consultation will identify the archaeological sensitivity of the site.

Following discussions with the county or national archaeologists the next step for the developer is to have researched exactly what is or might be there and how it will or could impinge on the proposed development.

This is a cost for the developer and will have to be paid for by the developer in the same way as any other site investigation exercise is paid for prior to a development being undertaken.

Options for archaeological investigations are potentially twofold.

Desktop studies

These draw on the archaeological records of the site itself and those of neighbouring sites. They are relatively quick and easy. Crucially they must be done by a trained archaeologist. The handbook of the Institute of Field Archaeologists will help in locating the right archaeologist or archaeological unit to undertake the study. Contact can be made on admin@archaeologists.net or by telephone on 01189 316446.

Discussions may however indicate that the next level of investigation is necessary.

Field evaluation

This is not a full archaeological elevation or 'dig' but a ground survey and small scale trial trenching.

The results from the desktop study and/or the field evaluation will inform the developer, the county archaeologist and the local planning officers, especially the conservation officer, as to the importance of the site in archaeological terms.

Model agreements between developers and the appropriate archaeological body regulating archaeological site investigations and excavations can be obtained from the British Property Federation, publications@bpf.org.uk or telephone 020 7828 0111.

Statutory protection for archaeological sites

Where Scheduled Ancient Monuments have been identified under the *Ancient Monuments and Archaeological Areas Act* 1979, these are sites of national importance and as such rank as the equivalent of Grade I (Grade A in Scotland) or Grade II* (Grade B in Scotland) buildings of special architectural or historic interest.

The protection of Scheduled Ancient Monuments is based on the requirement that scheduled monument consent has to be obtained from the Secretary of State (of the Department for Culture, Media and Sport whose website is www.culture.gov.uk).

Application has to be made to the Secretary of State for any works that would have the effect of demolishing, destroying, damaging, removing, repairing, altering, adding to, flooding or covering up a monument.

If you find a scheduled ancient monument standing on or laying below your site take great care. Ensure your professional advisors fully appreciate the implications before application is made. If in doubt, enter into the earliest possible discussions with the relevant heritage and conservation authorities covering the site. These will include the local authorities conservation officer, the county archaeologist, and the Inspectors of Ancient Monuments at English Heritage, Historic Scotland, CADW (Welsh Heritage) and the Environment and Heritage Service in Northern Ireland.

Above-ground archaeology

A Scheduled Ancient Monument is usually, although not exclusively, an unoccupied structure and can be either remains below ground and/or a standing structure above ground.

Above-ground Scheduled Ancient Monuments will require Scheduled Ancient Monuments Consent for works to the structure. To fully understand what is important in this structure in understanding 'ancient peoples by the study of their physical remains' was borne the concept of above-ground archaeology. This can involve the physical digging in to the structure above ground. This can equally involve the 'desktop study' approach of bringing together the known archive or history of the structure to fully understand what is important in the remains and what is less important.

This is because as structures are added to and/or changed over time there may well be pieces or parts of what is now extant that can well be removed or modified or changed and benefit the scheduled monument.

The final use of archaeology in standing structures is the extrapolation of the 'desktop study' for above-ground scheduled ancient monuments into the 'Conservation Plan' for all types of listed historic buildings.

Conservation Plans are increasingly required by Heritage and Listed Building authorities, particularly for the more important Grade I (Scottish A) and Grade II* (Scottish B) buildings as listed as being of Special Architectural and Historic Interest. This is as part of the application process for Listed Building Consent for works that will affect the special architectural or historic interest of these Listed Buildings.

Conservation plans have a number of practical and financial advantages for the developer/renovator of historic buildings. The key ones are:

- ❖ certainty for the design team in formulating in what can or cannot be done to the building and site before they formulate details for the Listed Building Consent and Planning Permission applications; and
- ❖ certainty for the developer/renovator that the scheme will not be stopped in its tracks by the heritage authorities discovering that the building contains important previously unknown historic elements in the structure that precludes all or part of the development going forward. The worst case would be the stopping of the scheme or at least making it less viable or completely unviable.

Project extranets as a method of coordinating project information

Some of the specific characteristics of the construction industry make the quality, quantity and timing of information flows difficult to administer. These include the following:

- ❖ large numbers of participating companies collaborating on projects of relatively short duration;
- ❖ diverse locations and working conditions related to the building site; and
- ❖ comparatively low levels of management support.

Despite this, the use of electronic systems for information management, 'project extranets', can have significant benefits including:

- ❖ direct 24-hour access to project-related material;
- ❖ enhanced communications, faster drawing/document approvals;
- ❖ reduced paper trails on labour intensive tasks;

- reduced distribution/production costs and associated time savings;
- improved management of information providing accountability and an audit trail;
- competitive differentiation;
- less chance of losing information;
- a platform to stimulate innovation; and
- the support of a green agenda.

Research

Independent research commissioned by the Network for Construction Collaboration Technology Providers (NCCTP) in 2006 showed that 74% of clients favoured contractors/consultants who are experienced in using web based collaboration systems (project extranets). In addition the *Proving Collaboration Pays* study carried out by Benchmark Research also found that teams welcomed the greater control afforded through collaboration technologies.

A number of benefits were identified in the NCCTP survey, which are included within the above list. In particular, the research indicated that drawing approval times were reduced by 26% from an average of 9.3 days to 6.9 days.

Relevant legislation/best practice information

The British Standards Institution's section for delivering information solutions to customers (BSI-DISC) sets out five principles which should be the starting point for coordinating information in DISC PD 0010:1997. BSI consider that the key principles of good practice for information management are to:

- be aware of all information types and sources;
- recognise your responsibilities in the use of the information;
- find a procedural solution;
- resolve a support network/resource for the solution; and
- review the results and apply lessons learnt.

Other relevant legislation/best practice information includes:

- DTI Building Centre Trust and Phrontis Limited construction best practice report entitled *Effective Integration of IT in Construction*, October 2001;
- DTI/CCPI *A Code of Procedure for the Construction Industry on Production Information*, September 2002;
- BS7799, *Information Security Management*; and
- *Data Protection Act* 1998.

Examples of project document management systems

The following list summarises a small sample of project document management systems currently available:

- Asite: www.asite.com
- BIW Technology: www.biwtech.com
- Business Collaborator: www.businesscollaborator.com
- Cadweb: www.cadweb.co.uk
- Citadon: www.citadon.com
- Meridian: www.mps.com
- Sarcophagus: www.sarcophagus.co.uk

Key issues

In order to ensure the successful adoption of a project extranet, a number of key issues need to be carefully considered and resolved, these include the following:

❖ Adopt document handling procedures within the project team that prevent double handling, e.g. the benefits of a project extranet system will only be realised if information is distributed electronically and not with simultaneous hard copy (perhaps because some members of the professional team are not IT literate or prepared to utilise the system).

❖ A principal barrier to entry is the selection of an appropriate system with appropriate pricing arrangements, reflecting the project particulars. The opportunities to purchase or procure project extranet systems appropriately scaled to project needs have greatly enhanced over recent years. Accordingly, further to appropriate research, it should be possible to identify a suitable system. System selection should include consideration of the following points:

- ownership of data;
- post project archive access;
- procedures for recovery of information should a hosting company cease trading;
- system redundancy;
- numbers of users; and
- other practical matters as set out in this section.

❖ A suitable policy or system feature is required to ensure that all required users are aware of and review new information when posted to the website. This can either be resolved through separate communication or an extranet site design that ensures all personnel are notified of new postings and are required to review them within a certain period, allowing the project manager to audit compliance.

❖ Policies are required concerning the information exchange format, e.g. are Autocad drawings to be posted in DWG format for design team use or in a finalised common exchange format such as Adobe PDFs. Perhaps both editable and fixed information is required.

❖ The system should provide different levels of ownership allowing data to be available to the whole project team, other stakeholders such as letting agents or tenants and to the contractor. However, full availability of data to all parties is unlikely to be appropriate.

❖ The system administration arrangements should be simple and clear as unlimited opportunity to amend the procedures and systems will inevitably generate a large barrier to the effective use of the system.

❖ Systems requiring a specialist appointed information coordinator may be less appropriate on all but the largest schemes, as this provides an additional workload to one particular team member and may delay information distribution. Of additional benefit can be a system allowing direct posting by all enrolled stakeholders, however, the notification points discussed above remain key.

❖ Team members experienced in utilising a project extranet should be a factor in the selection protocol for the team.

❖ Adopting a suitable framework to resolve the above matters throughout the team might most usefully be documented within the Project Execution Plan and matching provisions should be reflected in all appointments.

In conclusion, a complete understanding of the project, the environment and an active commitment by the people involved is necessary to effectively coordinate project information through the use of a project extranet. However, the benefits of a well organised approach are significant and the barriers to entry are reducing; accordingly, a project extranet can offer a real benefit on many schemes.

Modern methods of construction

Modern Methods of Construction (MMC) is a term used to describe a wide range of techniques whereby buildings or parts of buildings are manufactured and assembled off site. Generally, these systems or components are produced in a factory environment and delivered to site ready for installation. The aim of MMC or 'off-site' is to improve the cost, speed, quality and reliability of the finished product, in line with the recommendations set out in the influential 1998 Construction Task Force report *Rethinking Construction*. MMC is also variously referred to as off-site manufacturing (OSM), modular construction, prefabrication, pre-assembly, standardisation, off-site production and off-site fabrication.

Off-site systems

These can be broadly divided into the following categories:

❖ **Panel systems** – Flat panel units are manufactured in a factory and assembled on site. Open panels consist of a frame only, with external cladding, services, insulation and internal finishes applied on site. Closed panels have some or all of these elements, including doors and windows, fitted in the factory. Panels are then simply assembled on site and services connected.

❖ **Volumetric systems** – Complete units, or pods, are factory assembled, with the resulting 3D modules delivered to site ready for installation. Modules may or may not have all their component parts and finishes installed prior to leaving the factory.

❖ **Sub-assemblies and components** – These are factory-fabricated parts used with otherwise traditional construction methods. For example, floor or roof cassettes, precast foundations and preformed wiring looms would fall into this category.

❖ **Hybrids** – This method of construction is sometimes known as semi-volumetric: both panel and volumetric systems are used. For example, kitchen or bathroom pods may be used in a building otherwise constructed using panels.

What are the benefits?

Generally accepted benefits of MMC include:

Cost – Initial costs may be more expensive but economies of scale apply. The more factory-assembled components you use, the cheaper they become, hence the popularity of MMC in the social housing sector and with major fast food chains such as Pizza Hut and McDonalds.

Cost advantages may also result from:

❖ reduced risk of cost overruns;

❖ fewer defects, leading to less time – and fewer materials – wasted on site; and

❖ reduced life cycle costs.

Off-site manufacturer Kingspan has benchmarked its own off-site products against conventional construction methods and costs and the company asserts that they are both capital and whole-life-cycle cost competitive.

Time –

❖ less build time on-site; and

❖ more predictable completion dates.

The environment –

Kingspan has also made environmental comparisons with traditional construction, using the ARUP SPeaR sustainability assessment method. From this Kingspan concludes that off-site techniques 'significantly enhance sustainable construction'. Other benefits include:

❖ reduced waste on-site; and

❖ less noise and pollution from additional traffic.

Quality –

❖ consistent, quality-assured products manufactured in a controlled environment; and

❖ less accidental damage to or theft of construction components due to reduced on-site storage.

Safety issues – MMC has a major contribution to make in improving health and safety in the construction industry. By manufacturing large parts of a building in a controlled environment, fewer accidents are likely to occur on site. The necessity for site staff to work at height is also greatly reduced. Falling from a height continues to be the most common cause of accidents, accounting for 22% of fatal injuries to workers in 2005/06 (source: HSE).

In the light of existing skills shortages, another key benefit may be that off-site manufacturing reduces reliance on on-site 'wet trades' and other types of traditional skilled labour.

The market for MMC

Despite the advantages cited above, MMC only accounts for 2.1% of total UK construction output (source: Buildoffsite). However, this is set to change. A survey carried out in 2005 by market research company MSI forecast massive growth in the modular construction market during the next four years, particularly in the housing sector. Other sectors that MSI highlights for growth are:

❖ military buildings – up 193%;

❖ schools – up 103%;

❖ prisons – up 102%; and

❖ healthcare facilities – up 69%.

The biggest uptake of MMC in the UK to date has been in the social housing sector. As demand for housing continues to outstrip supply, MMC is increasingly gaining government support as a realistic solution to the problems of providing large numbers of homes quickly. Since 2004, the Housing Corporation has made a commitment that at least 25% of the housing that it funds should be built using MMC methods, regarding it as part of effective supply chain management. English Partnerships too is leading major innovations in the use of MMC, including it in the development briefs for a number of high profile exemplar projects such as the London Wide Initiative and Oakgrove Millennium Community. Like the Housing Corporation, English Partnerships has a target of 25% MMC by number of dwellings on projects for which it supplies funding.

Initiatives such as the Design for Manufacture competition launched in 2005 and the launch of the BRE's LPS 2020 Standard for Innovative

Systems, Elements and Components for Residential Buildings have helped promote greater use of off-site techniques. In addition, the government has allocated £1.3bn more to housing spending in 2007–08 than in 2004–05 (source: 2004 Spending Review), which can only be good news for the MMC sector.

Commercial clients are also taking MMC seriously. Off-site manufacture has successfully thrown off the stigma attached to post-war 'prefab' construction. It is now regarded as a legitimate way of improving quality and site safety while at the same time minimising waste, reducing delivery times and addressing skills shortages.

Private sector house builders, particularly those like Urban Splash who specialise in developing high density, city apartment schemes, are increasingly using MMC. Moho was the first private housing scheme to use off-site manufacturing techniques to build 120 apartments in the centre of Manchester.

One of the major players in the off-site manufacturing market is the Shepherd Building Group. Its subsidiary, Yorkon, has produced more than 200 ready-made buildings around the UK for the McDonalds fast food chain and has developed a partnership with Pizza Hut to build a number of UK restaurants for the company. Companies such as Yorkon are now developing their own ranges of exemplar designs for different building types to give clients more choice and to combat the perception that greater uptake of MMC means producing bland buildings with no design values.

Further information

- ❖ www.bre.co.uk
- ❖ www.buildoffsite.com
- ❖ www.englishpartnerships.co.uk
- ❖ www.housingcorp.gov.uk
- ❖ www.homein.org

Structural and civil engineering design

Design

The design process

The Institution of Structural Engineers defines structural engineering as:

> The science and art of designing and making, with economy and elegance, buildings, bridges, frameworks and similar structures so that they can safely resist the forces to which they may be subjected.

Generally, engineers use limit state design methods. These model the way in which loadings are applied to a building over the course of its life.

Limit state design utilises differing probability factors for separate types of loads and material stresses to reflect the degree of certainty in assumptions made about each. For instance, strength is checked at the ultimate limit state where the building or element is on the point of collapse.

Deflection and vibration are checked at the serviceability limit state, at which point the building is considered to be unserviceable, even though it will not collapse.

Today, design in concrete, steel and masonry is usually carried out using limit state methods, with timber design scheduled to change over with the imminent arrival of the new Eurocode. Foundation design, involving the much more unpredictable material of the soil, has still eluded the process.

An assessment of ground conditions is usually essential to ensure the proper performance of the superstructure.

Soils and foundation design

For very light residential building, a visual assessment of the soils with a minimum of physical testing may be sufficient, if local knowledge of the area is good. For larger buildings, a proper geotechnical investigation is usually recommended. This allows the measurement of relevant soils (geotechnical) data on which the foundation design will be based. Accurate testing of samples of soil obtained from boreholes usually leads to economies in foundation design. Samples are usually tested for consolidation, compressibility (both of these affect settlement) and shear strengths. In certain circumstances testing for chemicals, which could affect the structure, may be included.

Where soil conditions are good, and building loads are relatively light, a simple spread foundation is usually sufficient. This will be in the form either of simple strips or pad bases of non-reinforced concrete. As loads increase and soil conditions become more complex, foundations may need to be reinforced to allow loads to be spread sufficiently. Heavy building loads and poor ground often require piled foundations to take the foundation loads into suitable (deeper) soils.

Other features, such as trees (in shrinkable soils), groundwater, and basements, all require special consideration in foundation design.

The relevant British Standards to which reference should be made are BS 8004:1986 *Code of Practice for Foundations* and BS 5930:1999 *Code of Practice for Site Investigations*. See also BS EN ISO 14688-2:2004, *Geotechnical investigation and testing: Identification and classification of soil*.

For preliminary design purposes only, the following table gives typical allowable bearing values under static loading for various types of soils and may be used to size strip or pad foundations.

Category	Soil type	Presumed allowable bearing pressure (kN/m²)
Unweathered rocks	Strong igneous rocks,	10,000
	Strong sandstones and limestones	4,000
	Strong shales	2,000
Non-cohesive soils	Dense gravel	600
	Medium dense gravel or sand and gravel	200–500
	Loose gravel or loose sand and gravel	up to 200
	Loose sand	up to 100
Cohesive soils	Very stiff clay	300–600
	Stiff clay	150–300
	Firm clay	75–150
	Soft clay	75

Soil survey

Purpose

Soil surveys may be required to determine either, or both, of the following:

❖ environmental contamination; and

❖ geotechnical properties.

Environmental

An intrusive investigation may be required to establish the nature of any subsurface contaminated soil and/or groundwater. Site investigations are based upon site-specific factors such as the presence of likely contaminants, the anticipated subsurface geology and the location of the site. They are often referred to as Phase 2 investigations where they follow a non-intrusive Phase 1 audit. Samples of soil and groundwater are taken for laboratory analysis. The results are interpreted and a risk assessment undertaken for any contamination identified.

Geotechnical

The purpose of a geotechnical site investigation provides sufficient geotechnical information to enable design of foundations. Investigations will be designed specifically to suit the anticipated geology and development proposals. A geotechnical site investigation is intrusive and may include in-situ and laboratory tests.

A geotechnical site investigation is often procured with an environmental site investigation given a significant overlap with the fieldwork requirements.

Fieldwork

The following methods of soil and groundwater sampling are common to both environmental and geotechnical investigations.

Trial pits

Trial pits are extremely valuable if the depth of investigation is less than about 3 metres. They allow a detailed examination of the ground conditions in situ with some indication of stability and groundwater conditions. Trial pitting is a relatively fast and efficient means of exploring subsurface conditions.

Auger holes

Auger holes are normally made by hand-turning a very light auger into the ground, or by using light power-auger equipment. However, while auger holes are effective in preliminary investigations they do not provide the depth or range of sampling and in-situ testing provided by conventional site investigation boreholes.

Window samplers

A window sampler is a steel tube, usually about 1 metre long, with a series of windows along the tube through which to view disturbed soil conditions or extract samples. A lightweight percussion hammer drives the sampler into the ground, which is then extracted with jacks. A depth of approximately 10 metres can be achieved, depending on soil conditions, using a sequence of progressively smaller diameter samplers.

Boreholes

Light percussion drilling (shell and auger) is the most commonly used method in the UK. Samples are often unsuitable for soil description on the basis that the drilling process will have changed the strength of the soil by remoulding it and increased the moisture content of the soil through lubrication. For this reason U100 tube samples are often taken from boreholes at regular depths by driving a small diameter tube into the soil at the base of the borehole, thus extracting an undisturbed sample for laboratory analysis. Lubrication may be required if the subsurface is not cohesive making it unsuitable for some types of environmental site investigations.

Geotechnical in-situ testing

In-situ testing is typically undertaken on cohesionless soils where the strength characteristics may only be established on undisturbed in-situ samples.

Cone Penetration Test (CPT)

This technique involves hydraulically pushing a 10 or $15 cm^2$ cone into the ground at a standard rate of penetration and measuring the penetration resistance. The equipment necessary for this type of investigation is housed in a large truck. The results from a CPT can be very valuable providing a soil profile, estimates of the soil types encountered including consistency and density, and evidence of the presence of voids beneath the site.

Dynamic probing

Much less sophisticated than CPT, dynamic probing involves driving a steel rod into the ground by using repeated blows of a hammer of a specified mass falling through a fixed distance. The number of blows required for each 100mm is recorded and plotted as a depth versus blow-count log. However, the information given by dynamic probing is very restricted and is difficult to interpret. Further investigations are usually necessary to supplement this test.

The Standard Penetration Test (SPT)

This test involves driving an open-drive sampler into the bottom of a borehole with repeated blows of a hammer falling a predetermined distance. The number of blows necessary to drive the sampler six increments of 75mm are counted and recorded, giving the penetration resistance value. The test is undertaken on cohesionless soils such as gravels.

Other methods of testing and sampling are used depending on the soil type and conditions on site.

Geotechnical laboratory testing

Laboratory testing is typically undertaken on cohesive soils, i.e. clays, where an undisturbed sample may be retrieved from the field. Such testing is not appropriate to cohesionless soils such as gravels. Tests include:

❖   Soil Classification: Particle Size Distribution, Plasticity Index, Moisture Content.

❖   Consolidation: To assess the settlement characteristics.

❖   Triaxial: To assess the compressive strength characteristics.

Geotechnical reporting

The results of the fieldwork and laboratory tests are assessed. For development purposes preliminary designs for foundations may be prepared. Sufficient information would be provided to enable design of building foundations. For diagnostic purposes the investigation would assist with identifying the cause of defects with a building superstructure allowing remedial solutions to be specified with confidence.

Environmental sampling and analysis

Soil sampling

Soil samples are required for chemical analysis to determine the presence of any contamination. Methods of soil sampling differ depending on the contaminants being tested. Usually disturbed samples are adequate for testing most chemicals. These can be obtained from the excavator bucket when trial pits are being used, from the cuttings from boreholes or from the window within a window sampler.

Samples are analysed in the laboratory for a wide range of 'base line' contaminant chemicals often supplemented by further specialist testing depending upon the type of contamination present.

Water sampling

Water samples can be obtained by inserting a standpipe into a completed borehole. Water samples will be taken after insertion for further chemical analysis. The well may also be used for the monitoring of gas. Installation can be permanent/semi-permanent to facilitate further sampling at a later date. Laboratory analysis is similar to soil samples.

Gas sampling

The presence of methane and carbon-dioxide may be established on sites which are landfills or close to neighbouring landfills. Monitoring wells constructed for water sampling may also be used to sample the presence of land gas. In-situ measurements of gas concentrations and flow are taken at ground level on the head of the monitoring well using an infra-red gas analyser. Wells may be constructed to measure gas concentrations and flow at different depths.

A simpler broad-brush method of establishing the general presence of land gas is to undertake a shallow 'spike survey'. The presence and extent of contamination from a leaking underground petrol tank is a particularly common example.

Environmental risk assessment

On completion of the fieldwork and laboratory testing a risk assessment is undertaken. Where contamination has been identified it is important to consider the following:

- ❖ the client's requirements;
- ❖ the present use of the site and risk to occupants;
- ❖ the future intended use of the site and any considerations triggered by redevelopment;
- ❖ future excavations for foundations or buried services;
- ❖ contamination of groundwater particularly where abstracted for water supply;
- ❖ contamination of nearby water courses; and
- ❖ contamination to or from neighbouring sites.

Recommendations and budget costs should be provided for remediation.

Design loadings for buildings

Table 1 of British Standard 6399-1:1996 sets out details of the minimum recommended imposed loads for various types of buildings. Further details, together with an expanded list and limitations of use are also given in BS 6399:1996, Parts 1 and 3. Loads are usually quoted as uniformly distributed (kN/m²) or concentrated (kN).

Floor loadings for most residential purposes (other than hotels) are usually recommended at 1.5kN/m², although there are increased allowances for guest houses and communal areas in blocks of flats – 3.0kN/m².

Offices for general use are usually recommended to be designed to an imposed load of 2.5kN/m², although banking halls are usually slightly higher at 3.0kN/m². These allowances are less than the old 'institutional standard' of 4 plus 1 (100lbs per sq ft), reflecting the impact of modern technology in office use.

Loadings for warehousing can vary significantly, although as a general rule allow 2.4kN/m² per metre of storage height up to a maximum of 10m. In reality, the ground bearing capacity of a normal concrete floor slab will provide a good capability for most normal purposes. However, dense mobile stacking can prove to be very onerous and an allowance of 4.8kN/m² per metre of height is usual.

Floors in industrial and retail buildings

Use

In the UK, industrial buildings are being increasingly constructed for use as storage and distribution facilities rather than for production. In these buildings the floor forms a vital part of the operation of the facility, and the specification of the floor must suit the tolerances of the storage and materials handling equipment which is to be installed.

Specification

The main factors which need to be considered in the specification of a floor are:

- ❖ durability and suitability of floor finish for intended use;
- ❖ tolerance on finished levels across the floor;
- ❖ accommodation of movement due to constructional and in-service movements; and
- ❖ type and intensity of loading.

In bespoke facilities, where the use of the floor and the location of plant or storage racking and aisles are known, the specification of all of the above can be quite precise. Where the final use of the building and the layout of the facility is not known, as is the case for speculative development, assumptions must be made, but it may still be beneficial in terms of costs and usability to define as much as possible before design of the floor commences.

Support

Structurally, floors in industrial buildings may be either ground supported or suspended. Suspended construction is where the floor is supported on piles and not designed to bear directly onto the ground immediately below the building. The design of such slabs is not dissimilar to the design of concrete upper floors in multi-storey buildings, with the concrete section being reinforced to span between supports.

The more common arrangement, ground conditions allowing, is the use of a ground-bearing slab. With this type of construction, the load capacity of the floor is derived largely from the strength of the underlying ground and the imported capping (sub-base). Reinforcement is included in the slab but does not contribute to strength, being essentially there to control cracking which, in an un-reinforced concrete section, would result from shrinkage as water in the freshly placed concrete dries out. The rate of drying and resulting shrinkage depends on many things including the method of curing, the thickness of the slab, the concrete mix design and the presence of a membrane under the slab.

Loadings

Floor slabs are subject to distributed loads, for example from materials stored on the floor, and to concentrated loads from materials handling plant, storage racking, mezzanine floors and internal division walls. Of these, it is generally the concentrated loads which are more critical to the design of the slab and hence there are moves to specify floor capacities in these terms rather than in terms of distributed loadings.

In general, the weakest parts of a floor slab are the edges and the sections immediately adjacent to joints, particularly where joints intersect.

Construction methods

The proposed construction method will influence the design of the slab. Increasingly, large floor slabs are constructed using specialised plant which only trade contractors specialising in floor construction, rather than general contractors, are likely to have. With this type of procurement and construction much of the design and specification of materials is done by the contractor. In particular, the use of fibre reinforcement instead of conventional reinforcement is common for large bay construction.

Components

Concrete – the concrete mix will be specified by the structural engineer or specialist trade contractor to meet the requirements of the floor in terms of constructability, durability and finish. The concrete will include reinforcement in the form of either reinforcing bars or mesh, or fibres. Such fibres may be of steel or polypropylene.

Joints – joints are provided in a concrete floor slab to split it into easily constructed sections, and to cater for inevitable movement within the construction. This movement arises from shrinkage of the concrete soon after casting and from expansion and contraction due to changes in temperature over the life of the slab. Joints are expensive to provide and introduce weaknesses into the floor, and, therefore, much design and specifying expertise has been expended into trying to reduce their number, or even to omit them entirely.

Membranes – the provision of a membrane immediately below the concrete slab can assist in reducing the friction which develops between the shrinking concrete as it dries out and the material below (sub-base). Good preparation of the sub-base and the inclusion of a membrane can reduce the amount of reinforcement required to control cracking. A membrane may also be used to minimise loss of fine particles from the concrete mix during placing and, if specified and laid appropriately, as a damp-proof membrane to protect against rising damp.

Sub-base – this is the imported material which forms the foundation of the floor slab and is necessary on all but the best natural ground (sub-grade).

Sub-grade – an investigation, undertaken on site with laboratory testing, to determine the nature of the ground on the site, is required to allow design of the floor slab. This investigation is normally undertaken by geotechnical firms to a specification that is usually drawn up by the structural engineer.

Flatness

Sophisticated materials handling equipment in warehouse and distribution facilities requires tight control of variation in level between different parts of the slab. In general terms, it is not economic to construct all concrete floor slabs to meet these requirements. Where tolerances are inappropriately specified, the slab may be unnecessarily expensive or unsuitable for certain uses.

Specialist surveying equipment is necessary to confirm compliance with the higher categories of level specification. Such surveys are usually undertaken soon after construction and records of survey results should be sought where flatness is important. Visual survey will not pick up failure of a floor slab to meet level tolerances unless the variation in level is extremely large.

Finish

In contrast to the majority of upper floors in buildings, the concrete often forms the finished surface of the floor in warehouse and retail buildings. Durability of the concrete surface against impact damage and wear, including tendency to form dust, is important.

Defects

Most defects in floor slabs affect the serviceability of the floor, but occasionally more fundamental structural defects occur.

The most common defects are:

- ❖ dusting or breakdown of surface, or finishes;
- ❖ lack of flatness;
- ❖ cracking;
- ❖ breakdown of joints; and
- ❖ structural defects due to slab or sub-base defects, or poorer than anticipated ground.

Increasingly, floor slabs will be considered as important components of buildings in the way that cladding and services are, and recorded information on aspects of their construction and performance will be required during the life of the building, particularly at times of change in use or ownership.

Further information may be found in Technical Report No 34 *Concrete industrial ground floors – A guide to design and construction* (ISBN 1 904482 01 5) published by the Concrete Society.

Office floors

Suspended upper floors for modern office buildings are generally of some form of concrete construction, usually precast or cast in situ, but in some cases pre- or post-stressed concrete. Earlier buildings have a greater variety of floors, including some unusual or proprietary forms. Timber floors will be found in some older buildings. Modern concrete floors may take many forms, including solid, waffle or voided slabs. The concrete may have been cast on timber shuttering, subsequently removed, or on proprietary profiled metal decking, in which case the metal decking is incorporated into the final construction, providing part of the strength of the floor by acting as all or part of the tensile reinforcement to the combined steel and concrete floor construction.

Floor slabs are usually supported on a grid of beams which may be of steel or concrete construction, and which are normally visible below the soffite of the slab. The term 'flat slab construction' is used to describe concrete floor slabs supported directly off columns without the use of downstand beams. In these floors, bands of reinforcement within the slab perform a similar function to that of conventional beams.

Choice of floor construction normally includes consideration of issues such as cost, construction programme, proposed spans, column layout, and distribution of building services between and through floors, etc. Increasingly, environmental aspects of the building construction will also influence the type of construction chosen.

Service distribution through floor structures

Various structural systems are available which allow horizontal service distribution within the overall depth of the structure. Generally, with these systems, the overall depth of the floor structure is increased, but savings in overall floor depths are made because there is no need for a service distribution zone between the ceiling and the underside of the structure.

Small openings can often be formed through floors to allow distribution of building services between floors, but larger openings will normally require some form of trimming to avoid compromising the strength of the floor. The acceptability of forming openings in floors varies depending on the type of structure and on the location of the hole relative to spans and columns.

Environmental aspects

Environmental issues may influence the choice of floor structure used in a new building. In particular, the use of heavier reinforced concrete floors can be utilised as a heat sink to reduce fluctuations of temperature within a building.

Loading

Load on floors is commonly categorised as being either dead or live, with live load often being referred to simply as superimposed or imposed.

Dead load refers to the load arising from construction present at the time of construction and likely to be in place throughout the life of the building, and which can therefore be assessed relatively accurately by the designer. This normally includes the weight of the structure, any finishes (topping, screeds, raised floors, etc.) and the weight of floor coverings, ceilings, and building services, as well as any permanent partitions, such as those around cores.

Imposed load refers to loads arising from the occupation of the building which may vary substantially from user to user and cannot always be accurately assessed when the building is designed. This includes the load from people in the building, furniture, and de-mountable partitions and screens.

Occupiers are primarily interested in the capacity which the floor has to accommodate the latter of these two categories, i.e. the imposed load.

Imposed loadings in offices have not changed greatly over the years, with modern office equipment such as personal computers weighing no more than typewriters. BS 6399: Part 1, the current British Standard, sets out the statutory minimum requirement for different uses of building including offices and banks, and gives loadings for areas of general use and for filing and storage spaces, ranging from 2.5 kN/m² to 5.0 kN/m². These values have led to the blanket use of 5.0 kN/m² in many office buildings, although more recent research suggests that this leads to uneconomical construction: lower values are now more usually accepted. However, it should be noted that even the higher loading of 5 kN/m² will not accommodate proprietary rolling filing systems which can impose far greater loads on floors and need special consideration.

Sources of information on appropriate design loads for floors in office buildings are given below:

- BS 6399: Part 1 *Loading in buildings* – published by British Standards
- BCO Guide 2005 *Best practice in the specification for offices* – published by the British Council for Offices
- *Office floor loading in historic building* – published by English Heritage

Equivalent loadings in metric and imperial units for common floor loadings in office buildings are as follows:

2.5 kN/m²	=	50lb / sq ft
3.5 kN/m²	=	70lb / sq ft
4.0 kN/m²	=	80lb / sq ft
5.0 kN/m²	=	100lb / sq ft

Floor dynamics

The perception of floor vibration due to pedestrian walking has become a growing issue in modern lightweight buildings, especially those with large floor spans.

Where walking pace matches the floor's natural frequency the energy from walking will be transferred into the floor structure, causing the floor to vibrate more strongly than would otherwise be the case. The perception of vibration in floors varies significantly between persons. Vibration of floors can also cause problems for users of large panel monitors or sensitive equipment.

Recommendations for the design of new buildings include guidance on design checks on the responses of structures to loading, which seek to minimise the likelihood of occupants being aware of floor vibration.

In existing buildings, testing can be carried out to assess the natural frequency of floors, and from this a comparison with other buildings can be made so that the probability of discernable vibration under footfall can be made.

Finishes

Office floors may be directly finished concrete, or finished with some form of sand-cement screed or concrete topping, or be finished by the addition of a raised floor system, usually a proprietary product, often supported on pedestals.

Whereas screeds are generally used solely to provide a level wearing surface to a floor, concrete toppings usually have a structural function as well, providing strength and lateral stiffness to the floor.

Defects

Some forms of floor construction have a higher incidence of defects in certain circumstances than others. Some defects may be common to all types of floors, whereas others are specific to certain types of construction. Defects may relate to structural or to serviceability aspects of the construction. Although not exhaustive, the following list comprises some of the more common defects:

❖ Requirement for strengthening, where particularly heavy equipment or storage is required, or where additional finishes are required, such as when kitchen facilities or shower rooms are to be installed, or where heavy acoustic or sliding partitions are added.

❖ Occupants being disturbed by vibration of the floor, as a result of people walking in open areas or corridors.

❖ Weakening of floor structures as a result of inappropriate alterations, overloading, removal of structural toppings, etc. or as a result of fire, or reduction in fire resistance following inappropriate work.

❖ Cracking of finishes, which sometimes occurs where brittle finishes are laid onto floors not designed specifically for them.

❖ Floor constructions containing high alumina cement (HAC). High alumina cement concrete has been found to lose strength over time, associated with a chemical process referred to as conversion. Concrete containing HAC can be identified by visual survey supplemented by the taking of samples on site for subsequent testing in the laboratory. Where HAC is found, further investigation and appraisal of the structure is necessary to assess its capacity.

❖ Defects in the original construction, such as inadequate concrete cover to reinforcement, poor compaction of concrete between pots or in narrow ribs, or in concrete cast on certain types of formwork, which may affect strength, reduce durability and/or fire resistance.

❖ Filler-joist floor constructions with clinker-aggregate concrete that may contain inclusions, which in damp conditions can create an acidic and therefore corrosive environment to the embedded steel sections.

❖ Floor construction which contains concrete with high levels of calcium chloride, which can lead to severe pitting corrosion of embedded steel sections or reinforcement.

❖ Floor constructions containing reinforced autoclaved aerated concrete planks which, in early designs before 1980, may have insufficient strength leading to excessive deflection.

Building services design

Design

Air-conditioning systems

Air-conditioning refers to a system or process for controlling within predetermined limits the temperature, humidity and sometimes the purity of the air in a building, accommodating the internal heat gains in conjunction with the external ambient conditions. The air, as well as being filtered, is heated or cooled as necessary and moisture is added or extracted to give a controlled humidity.

A comfort cooling system is essentially an air-conditioning system but without full control of the humidity.

The table overleaf provides a comparison of some of the more common floor/ceiling system type characteristics. Wall positioned systems may be utilised however, these have different features. The abbreviations used in the table relate to the following system configurations:

- ❖ **DX:** Direct expansion split type unit system operating with a minimum fresh air system.
- ❖ **VRV/VRF:** Variable refrigerant volume/flow system operating with a minimum fresh air system.
- ❖ **Heat Pump:** Unitary reverse cycle heat pump system operating with a minimum fresh air system.
- ❖ **FCU:** Four pipe fan coil unit system operating with a minimum fresh air system.
- ❖ **VAV:** All-air variable air volume system incorporating terminal reheater batteries.
- ❖ **Underfloor swirl:** All-air underfloor system with perimeter heating.
- ❖ **Displacement:** Underfloor displacement system with ceiling positioned chilled beams and perimeter heating.

Mixed mode ventilation systems

Mixed mode is a term used to describe engineering strategies that normally combine natural ventilation and/or mechanical ventilation and/or cooling in various combinations to achieve acceptable indoor environmental conditions in the most effective manner. It involves maximising the use of the building fabric and envelope to modify the internal climate/temperature swings, such as the use of night time pre-cooling of the building structure via the mechanical fresh air system. This approach has generally been used in offices; however, it is suitable for a wide range of building types.

Comparison of floor/ceiling based AC system type characteristics

	DX	VRV/VRF	Heat Pumps	FCU	VAV	Underfloor Swirl	Displacement
Installation costs	Low	Medium	Medium	Medium/high	High	Medium	Medium/high
Flexibility to change	Poor/average	Average/good	Poor	Good	Very good	Average	Average
Maintenance costs	Medium	Medium	Poor	Poor/medium	Good	Very good	Good
Operating costs	Medium	Low/medium	Low/medium	Poor	Very low	Low	Low
Ceiling void depth	Medium/low	Medium/low	Medium/high	Medium	High	Very low	Low
Floor void depth	Low	Low	Low	Low	Low	High	Medium
Suited to refurbishments	Average	Good	Average	Good/average	Poor	Poor	Poor
Resultant noise level	Average	Good	Poor	Average	Good	Good	Very Good
Plant space requirement	Medium	Medium	Medium	Low/medium	High	Medium	Low/medium
Riser space requirement	Low	Low	Low	Low/medium	High	Medium	Low/medium
Environmental control	Poor	Average	Poor	Good	Very Good	Good	Very Good

Plant and equipment

Boilers – (purpose is to heat water for distribution)

❖ fuel can be gas, oil, coal, electric or dual fuel

❖ air is required for combustion and cooling (not for electric)

❖ some form of flue is required (not for electric)

❖ usually quiet in operation with insignificant vibration.

Water chillers – (purpose is to cool water for distribution)

❖ normally electrically driven, but can be gas driven

❖ conventionally air cooled to avoid the need for cooling towers that can be susceptible to bacteriological contamination (if near large body of water, water cooled chiller can be used)

❖ best externally located but can be internal and ducted to atmosphere

❖ refrigeration machines are complex and expert maintenance is required

❖ high noise and vibration levels can be generated

❖ old machines incorporated CFCs and HCFCs but new ones must not.

Air-handling units – (purpose is to deliver heated/cooled and filtered air to various spaces)

❖ units incorporate fans, heaters, coolers, humidifiers and filters in various combinations

❖ may be located externally or internally with fresh air ducts to outside

❖ low tech equipment and easily maintained

❖ noise and vibration levels can be contained (but additional space required in plant room for silencers).

Diesel generators – (purpose is to provide a standby electrical supply to compensate for a breakdown in the main utility supply)

❖ normally diesel oil fed for commercial developments

❖ high fresh air and exhaust requirements demanding large louvred areas (for cooling)

❖ noise and vibration levels require special attention

❖ oil storage facility – daily use and possibly long term storage

❖ flue is required.

Lift terminology

Power systems

Traction

- ❖ ideally requires motor room above (possible planning problem)
- ❖ can be positioned at other levels, usually below or adjacent to lift pit – more expensive (doubles load on structure)
- ❖ machine room – less (MRL) models now available
- ❖ incorporates counterbalance weight
- ❖ high efficiency
- ❖ high speed available.

Types

- ❖ single speed AC motor: up to 0.5m/sec jolt stop
- ❖ dual speed AC motor: up to 1.0m/sec, more accurate levelling
- ❖ geared variable voltage (VVAC and VVVF): smoother ride and greater speed (VVAC and VVVF)
- ❖ gearless variable voltages above 2.0m/sec, very quiet, long travel.

Hydraulic

- ❖ higher starting current, but not significant as compared to electric traction lifts
- ❖ maximum travel 20m
- ❖ less efficient, higher energy consumption
- ❖ no counterbalance
- ❖ limited starts per hour
- ❖ motor and pump house can be remote from shaft (up to 10m from lift pit), ventilation important for cooling
- ❖ lower speed, up to 1.0m/sec.

Types

- ❖ direct acting: ram and bore hole below car
- ❖ side acting: usually 'fork lift' action ram and cylinder within shaft
- ❖ indirect: combined ram and ropes, ram raises and lowers pulley.

Control systems

Automatic push button

- ❖ responds to first push – no calls stored; preference given to car button calls – flats and small offices.

Down collective

- ❖ answers landing calls in down direction only – mainly used for flats.

Full collective

- ❖ calls stored and answered in sequence in both up and down direction.

Destination despatch

- ❖ requires passengers to enter their destination at the landing – can improve overall journey time.

Door arrangement

Manually operated

Power operated

❖ single sliding: cheapest – larger shaft size required
❖ two speed side opening: expensive – minimum shaft size
❖ centre opening: quickest to full opening position.

Safety provisions

❖ retractable door safety edge – operating micro-switch
❖ pressure sensitive doors – operating micro switch on door operating mechanism
❖ electronic proximity detectors – detects presence of obstruction
❖ light ray or sonar.

For further information refer to BS EN 81 Parts 1 and 2.

Lighting design

Categories of lighting, their respective lux levels, and the areas for which they are typically suitable are identified in the following table.

Category	Lux	Typical areas
Casual	100–150	Storage areas, plant rooms, lifts, circulation areas, bathrooms
Casual rough work	200–300	Dining areas, lounging rooms, bars, sports halls, libraries, rough machining
Routine work	300–500	General office, retail areas, lecture rooms, laboratories, kitchens, medium machining, supermarkets
Demanding work	750	Drawing offices, inspection of medium machining
Detailed work	1,000	Colour discrimination, fine machining and assembly, inspection rooms
Very fine work	1,500–3,000	Hand engraving, precision works, inspection of fine works

Lighting design should generally comply with the recommendations as laid down in the CIBSE/SLL Code for Lighting.

Lighting in offices should comply with the requirements of CIBSE/SLL Lighting Guide LG7. The purpose of LG7 is to promote the overall visual environment (i.e. surface reflections, direct daylight, etc.) and its effect on display screens and their users. Emphasis is also placed on designing schemes that avoid very high luminance patches in a space and abrupt changes in luminance across a surface or between adjacent surfaces.

Data installations

Data installations and information technology require extensive cabling which, in turn, demands adequate access through the building. Therefore, it is important to consider access via risers, suspended floors or floor trunking in order to present the user with these services.

A raised floor is normally a basic pre-requisite to enable full flexibility of outlet positions. Minimum clear void typically 100 – 150mm depending upon floor plate size and riser arrangement.

Modern buildings are now usually block wired for voice and data using common telephone/data jack outlets.

Definitions

MER: Main equipment room
Typically houses: main servers, switches, patching frames, UPS equipment.

SER: Satellite or secondary equipment room
Typically houses: switching, patching frames.

Field wiring types:

❖ Backbone – typically fibre cabling – used to interconnect MERs to SERs.

❖ UTP – unshielded twisted pair – commonly used where low risk of electromagnetic interference.

❖ STP – shielded twisted pair – used where medium risk of electromagnetic interference.

❖ FSTP – fully shielded twisted pair – used where high risk of electromagnetic interference.

Site analysis

Design

Measured surveys

It is strongly advisable to invest in measured surveys at all stages of a project, as early collection of the correct data will pay dividends.

The surveys are best carried out by a reputable measurement surveyor with independence and integrity. Most projects can be broken down into the following stages – the type of surveys recommended at each stage are listed.

Property acquisition – Check the floor areas (gross or net) independently (the RICS produce a booklet *Code of Measurement* which is worth reading).

Check the lease or conveyance plans with the latest Ordnance Survey (OS) maps (1:1250 or 1:2500 scale). Check boundaries on site against legal documentation – resolve boundary disputes before completing the contract. The new Land Registration enables owners to determine their own boundaries and should be considered if any doubt arises or in fact to prevent potential disputes.

Development – Existing measured surveys of the topography and/or buildings may exist. If they do, be sure to check their completeness and whether they are up to date. Consider employing a land surveyor to make checks. If none exist, then purchase the latest OS mapping (available digitally) for contextual purposes but be aware that the data will only be accurate to a metre or two.

It is strongly advised that you invest in a new measured survey. The RICS or TSA (the UK Land Survey Association) can provide assistance. The RICS has a document for large scale surveys which needs you to 'tick the boxes' to provide a specification. Also be aware that the more boxes you tick – the more cost and time is involved!

Various techniques are available now for obtaining data for adjoining properties such as large scale aerial photography and laser scanning (LIDDAR). This enables 3D data to be collected without gaining access to the property. Various 3D models of cities are now available on the internet but be very wary of their accuracy.

Architectural engineering and services, design and construction

The architect, engineer and services consultant will need measurements.

Everyone can and does take measurements. Modern equipment, such as Leica's 'Disto' and electronic theodolites make the task of surveying ever easier. It is strongly advisable though to seek the services of a good, reputable and honest land surveyor (preferably RICS or ICES qualified) whose job it is to 'measure'. Such a surveyor will understand the complexities of the instrumentation and the necessary precision and accuracy for the task.

The culture within the property and construction industry is not to rely on others' dimensions and measurements. This all too often leads to disputes over measurements. It is worth considering employing an independent surveyor to collect the necessary measurements and supply these to all parties involved. A good surveyor will stand by his dimensions and this will lead to an improvement in time and less confrontation. Laser scanning technology provides an accurate 3D model instantly, from which measurements can be taken. This can be used to record progress and be displayed at design team meetings for all to see and take measurement from. Due to the fact this is 3D there is instant 'clash detection' (important for M&E Services), there is less ambiguity and misunderstanding than with 2D drawings and finally (and most importantly) it is understood by non-technical professions (e.g. finance and legal advisers).

During construction it will be advisable to have a land or engineering surveyor on site, all the time if possible, or at least at regular intervals to ensure adequate dimensional control is established (in X, Y and Z planes) for the trade contractors to use.

After completion a true 'as-built' survey is recommended. This can be used to check the area (gross and net) of the building and then be retained as part of the log book of the property. Ensure this is available in digital form to be used in CAD systems as well as a format suitable for Microsoft Office.

The plans will help the maintenance of the building and any future disposal. It is surprising how few reliable drawings exist.

An information system (e.g. GIS) is worth considering to help the operation of the property. Each space can be allocated a unique reference number attached to the drawings to enable instant reporting. Additional data can be added about size, condition, occupancy, etc.

Flooding

Design

Flooding and its impact on property

Around five million people in two million properties live in flood risk areas in England and Wales and these figures are set to rise. The government's Foresight Future Flooding report, released in April 2004 by the Department of Trade and Industry (DTI) is the most wide-ranging analysis of flood risk carried out to date in the UK. The report predicts that climate change will be an important factor in increasing flood risk, and that both the number of people in danger from flooding and the costs of damage from floods will rise significantly. It uses scenarios of potential social and economic change, as well as information on climate change, to identify future risks and to inform both public and government bodies about what will need to be done to mitigate these risks.

The report concludes that:

* the amount of carbon we burn must be reduced in order to help slow down the rate of climate change;
* more must be spent on flood and coastal defences to protect against the impacts of climate change;
* tougher restrictions are needed on building on flood plains; and
* new developments must be resilient to flooding.

Who is responsible?

Defra has overall policy responsibility for flood and coastal erosion risk in England and the Environment Agency has statutory responsibility for flood management and defence. The Environment Agency, Internal Drainage Boards and local authorities are responsible for maintaining, operating and improving flood defences. Defra funds most of the Environment Agency's flood management activities in England, it does not build defences, nor direct the authorities on which specific projects to undertake. The works programme to manage risk is driven by the operating authorities.

Since 1 April 2006, Defra's Flood Management Division has been reorganised into a programme-led structure. In future, the Environment Agency is expected to take on responsibility for operating the national capital investment prioritisation system across all operating authorities, approving the various authorities' capital improvement projects and distributing grants to them.

Managing the risk

One of the main goals of the Environment Agency, through its Flood Defence Committee, is to reduce flood risk. Defra's 2004 national assessment of defence needs and costs report, estimated the capital value of assets at risk from flooding to be approximately £250 billion. Average annual damages from flooding were estimated at some £1bn per year. Average damages that would occur if nothing were done to manage the risk were estimated at more than £3 billion per year. The British Government now spends more than £300m each year on flood defences: since 2000, 70km of defences have been built, reducing flood risk to more than 25,000 people. And around 80 new flood defences were approved in the two years to 2006.

The government now believes that the most effective way to reduce flood risk is to adopt a portfolio of measures tailored to conditions in each location. These measures include the way in which land is used, what flood defences are built and the way in which flood warnings are given. A five-year strategy for flood risk management is now in place, with the aim of reducing the risk of flooding to around 80,000 homes.

This is being achieved by:

* ensuring more residents in flood risk areas know they are at risk and are aware of the action they need to take to protect themselves;

- ❖ improving the coverage of flood warning services to reduce the number of properties exposed to a high risk of flooding;
- ❖ planning flood defences based on how a whole area is affected, rather than individual locations; and
- ❖ preventing all inappropriate development inside flood plains.

Longer term, as set out in *Making space for water*, published by Defra in July 2004, the government will continue to implement 'a more holistic approach' to managing flood and coastal erosion risks in England. Its stated aim is 'to manage risks by employing an integrated portfolio of approaches which reflect both national and local priorities so as to reduce the threat to people and their property and deliver the greatest environmental, social and economic benefit consistent with the government's sustainable development principles'.

The quotes above are Crown copyright and are reproduced from the report *Making space for water*, published by Defra.

Forecasting floods

According to the Meteorological Office, the ability to accurately forecast floods depends on the nature of the events which trigger them. Short periods of intense rainfall can cause flash flooding; longer periods of widespread heavy rain can cause rivers to overflow and storm surges can cause coastal flooding. The severity and extent of flooding depends to a large degree on the state of the underlying ground – if the soil moisture content is already high, flooding occurs much more quickly because surface water cannot soak away.

The Met Office is currently addressing this issue by developing tools and services to help combat the problem, including working closely with the Environment Agency and other experts in hydrology, and development of the National Severe Weather Warning Service (NSWWS). Using a wide range of technologies, it provides local authorities and the public with warnings of potentially dangerous weather events. In addition, a high-resolution rainfall forecasting and warning system, which has been developed in partnership with the Environment Agency, uses radar, satellite and Met Office numerical weather prediction model data to forecast rainfall rate and accumulation over England and Wales.

Rising groundwater

During the latter part of the 20th century, the level of groundwater beneath major UK cities rose rapidly, leading to increasing concern that huge costs could be incurred from damage to buildings and infrastructure if preventative measures are not taken. The problem stems from the city-centre industries that populated the areas during the industrial revolution and their demand for water. Beneath London this led to a reduction in the level of up to 90 metres. The usage has declined significantly since the late 1960s as the industries relocated and without this extraction levels have recovered, rising by 1.5 metres a year initially and by as much as 3 metres a year recently. By the late 1990s, water levels in central London had recovered by 35 metres, close to the 1900 level.

It was therefore realised that action to minimise the damage was needed urgently to allow time for planning and implementation. A group was formed from interested parties and in March 1999 it announced that a five-stage plan had been developed to safeguard London from the effects of rising groundwater. The plan involved controlled increased abstraction from 50 or more existing and new boreholes, with the amount that could be used for drinking water maximised and the remainder to be used for industrial or agricultural processes. The five phases of the strategy are:

- ❖ Utilise four existing licensed water supply boreholes on the outskirts of London.

- ❖ Equip three proven borehole sites near central London with the latest filtration technology to provide further water for drinking purposes.
- ❖ Encourage the use of existing and new private boreholes, in and around central London where the water quality is lower, for non-potable uses.
- ❖ Identify locations for new control boreholes in central London, initially to be pumped to waste until end uses can be determined.
- ❖ New control boreholes in outer London to intercept the flow of water towards the central basin.

The plan has the backing of government and is being managed by Thames Water, working in conjunction with the Environment Agency. Although the threat to London is the most immediate, other cities are at risk and it is likely that similar strategies will be implemented as required.

Flood plans

Predicting flooding is only the first part of the equation. When flooding occurs, by managing excess water as effectively as possible, the Environment Agency aims to save money, spare the environment as much as possible from catastrophic and often extremely damaging events, and keep greater numbers of people safe. Catchment Flood Management Plans (CFMPs) and Shoreline Management Plans (SMPs) have a key role to play in this strategy.

Instead of simply building flood defences, CFMPs look at land use across a larger area – or 'catchment' – seeing if the water can be moved to where it will do least harm to people and the environment. A catchment is an area that serves a river with rainwater and every part of land where the rainfall drains to a single river is in the same catchment. For this reason, hills and high ground are often the boundaries between catchments – rain falling on one side of the hill drains to one river; rain falling on the other side drains to another river.

The main aims of Catchment Flood Management Plans are to:

- ❖ understand the factors that contribute to flood risk within a catchment, such as how the land is used; and
- ❖ recommend the best ways of managing that risk during the next 50 to 100 years.

All land use changes will be decided in full consultation with those affected, such as local authorities that have responsibility for planning permission, land owners and conservation and marine organisations. It is anticipated that the majority of CFMPs will be written and ready for consultation by 2008.

Planning to avoid flooding

Planning has a vital role to play in flood risk management. The Department for Communities and Local Government (DCLG), formerly the ODPM, is responsible for the planning system, which aims to prevent inappropriate new developments in flood risk areas, and to direct development away from areas at highest risk.

The DCLG estimates that around 10% of the total land in England lies within areas of flood risk, including large areas of Eastern England and much of London, Hull and York. The government is committed to continuing development in these areas and so in order to manage flood risk so that new development is safe and sustainable, former planning guidance detailed in PPG25 was superseded in December 2006 by a new Planning Policy Statement: PPS25.

This new planning policy statement aims to:

❖ ensure flood risk is taken into account at all stages in the planning process;

❖ avoid inappropriate development in areas at risk of flooding; and

❖ direct development away from high risk areas.

It will:

❖ focus on core policies that are clearer and easier to understand;

❖ provide a more strategic approach, emphasising the need to consider flood risk as early as possible in the planning process;

❖ clarify the sequential test that matches types of development to degrees of flood risk; and

❖ strengthen guidance on the need to include Flood Risk Assessments at all levels of the planning process.

Flood risk assessments

It is vital that checks are carried out at an early stage of all new developments to determine whether or not they are located in areas that fall within the Environment Agency's flood plain map. This map does not, however, take into account any mitigating effects of planned or existing flood defences or site specific features and therefore it is important to carry out a site specific flood risk assessment (FRA) at an early stage on those projects considered to be at risk.

An FRA must include:

❖ the location of the development or redevelopment, showing streets, water courses, etc. with property clearly marked;

❖ site plan showing existing and future floor levels;

❖ cross section of the site showing floor levels and river banks;

❖ details of proposed Flood Alleviation Measures;

❖ sources of possible flooding;

❖ existing information on flooding;

❖ assessment of the probability of flooding and the expected impact of climate change;

❖ assessment of rate and duration of flooding;

❖ assessment of the likely rate and speed with which flooding might occur;

❖ assessment of the potential impact of any development on fluvial morphology (ground movement as a result of the action of water);

❖ assessment of the need for preventative measures, such as internal flood barriers, raising of threshold levels, flood attenuation using SUDS (sustainable urban drainage);

❖ assessment of the impact of the development on drainage, i.e. will there be increased run-off and if so, how this could be remedied; and

❖ assessment of escape routes and evacuation procedures.

Protecting property from floods

Despite disturbing scenes of flooding both at home and abroad in recent years, many of those homeowners and businesses most at risk in England and Wales are still denying that flooding could happen to them. Environment Agency research shows that, while 95% of people at risk agree flooding is a serious issue, less than half believe that it relates to them. And only one person in 20 takes any advance action to prepare for floods. The Agency thinks this could be due not only to apathy but also to public fears that acknowledging the risks and taking steps to protect against flooding could in some way have a negative effect on property values.

Although it is not possible to avoid floods occurring, there are a number of ways in which property owners can help safeguard their property from water damage. Sand bags have now largely been replaced by a range of more sophisticated flood protection products, such as flood boards and air brick covers. The Environment Agency in conjunction with CIRIA has published a new leaflet outlining some of the many products on offer and giving advice on protecting premises against flooding. *Flood products – using flood protection products* helps homeowners assess the risk to their property from flooding and understand the routes of floodwater entry. It also introduces the range of flood protection products available, the level of protection that can be expected and other measures that can be applied to reduce the entry of floodwater. Both organisations are also supporting the BSI's new Kitemark scheme for flood protection products.

In addition to using specialist flood protection products, property owners living in high risk areas should take the following precautions if flooding is likely:

- ❖ Check that all buildings insurance policies include cover for flood damage and inform insurers as soon as possible after the event so that a claim can be made immediately.
- ❖ Protect people, data and equipment – make sure that records and other business information are archived and stored off the premises.
- ❖ Businesses could consider investing in a generator to maintain emergency power supplies.
- ❖ Move valuable items away from lower floors where possible.

After a flood:

- ❖ Open doors and windows to ventilate the building.
- ❖ Don't heat the building to more than 4 degrees centigrade until all the water is removed and expose as much damp timber as possible to accelerate the drying out process.
- ❖ Don't forget about security. Burglar alarms may not be working if the electricity supply has been affected by the high water level: if necessary cover open or broken windows with security mesh.
- ❖ Never attempt to move back into a property that still contains standing water: it is a potential health hazard and should be pumped or baled out. Open up all the floor voids to check there is no water there.
- ❖ Saturated buildings take time to dry out. The rule of thumb for masonry is one month per inch of thickness. However, it may not be possible to save plaster walls. Older sand and cement renders should dry out but some may need to be removed. Gypsum plaster or plasterboard will hold water so remove and dispose of it quickly. Non-waterproof grades of chipboard and plywood should also be treated with suspicion: if it swells, replace it.

Help and support for flood victims

The National Flood Forum is a community-based network set up by people who have been through the experience of flooding and suffered the distress, losses and frustration that follow. The forum was established in 2002 to give communities and individuals who have been flooded or are at risk the support, knowledge and help they need to organise themselves, to manage the effects of flooding, to promote self-help and to campaign for flood alleviation.

The forum works closely with The Environment Agency, water companies, local authorities, the government, flood protection companies and the insurance industry.

It can provide information on all types of flooding, from main rivers, local watercourses, sewers, storm water and highway drains, tidal and coastal flooding, groundwater, to run-off from urban areas or agricultural land. The forum also offers free advice to individuals or groups on where to source flood protection products, specialist help or advice on insurance issues.

The surveyor's role in flooding

Construction professionals have an important role to play in advising clients about the impact of flooding. This applies both to those providing advice on proposed developments and those inspecting and reporting on existing buildings that may have suffered flood damage. However, according to recent research carried out for the Royal Institution of Chartered Surveyors (RICS), despite 'areas of good practice and pockets of experience in dealing with flooding and reinstatements ... information remains uncoordinated and somewhat overgeneralised. There is little in the way of agreed professional procedures for dealing with flood risk and flood damage'. In response, RICS is developing guidance for chartered surveyors with the aim of enabling them to take a more active role in this area of work.

There is, however, already some useful guidance on renovation procedures published by other construction industry bodies. BRE Digest 152: *Repair and renovation of flood damaged buildings* and the BRE Guide: *Dealing with flood damage*, offer guidance on:

- ❖ draining;
- ❖ cleaning – mud above damp-proof courses, under-floor spaces and cavity walls;
- ❖ drying – brickwork and plaster, masonry and timber;
- ❖ effect of water on materials – brick, stone and concrete, wall finishes, timber, floor finishes and metals;
- ❖ structural damage – foundations, walls, floors and roofs, paths, driveways and drains;
- ❖ renovation of interiors – walls and timbers;
- ❖ electrical installations – connections, ducts, cables and conduits, tests and future arrangements; and
- ❖ sea water flooding.

A new guide produced by the BRE's Flood Repairs Forum may also be useful. Titled *Repairing flooded buildings: an insurance industry guide to investigation and repair of flood damage to housing and small businesses*, it is available from the BRE bookshop.

CIRIA has produced a series of online advice sheets giving detailed technical information on assessing and inspecting properties and techniques for improving the flood resilience of a property. The advice sheets are designed to help homeowners carry out any necessary work, but may also prove useful to surveyors and other construction professionals involved in repairs and refurbishment needed as a result of flooding. The advice sheets look at:

- ❖ identifying flood risk;
- ❖ how floodwater enters a house above ground;
- ❖ how floodwater enters a house below ground;
- ❖ flood-resilient walls;
- ❖ flood-resilient windows and doors;
- ❖ flood-resilient floors;

- ❖ flood-resilient services; and
- ❖ flood-resilient sewers and drains.

Another CIRIA publication, *Standards for the repair of buildings following flooding*, published in 2005, describes the causes of flooding and the impact it can have on buildings, gives advice on what to do in the immediate aftermath of flooding, sets out how to conduct post-flood surveys and future flood risk assessment and offers standards for repairing buildings that have been affected by flooding to improve their flood resistance. The guide is aimed primarily at building professionals and insurers experienced in flood damage and repair. However, it could also be used by general builders, surveyors and building owners needing advice when commissioning repair work.

Compensation for flooding

It has been the policy of successive governments that individuals should not be compensated for any flood loss. The thinking behind this is that, as flooding is generally an insurable risk, government compensation for flood losses would disrupt this private insurance market.

However, local authorities can apply for compensation under the Bellwin Scheme of Emergency Financial Assistance to Local Authorities. A Bellwin scheme can be brought into effect in any case where an emergency or disaster involving destruction of, or danger to, life or property occurs and, as a result, one or more local authorities incur expenditure in connection with the taking of immediate action to safeguard life or property in their area. There is no automatic entitlement to financial assistance and the government has discretion to decide whether or not to activate a scheme after considering the circumstances of individual cases.

The onus is therefore on individual home and business owners to ensure that if their property is in an area susceptible to flooding, that they have adequate insurance in place to cover the risk. Between October and November 2000, claims for flood and storm damage due to extreme weather conditions cost the insurance industry more than £750m in total. However, despite the enormous cost to insurers, the Association of British Insurers (ABI) stresses that its members are committed to ensuring that flood insurance remains as widely available as possible. ABI members tend to deal with flooding risks as follows:

- ❖ for existing customers in higher risk flood areas, premiums may be higher or the customer may be asked to pay a higher excess to reflect the increased frequency of flood claims;
- ❖ for new customers in high risk areas, all cases are considered on an individual basis; and
- ❖ in exceptional cases, where flooding has occurred frequently and where no flood defences are planned 'within a reasonable timescale', flood cover may be withdrawn completely.

Further information

www.defra.gov.uk
www.environmentagency.gov.uk
www.abi.org.uk
www.norwichunion.com
www.devon.gov.uk
www.ciria.org.uk
www.communities.gov.uk
www.floodforum.gov.uk
www.rics.org.uk

Materials

Materials and defects

Deleterious materials

The presence of deleterious materials in a building may affect its market value and could, in severe cases, result in element failure or affect the health of persons working or living there.

The reaction of investing institutions to these materials depends on a number of factors and often the presence of a deleterious substance will not prevent a purchase. However, great care must be taken to assess the actual risks or consequences involved, so that a value judgement can be made.

Materials hazardous to health

The more common hazardous materials, and associated risks, are identified in the following table.

Materials	Common use	Use risk
Lead	When used in water pipes and lead paint (lead roofing materials pose little or no risk).	Risk of contamination of drinking water in lead pipes, or from lead solder used in plumbing joints. Risk of inhalation of lead dust during maintenance of lead based paint. Risk to children of chewing lead painted surfaces (Pica). Concentration of lead in paint now generally much reduced. Beware of lead content in brass fittings.
Urea Formaldehyde foam	Cavity wall insulation. Some insulation boards but rare in UK.	There is some evidence that UF foam may be a carcinogenic material although this is not proven. Vapour can cause irritation. Poorly installed insulation can lead to passage of water from outer leaf of brick to inner leaf in cavity wall situation. There are some worries over formaldehyde used as an adhesive in medium density fibreboard and chipboard but this is likely to be a problem only in unventilated areas with large amounts of boarding.
Asbestos See also page 202	Commercial and residential buildings as boarding, sheet cladding, insulation and other uses particularly in the 1950s, 1960s and 1970s.	Airborne asbestos fibres may be inhaled and eventually lead to either asbestosis, lung cancer or mesothemelioma.

Materials damaging to buildings

Those materials which may affect building performance or structure are identified in the following table.

Materials	Common use	Use risk
Calcium silicate brickwork	Used in lieu of concrete or clay bricks, often as an inner leaf in cavity work. Often cited as deleterious but if used correctly will perform well.	Calcium silicate brickwork shrinks after construction with further movement due to wetting. Construction must provide measures of control to distribute cracking. Concrete bricks may display a similar propensity to shrinkage and again care must be taken in the design of movement joints, etc.
Calcium chloride concrete additive	Commonly used in in-situ concrete as an accelerator and often added in flake form. Often found in buildings constructed before 1977. (May also be present from atmospheric or traffic exposure).	Reduces passivity of concrete in damp conditions. Subsequent risk of corrosion of steel reinforcement.
High Alumina Cement (HAC) Further details on page 211	Mainly used in the manufacture of pre-cast X or I roof or floor beams together with some lintels, sill members, etc. between 1954 and 1974. HAC has existed since about 1925.	Strength of concrete can decrease significantly often when high temperatures and/or high humidity is involved. Defects may be due to faulty manufacture.
Sea dredged aggregate	In-situ concrete or precast concrete.	May contain salts such as sodium chloride. If salts not properly washed out, risk of corrosion reinforcement sodium may contribute to alkali silica reaction. Provided the aggregates are properly washed and controlled in accordance with British Standard requirements the indications are that there are no greater risks involved than with the use of aggregates from inland sources.

Materials	Common use	Use risk
Mundic blocks and Mundic concrete	Concrete blocks and concrete manufactured from quarry shale commonly found in the West Country.	Loss of integrity in damp conditions. Further research required to identify level of risk across the country.
Woodwool slabs (also woodcrete and chipcrete)	Often used as (a) decking to flat roofs, or (b) as permanent shuttering.	Use in (a) may be considered acceptable providing material is kept dry. Use in (b) as a permanent shutter may result in grout loss (honeycombing) or voidage of concrete near to or surrounding reinforcement, particularly with ribbed floors. May result in reduced fire resistance, reinforcement corrosion or in extreme cases loss of structural strength. May be repaired by application of sprayed concrete. Condition investigated by cut-out removal of woodwool in many locations.
Brick slips	Typically 1970s and 1980s to conceal flow nibs in cavity walls.	Risk of poor adhesion, lack of soft joints can transfer load to slips and cause delamination.

For a fuller description refer to *Investigating Hazardous and Deleterious Building Materials*, Rushton, T., RICS Books, 2006 (ISBN 1 84219 291 4).

Asbestos

Asbestos is the generic term for several mineral silicates occurring naturally in fibrous form. Because of its various useful properties (resistance to heat, acids and alkalis, and good thermal, electrical or acoustic insulator) it has been extensively used in the construction industry.

Three main types in the UK are Chrysotile (white), Amosite (brown) and Crocidolite (blue). It is used in a variety of forms varying from boards or corrugated sheets to loose coatings or laggings and, generally, the more friable the material, the greater the asbestos content.

Health risk

Inhalation of its microscopic fibres can constitute a serious health risk and is associated with several terminal diseases.

Not all asbestos, irrespective of its circumstances, constitutes an immediate risk, although the effects of possible future disturbance or deterioration must be considered. Factors to be taken into account are the type, form, friability, condition and location of the source material.

The (1987) Joint Central and Local Government Working Party on Asbestos concluded that 'Asbestos materials which are in good condition and not releasing dust should not be disturbed ... Materials that are damaged, deteriorating, releasing dust or which are likely to do so should be sealed, enclosed or removed as appropriate. Materials which are left in place should be managed and their condition periodically reassessed. The risk to the health of the public from asbestos materials which are in sound condition and which are undisturbed is very low indeed. Substitute materials should be used where possible, provided they perform adequately'.

The HSE actively discourages the unnecessary removal of sound asbestos materials and each case should be decided on its own merits following an assessment of the risks arising.

In the past the people most at risk have been workers in the asbestos industry involved in the importation, storage, manufacture and installation of materials or components containing this material.

These activities are now banned in the UK and the removal, treatment or intentional working with asbestos is strictly controlled and generally limited to specialists. The risk however continues for anyone who inadvertently disturbs the asbestos in the course of their routine business, including builders, maintenance workers, electricians and the like, and the most recent legislation is intended for their protection.

Legislation

The enabling act for asbestos legislation is the *Health and Safety at Work etc. Act* 1974 and failure to comply with its requirements is a criminal offence.

The principal Regulations that apply to works that could expose persons to the risk of respirable asbestos fibres are the *Control of Asbestos Regulations* 2006 (CAR 2006) which came into operation on 13 November 2006 and implement the 2003/18/EC amendment to the European *Asbestos Worker Protective Directive* 83/477/EEC.

These supersede the *Control of Asbestos at Work Regulations* 2002 (CAWR), the *Asbestos (Licensing) Regulations* 1983 (as amended) and the *Asbestos (Prohibition) Regulations* 1992.

In addition the HSE has produced various Approved Codes of Practice and Guidance:

* L143, *Work with materials containing asbestos*, Control of Asbestos Regulations 2006 (ISBN 0 7176 6206 3); and
* L127, *The management of asbestos in non-domestic premises*, Regulation 4 of the *Control of Asbestos Regulations* 2006 (ISBN 0 7176 6209 8).

In addition to legislation specifically focussed on asbestos, more general health and safety legislation that may also need to be taken into account includes:

* the *Management of Health and Safety at Work Regulations* 1999; and
* the *Construction (Design and Management) Regulations* 1994 (as amended).

CAR 2006 has introduced fundamental changes to the previous legislation and these are set out below:

* The concept of 'action levels' is abandoned and a **single** 'control limit' is applicable to **all** types of asbestos.
* The applicability of specific regulations and methods of control are based on risk assessment, using the hierarchy of risk assessment of COSHH.
* In principle, CAR 2006 changes the concept of previous legislation by applying all of its many and varied regulatory requirements to **any** work involving **any** form of asbestos, subject to only a few limited and specific exceptions on a risk-based assessment basis.

These are known as the regulation 3(2) exceptions and in such cases the regulatory requirements relating to licensing, notification, arrangements to deal with accidents, incidents and emergencies, designation of asbestos areas and of health records and medical surveillance do **not** apply.

Control limit

This is a specific level of concentration of asbestos in the atmosphere, measured in accordance with the World Heath Organisation (WHO) recommended method, or approved equivalent. It is the trigger point for the application of specific regulations and/or controls. If the risk assessment for the works indicates it is liable to be exceeded, then regulation 18(1)(2) 'Designated areas' requires the establishment of 'respirator zones', where access is restricted to 'competent' persons and suitable respirators must be worn at all times. In addition, if it is **not** liable to be exceeded, then this is one of a number of circumstances set out in regulation 3(2) for which specific regulatory requirements may not necessarily apply.

The current control limit is 0.1 fibres per cubic centimetre of air averaged over a continuous period of four hours. This is more stringent than that contained in the previous CAWR 2002, which was 0.3 fibres for White asbestos and 0.2 fibres for any other type or mixture of asbestos.

What are the regulation 3(2) exceptions?

The regulations in the table below do **NOT** apply to the circumstances set out in regulation 3(2) i.e. where:

    a)   'the exposure of employees to asbestos is *sporadic and low intensity*;

    b)   it is clear from the risk assessment that the exposure of any employee to asbestos will not exceed the control limit; and

    c)   the work involves:

        i)   *short, non-continuous maintenance activities*,

        ii)   removal of *materials in which the asbestos fibres are firmly linked in a matrix*,

        iii)   encapsulation or sealing of asbestos-containing materials which are in good condition, or

        iv)   air monitoring and control, and the collection and analysis of samples to ascertain whether a specific material contains asbestos.'

Crown Copyright material is reproduced with the permission of the Controller of HMSO and the Queen's Printer for Scotland.

The phrases in italics are explained in the ACOP and guidance accompanying the Regulations and should be referred to for detail.

Number	Title	Details
8	Licensing of work with asbestos	Licensed asbestos contractor
9	Notification of work with asbestos	Informing enforcement authority
15(1)	Accidents, incidents and emergencies	Arrangements in anticipation
18(1)(a)	Asbestos areas	Designated area where employee(s) liable to be exposed to asbestos
22	Health records and medical surveillance	

Generally this means that, subject always to the results of the risk assessment in the specific circumstances, work to asbestos-containing decorative coatings will fall into this exclusion category. Also, subject to the control limit not being likely to be exceeded, the definition of 'sporadic and low intensity' will also apply to:

❖ asbestos cement;

❖ bituminous, plastic, resin or rubber articles where thermal and acoustic properties are only incidental; and

❖ sundry products with no insulation purposes, including paper linings, cardboard, felt, textile, gaskets, washers and ropes;

effectively thus taking these low risk materials outside of the previous licensing requirements and allowing the works to be carried out by competent contractors, but who need not necessarily be licensed by the HSE.

Training

The list of training requirements is also augmented and the accompanying ACOP sets out the detailed requirements.

In addition to the general training requirements for any employee, set out in the *Management at Work Regulations*, regulation 10 of CAR 2006 requires every employer to ensure that adequate information, instruction and training is given to employees who:

a) are, or are liable to be, exposed to asbestos, and to their supervisors,

and

b) carry out work in connection with the employer's duties under these Regulations so that they can carry out that work effectively.

The ACOP which accompanies CAR 2006 provides a full and detailed list of these training requirements.

There are three main types of information, instruction and training, namely:

Type	For
Awareness training	Those who are liable to be exposed to asbestos while carrying out their normal everyday work, e.g. maintenance staff; electricians; demolition and construction workers; installers of computers, fire or burglar alarms; and **'construction professionals'**.
For non-licensable asbestos work	For example, a roofer removing whole asbestos cement sheet in good condition.
For licensable asbestos work	For example, a contractor removing asbestos lagging or asbestos insulating board.

The topics which the training should cover are listed and should be given in appropriate detail by both written and oral presentation and by demonstration (as necessary). In particular, training is to be in a manner appropriate to the nature and degree of exposure identified by the employer's risk assessment giving the significant findings of the assessment and the results of any air monitoring carried out, together with an explanation of the findings.

The training should be given by a competent person and the procedures for providing the information, instruction and training should be clearly defined and documented and reviewed regularly, particularly when work methods change.

Records should be kept of the training undertaken by each individual. For licensable work copies should be given to each individual.

Refresher training should be given at least **every year** and more frequently if the work methods, equipment used or type of work changes.

Where **non-employees** are on the employer's premises, they should also be given adequate information, instruction and training as far as is reasonably practicable.

Management of asbestos

There is **no change** to the duty to manage asbestos, regulation 4.

Regulation 4 requires the dutyholder(s) to 'manage' asbestos in 'non-domestic premises' and also, for 'every person' to cooperate with the dutyholder so far as is necessary to enable him or her to comply with his or her duties.

Accredited personnel

Regulations 20 and 21 require, respectively, that only persons accredited as complying with ISO 17025 must be employed to measure the concentration of airborne asbestos fibres and analyse a bulk sample of material to determine whether it contains asbestos.

In addition, from 1 April 2007, anyone issuing a clearance certificate for reoccupation following asbestos removal work must meet the relevant accreditation requirements of ISO 17025 and ISO 17020 extended to include all four stages of the clearance and not just the air testing part.

Distinguishing between asbestos insulating board and asbestos cement

Because of the relatively higher potential risks to health arising, working with asbestos insulating board (AIB) is subject to different and more stringent controls than working with asbestos cement.

As the two materials are very similar in physical appearance, depending upon the circumstances, it is necessary to distinguish between them.

The distinction is one of density, the general rule being that the greater the proportion of cementitious matrix to asbestos, the greater the density. Conversely, the more friable the material, the greater the asbestos content.

The Approved Code of Practice that accompanies CAR 2006 defines asbestos cement as 'a material which is predominantly a mixture of cement and asbestos and which in a dry state absorbs less than 30% water by weight'. The guidance in the document includes a comprehensive description of the testing procedure.

Asbestos insulating board is defined as a flat sheet, tile or building board consisting of a mixture of asbestos and other material except asbestos cement or any article of bitumen, plastic, resin or rubber which contains asbestos, and the thermal or acoustic properties of which are incidental to its main purpose.

It is relatively easy to identify asbestos cement when it is used in preformed components such as corrugated sheeting, tanks or toilet cisterns, but when it is used in flat board form the only sure way of distinguishing the material from AIB is by laboratory analysis.

Where there is doubt, the regulations require that caution be taken, and the material is presumed to be AIB until proven otherwise.

Summary of CAR 2006

Regulation(s)	Title (in italics) plus explanatory notes
1	*Citation and commencement*
2	*Interpretation*
3	*Application of the Regulations* – see 'regulation 3(2) exceptions' above
4	*Duty to manage asbestos in non-domestic premises* – see separate detailed explanation below
5	*Identification of the presence of asbestos*
6	*Assessment of work which exposes employee to asbestos* – prior to the works, assess the likely level of risk, determine the nature and degree of exposure and set out steps to control it
7	*Plans of work* – produce a suitable written plan of the proposed works
8*	*Licensing of work with asbestos* – previously *Asbestos (Licensing) Regulations* 1983 (as amended). All work except 'regulation 3(2) exceptions' must only be undertaken by licence holders
9*	*Notification of work with asbestos* – notify the enforcing authority of licensable work (min. 14 days notice)
10	*Information, instruction and training* – see 'Training' above
11	*Prevention or reduction of exposure to asbestos* – prevent exposure to employees as far as is reasonably practicable, and where not reasonably practicable, reduce to lowest level reasonably practicable, both the exposure (without relying on use of respirators) and the number of employees exposed
12	*Use of control measures* – ensure that any control measures are properly used or applied
13	*Maintenance of control measures* – maintain control measures and equipment (keeping records of the latter)
14	*Provision and cleaning of protective clothing* – provide suitable PPE and ensure it is properly used and maintained
15*	*Arrangements to deal with accidents, incidents and emergencies*
16	*Duty to prevent or reduce the spread of asbestos* – where not reasonably practicable, reduce to lowest level reasonably practicable

Regulation(s)	Title (in italics) plus explanatory notes
17	*Cleanliness of premises and plant* – keep asbestos working areas and plant clean and thoroughly clean on completion; four-stage clearance procedure and certification for reoccupation
18*	*Designated areas for asbestos work* – 'asbestos areas' where any employee would be liable to be exposed to asbestos and 'respirator zones' where control limit liable to be exceeded
19	*Air monitoring* – monitor exposure of employees to asbestos
20	*Standards for air testing and site clearance certification* – see 'Accredited personnel' above
21	*Standards for analysis* – of bulk samples, see 'Accredited personnel' above
22*	*Health records and medical surveillance* – of employees liable to be exposed to asbestos
23	*Washing and changing facilities*
24	*Storage, distribution and labelling of raw asbestos and asbestos waste* – if received, despatched from, transported or distributed, waste must be in sealed, labelled, appropriate bags or containers
25–31	*Prohibitions and related provisions* – previously *Asbestos (Prohibition) Regulations* 1992
32–37	*Miscellaneous* – exemptions, etc. and defence 'must have taken all reasonable precautions and exercised all due diligence'

Regulations marked with an asterisk do **not** apply in whole or part where the work falls within any of the circumstances set out in 'regulation 3(2) exceptions'.

Duty to manage asbestos in non-domestic premises (regulation 4)

The dutyholder responsible for the management of asbestos in non-domestic premises as set out in regulation 4(1) is every person, who has by virtue of a contract or tenancy, an obligation for its repair or maintenance, or, in the absence of such, control of those premises or access thereto or egress therefrom.

This includes those persons with any responsibility for the maintenance, or control, of the whole or part of the premises.

When there is more than one dutyholder, the relative contribution required from each party in order to comply with the statutory duty, will be shared according to the nature and extent of the repair obligation owed by each.

This regulation does not apply to 'domestic premises', namely a private dwelling in which a person lives, but legal precedents have established that common parts of flats (in housing developments, blocks of flats and some conversions) are not part of a private dwelling.

The common parts, are classified as 'non-domestic' and therefore regulation 4 applies to them, but not to the individual flats or houses in which they are provided.

Typical examples of common parts are entrance foyers, corridors, lifts, their enclosures and lobbies, staircases, common toilets, boiler rooms, roof spaces, plant rooms, communal services, risers, ducts and external outhouses, canopies, gardens and yards.

The regulation does not however apply to kitchens, bathrooms or other rooms within a private residence, that are shared by more than one household, or communal rooms within sheltered accommodation.

The duties are identified in the following table.

Subject	Requirement
Cooperate (see also next page)	Cooperate with other dutyholders so far as is necessary to enable them to comply with their Regulation 4 duties.
Find and assess condition of ACMs	Ensure that a suitable and sufficient assessment is made as to whether asbestos is or is liable to be present in the premises and its condition, taking full account of building plans or other relevant information, the age of the building and inspecting those parts of the premises which are reasonably accessible. (Must presume that materials contain asbestos unless strong evidence to the contrary.) (See MDHS 100 for guidance on asbestos surveys.)
Review	Review assessment if significant change to premises or suspect that it is no longer valid and record conclusions of each review.
Records	Keep an up-to-date written record of the location, type (where known), form and condition of ACMs.
Risk assessment	Where asbestos is or is liable to be present assess the risk of exposure from known and presumed ACMs.
Management plan (see also next page)	Prepare and implement a written plan, identifying those parts of the premises concerned, specifying measures for managing the risk including adequate measures for properly maintaining asbestos or where necessary, its safe removal.
Provide information to others	Ensure the plan includes adequate measures to ensure that information about the location and condition of any asbestos is provided to every person likely to disturb it and is made available to the emergency services.
Review and monitor	Regularly review and monitor the plan to ensure it is valid and that the measures specified are implemented and that these are recorded.

Management plan

The management plan is an important legal document which in addition to its health and safety significance will be required to be made available to, and inspected by, a variety of interested parties.

The absence of such a document may thus have significant financial implications or affect the liquidity of the premises as an asset.

A plan is not required when the assessment whether asbestos is present or is liable to be present in the premises confirms that it is not. For example, the building is new and there is confirmation from the project team that asbestos has not been used in its construction.

Nevertheless a record must be kept of the assessment carried out and its conclusion to show to an inspector or prospective purchaser or occupant.

The dutyholder owns and is responsible for the safekeeping of the plan, however he is obliged to make the information available 'at a justifiable and reasonable cost' to anyone who is likely to disturb asbestos and this includes new owners or occupants.

(See HSE publication *A comprehensive guide to managing asbestos in premises* HSG227.)

Duty to cooperate

Every person has a duty to cooperate with the dutyholder so far as is necessary to enable the dutyholder to comply with his or her duties under regulation 4.

This includes the landlord, tenants, occupants, managing agent, contractors, designers and planning supervisor.

The possible scenarios envisaged by the ACOP include:

- ❖ anyone with relevant information on the presence (or absence) of asbestos; and

- ❖ anyone who controls parts of the premises to which access will be necessary to facilitate the survey and management of asbestos (i.e. its removal or treatment or periodic inspection).

Cooperation does not extend to paying the whole or even part of the costs associated with the management of the risks of asbestos by the dutyholder(s), who must meet these personally.

Where there is more than one dutyholder for premises, the costs of compliance will be apportioned according to the terms of any lease or contract determining the obligation to any extent for repair and maintenance of the premises.

If there is no such documentation then the apportionment of costs will be based on the extent to which parties exercise physical control over the premises.

In the final analysis, the courts will decide financial responsibility using the principles outlined above.

Guidance in the ACOP states that architects, surveyors or building contractors who were involved in the construction or maintenance of the building and who may have information that is relevant 'would be expected to make this available at a justifiable and reasonable cost'.

The duty to cooperate is not subject to any limitation or exclusion, thus there is an obligation to do whatever is necessary to cooperate with the dutyholder.

Short lease tenants, licensees or other occupants who control access, but do not have any contractual maintenance liabilities would be required to permit the landlord access to fulfil his duties.

In June 2003, RICS published a guidance note *Asbestos and its implications for members and their clients* (ISBN 1 84219 063 6).

High Alumina Cement concrete

Background

The manufacture of High Alumina Cement (HAC) commenced in the United Kingdom in 1925 to provide concrete that would resist chemical attack, particularly for marine applications. This cement developed high early strength, although its relatively high cost prevented extensive use.

During the late 1950s and 1960s the main use of HAC was for the manufacture of precast prestressed components which could be manufactured quickly, therefore offsetting the additional cost of the material.

The earliest UK failures were experienced during 1973–74 when several school roofs collapsed. There followed considerable investigation and testing. In 1975, the Building Regulations Advisory Committee (BRAC) Subcommittee P published design criteria to be used in checking the adequacy of buildings containing HAC structural members. The two main aspects of the investigation were, firstly, a strength assessment and, secondly, a durability assessment.

In 1976 HAC concrete was banned for structural use.

Problems with HAC

HAC concrete undergoes a mineralogical change known as conversion. This conversion is accompanied by a loss of strength and increased porosity. Consequently there is also a reduction in resistance to chemical attack. The higher the temperature during the casting of the concrete, the more quickly conversion takes place.

The relationship between conversion and strength is complex, however the strength of highly converted concrete is very variable and is substantially less than its initial strength. Typically the original design strength of $60N/mm^2$ may be reduced to $21N/mm^2$.

Highly converted HAC concrete is vulnerable to acid, alkaline and sulphate attack. For this to take place water as well as the chemicals must have been present persistently over a long period of time at normal temperatures. Chemical attack is usually very localised in nature and the concrete typically degenerates to a chocolate brown colour and becomes very friable, often due to sulphate attack.

Given the sensitivity to moisture the greatest risk therefore lies in the use of HAC concrete in roof members. It is therefore important to appraise the condition of the concrete and any waterproof coverings before making any formal judgement as to the remedial work required.

In a warm and moist environment there is the possibility of chemical action occurring where high alkali levels may be present as a consequence of the use of certain types of aggregate or where alkalis may have ingressed from plasters, screeds and woodwool slabs. In such circumstances, HAC is vulnerable to chemical attack.

Investigation

There are three generic stages in an investigation, namely:

- ❖ Stage 1 – identification
- ❖ Stage 2 – strength assessment
- ❖ Stage 3 – durability assessment.

A Stage 2 strength assessment is required to determine if the precast concrete members have sufficient structural capacity, even at the reduced fully converted strength, to safely withstand the applied loading. Subcommittee P sets out the guidelines for concrete strength based on

21N/mm². The strength assessment requires the section properties of the beam to be established. Thereafter the structural strength of the element can be calculated. In cases where the section properties are unknown, or cannot be determined by investigation, then assessments are limited to determining the concrete strength using near-to-surface tests.

A Stage 3 durability assessment is required to determine the long-term durability where affected by chemical attack and reinforcement corrosion. Testing can be undertaken to determine the presence of alkalis and sulphates. Laboratory testing may be supplemented by a detailed visual inspection and the removal of lump samples for petrographic examination. A durability assessment should also include a visual examination of the reinforcing steel where lump samples are removed. In recent years it has been found that HAC is less durable than members containing ordinary Portland cement.

Assessment

Putting all of this in context, however, there have been no recorded instances in this country of a failure of a floor incorporating HAC concrete. It is important to know that in the case of the original historic failures, manufacturing faults were eventually discovered. The greatest reduction in strength occurred where a high water content was present during the period of mixing and high temperatures took place during curing.

Of the five failures or new failures of roof constructions, two did not directly involve the quality of the concrete, one was aggravated by chemical attack and two were apparently due to defective cement which should have been rejected at the time of casting. On no occasion has weakening of the concrete due to conversion been the sole cause of failure.

Chlorides

The presence of chlorides, whether added as calcium chloride or ingressed as de-icing salts, may result in 'chloride induced corrosion' and is less common than corrosion caused by low cover. When chloride corrosion does occur its effects may be wide ranging including a reduction in structural capacity.

Natural alkalinity of concrete

Steel does not corrode when embedded in highly alkaline concrete despite high moisture levels in the concrete because a passive film forms on the steel and remains intact as long as the concrete surrounding the bar remains highly alkaline.

Chloride induced corrosion

Corrosion may occur in concrete that contains sufficient chlorides even if it is not carbonated or showing visible signs of deterioration.

The presence of free chloride ions within the pore structure of the concrete interferes with the passive protective film formed naturally on reinforcing steel.

Chloride ions exist in two forms in concrete, namely free chloride ions, mainly found in the capillary pore water, and combined chloride ions which result from the reaction between chloride and the cement hydration process. These occur in proportions that depend on when the chloride entered the concrete. If chloride was introduced at mixing, for example, as calcium chloride, approximately 90% may form harmless complexes leaving only 10% as free chloride ions. If, on the other hand, sea water or de-icing salts penetrate the surface of the concrete, the ratio of free to combined chloride may be 50:50.

The corrosive effect of chlorides is significantly affected therefore by the presence of free chlorides. The effects of chlorides are classified in terms of risk of corrosion because in certain conditions even low levels of chloride may pose some risk. The permissible level of chloride added at mixing specified in BS 8110 is 0.4% by weight of cement. For pre-stressed concrete the level is lower at 0.06%. The overall effect of reinforcement corrosion caused by chlorides must therefore be considered with the depth of reinforcement and the depth of carbonation.

There are two methods by which chlorides can be the cause of corrosion in reinforced concrete:

- ❖ as cast-in chloride, usually calcium chloride added at the time of mixing or from sea-dredged aggregates; and
- ❖ as ingressed chloride, i.e. by the penetration of the outer surface of the concrete from de-icing salts.

Chloride induced corrosion results in localised breakdown of the passive film rather than the widespread deterioration that occurs with carbonation. The result is rapid corrosion of the metal at the anode leading to the formation of a 'pit' in the bar surface and significant loss of cross sectional area. This is known as 'pitting corrosion'. Occasionally a bar may be completely eaten through.

Chloride induced corrosion may occur even in apparently benign conditions where the concrete quality appears to be satisfactory. Even if there is poor oxygen supply reinforcement corrosion may still take place. Failure of reinforcement may therefore occur without any visual sign of cracking or spalling.

All aggregates used commonly for concrete mixing contain a background level of chlorides usually less than 0.06% by weight of cement. The use of calcium chloride as an accelerating additive at the time of mixing was popular during the 1950s and 1960s. It was used in precasting yards to speed up the re-use of expensive moulds and was used on site during cold weather to increase the rate of gain in strength. The use of calcium chloride additive was banned in 1977. The presence of calcium chloride cast-in within the mix usually attracts a chloride level significantly greater than 0.4% by weight of cement. Ingressed chlorides through the outer surface of the concrete are variable in nature. However the use of de-icing salts on, for example, external staircases and balconies is popular and may result in localised high concentrations of chlorides in excess of 1.0% by weight of cement. Concentrations of ingressed chlorides on the top surface of a car park deck may typically occur up to 3 or 4%.

The presence of calcium chloride is further exaggerated by the presence of deep carbonation. Carbonation releases combined chlorides into solution to form free chloride ions, thus increasing the likelihood of corrosion. For this reason many properties built approximately 20–30 years ago may only now start causing problems.

Risk assessment

Guidance on assessing the risk of reinforcement corrosion is provided by the BRE in Digest 444 Part 2. Here the risk of corrosion for structures of various ages is presented in the range negligible, to extremely high risk. Factors affecting the risk assessment are either a dry or damp environment, the depth of carbonation and of course the level of chlorides present.

Repair

The successful repair of chloride induced corrosion is notoriously difficult because of the tendency for new corrosion cells to form at the boundary of the repair. This mechanism is called 'incipient anode effect' and should be minimised by removing, wherever possible, all concrete with significant chloride contamination. In recent years the introduction of proprietary sacrificial zinc anodes embedded within the patch repair and attached to the reinforcement can help to reduce this effect. For high levels of chlorides and long-term protection this may not be sufficient.

For heavily chloride contaminated structures, particularly car parks, the only tried and tested long term solution is cathodic protection. The cost and complexity of installing cathodic protection is not usually warranted within building structures. A variation of cathodic protection is desalination – a short-term process using higher current densities than cathodic protection. Migrating corrosion inhibitors have found some success; these are penetrating surface coatings applied under strict conditions.

Alkali aggregate reactions – ASR

ASR – the problem

Alkali aggregate reactions, of which alkali silica reactions (ASR) are only one variant, are relatively uncommon in construction in this country and tend to occur in civil engineering structures rather than conventional buildings.

Concrete is a highly alkaline material: it follows that pore water contained within the concrete will also be highly alkaline, and can, given the correct combination of conditions, react with certain types of aggregate to produce a gel.

The gel imbibes water, expands and can cause the concrete to crack or disrupt. Sometimes a pattern of 'map' cracking occurs but in others small 'pop-outs' can occur – rather like concrete with acne. The durability of the concrete can thus be compromised and in extreme cases the tensile strength of the concrete component can be reduced.

For ASR to occur, three factors must be present. Remove one of the following three factors and ASR will not take place:

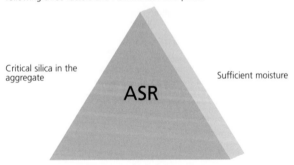

Critical silica in the aggregate

Sufficient moisture

ASR

High alkalinity

Most of the aggregates used in the UK are considered to be of 'normal' reactivity rather than high reactivity, although there are some troublesome types in the South-West.

The Building Research Establishment (BRE) and the Concrete Society have prepared guidelines and flow charts to assist the designer in the selection of appropriate measures to reduce the risk of ASR. By adopting a 'sodium oxide equivalent' scale, cement can be classified according to low, moderate or high alkalinity. High alkalinity cement means an equivalent of 0.75% sodium oxide equivalent or greater. When dealing with the total alkali content of concrete it is usual to consider the equivalent sodium oxide in the concrete expressed as kilogrammes per cubic metre (kg/m³).

However, the use of cement at high risk does not necessarily mean that ASR is inevitable. For the reasons given above, two other factors must be present. Where the aggregate was sea-dredged, marine flint classified in accordance with current guidelines as being of normal reactivity, it would present no particular concerns when used in combination with highly alkaline cement. A combination of normal reactivity aggregate with high alkalinity cement is permissible, if the total alkalinity of the concrete is kept within certain limits. However, good construction practice dictates that for normally reactive aggregates, the total alkali content of the concrete should not exceed 3.0kg/m³.

What if ASR occurs?

Concrete Society Report 30 and Part 4 of BRE Digest 330 are mainly concerned with the selection of materials to reduce the risk of ASR occurring. The available records seem to point to a low risk of the development of ASR, but it will be remembered that the third component necessary for the formation of a reaction is sufficient moisture.

If the concrete was reinforced, then any potentially expansive reactions in the concrete could be restrained (the degree of restraint depending upon the arrangement of the reinforcement).

A risk assessment based approach to analysis is advocated – taking into account whether the concrete is wet or dry, restrained with reinforcement or not and finally the consequences of failure – the structural significance of a component. The structural significance of an element is a function of the consequences of its failure. These are judged to be slight or significant as defined below:

❖ slight – the consequences of structural failure are either not serious or are localised to the extent that a serious situation is not anticipated; and

❖ significant – if there is risk to life and limb or a considerable risk of serious damage to property.

Further information

BRE Digest 330, *Alkali-silica reaction in concrete*

Structural effects of alkali-silica reaction: Technical guidance on the appraisal of existing structures, Institute of Structural Engineers, 1992

Concrete Society Report 30, *Alkali-silica reaction – Minimizing the risk of damage* (3rd edition), TR30, 1999

Investigating Hazardous and Deleterious Building Materials, Rushton, T., RICS Books, 2006

Corrosion of metals

Bi-metallic corrosion

Bi-metallic or galvanic corrosion is experienced when two dissimilar materials are in electrical contact and are bridged by an electrolyte. The electrolyte could be water containing salt, acid or a combustion product. The electrolytic cells comprise a series of positive anodes and negative cathodes between which current flows and at which electrochemical reactions take place. The degree to which a metal is subject to this form of attack is determined by the difference in voltage potential between two metals, the amount of moisture present, the relative areas of contact, the corrodent concerned and whether either or both of the metals have naturally occurring oxide films.

If it is necessary to use dissimilar materials they should be isolated with washers of a non-conductive material, e.g. neoprene, PTFE, SRBF, etc. Painting of the contact surfaces with bitumen is an alternative, but less reliable, solution.

PD 6484:1979 *Commentary on corrosion at bimetallic contacts and its alleviation* sets out helpful guidance and detailed tables showing the corrosion of steels resulting from contact with other metals.

The electrochemical series

The further apart two metals appear in the following table the more actively the two metals will react when placed in contact in a slightly acid aqueous solution.

Metal	Chemical symbol	Normal electrode potential (volts)
'Noble' or Cathodic, i.e. protected end		
Gold	Au	+1.42
Platinum	Pt	+1.20
Silver	Ag	+0.80
Mercury	Hg	+0.80
Copper	Cu	+0.345
Lead	Pb	-0.125
Tin	Sn	-0.135
Nickel	Ni	-0.24
Cadmium	Cd	-0.40
Iron	Fe	-0.44
Chromium	Cr	-0.71
Zinc	Zn	-0.76
Aluminium	Al	-1.66
Magnesium	Mg	-2.38
Sodium	Na	-2.71
Potassium	K	-2.92
Lithium	Li	-3.02
'Base' or Anodic, i.e. corroded end		

Effects of bi-metallic combinations

For cladding supports, aluminium alloys are often employed. When aluminium and stainless steel are in contact, there is the potential for corrosion to occur. The extent of corrosion will depend upon the respective sizes of the two metal components.

For example, large aluminium fitting with small stainless steel bolt: little corrosion.

Filiform corrosion (on coated aluminium)

This variety of corrosion can be found in the form of long filaments of growth between aluminium and its particular paint coating. The depth of penetration of this corrosion is generally found to be 10–20μm and is therefore considered to be cosmetic rather than structural. The deterioration process is primarily caused by a break or defect in the coating itself and is most commonly found in moist or wet environments (which may be internal or external) where sections of coated aluminium have been cut to form joints, or sections of cladding have been cut, drilled or damaged. Even the most microscopic of marks or breaks in the paint effectively cause the formation of a battery circuit between the exposed metal and adjoining sections which are protected from the air. The corrosion takes the appearance of a worm trail as the 'battery cell' moves along the surface of the aluminium underneath the paint.

Liquid waterproofing systems

Description

Advances in technology over the last 30 years or so have resulted in the development of many polymer-based roofing materials, offering favourable advantages to petroleum-based systems, which, since the 1970s oil crisis, have become increasingly expensive and in some cases of unpredictable quality. Furthermore, rising labour costs have resulted in a need to gain a competitive edge by providing materials that can be laid quickly and efficiently, without necessarily the intensive labour associated, for example, with built up felt (BUR) roofing applications.

But not only have materials had to cope with changes in the cost and nature of raw products, the method of forming buildings has changed: lightweight, highly insulated structures with increased propensities for movement place very onerous demands on roof membranes, which only some systems are capable of accommodating. Most of the new roofing materials are polymeric in nature, meaning that they are made up of many (poly) molecules (mer) that are linked together in a chain – in effect forming very large molecules of different chemicals, for example, poly(propylene) or poly(isoprene).

Broad categories

European Technical Approvals (ETAs) exist for the following:

- ❖ polymer modified bitumen emulsions and solutions;
- ❖ glass reinforced resilient unsaturated resins;
- ❖ flexible unsaturated polyester resins;
- ❖ hot applied polymer modified bitumen;
- ❖ polyurethanes;
- ❖ bitumen emulsions and solutions; and
- ❖ water dispersible polymers.

In addition, solvent-based acrylic roofing systems are available: these are not covered by ETAs and are often used for emergency repairs. Most of the above products are cold-applied, but polymer modified bitumens are very popular for new build applications whereas cold-applied materials are generally (but not exclusively) used for remedial works. Both have good performance characteristics and, if properly laid, a life expectancy in excess of 30 years would not be an unreasonable expectation, although as with most materials this is highly subject to workmanship, protection, maintenance, etc. An 'as installed' cost for a two-part, fleece reinforced polyurethane membrane could be somewhere in the region of £45–£50 per m² and whilst hot-applied systems used to be more expensive (because of the need for protection layers) roofing contractors now report that costs are becoming comparable.

Hot-applied rubberised bitumen membranes

By dispersing virgin or reclaimed rubber in asphalt together with limestone powder, oil and styrene butadiene styrene (SBS) it is possible to manufacture a very flexible roofing membrane that can form a seamless membrane about 3–4.5mm thick. Some formulations include an additional spun bond polyester fabric interlayer with a further 3mm layer to form a roofing system. However, these materials are not usually resistant to UV light and so it is important to add a bonded membrane or alternatively a ballasted insulation layer to provide mechanical and solar protection.

The materials are usually supplied as cakes wrapped in polyethelene wrapping which are melted in a heater to around 200°C. The melt is discharged from the heater into a suitable container and applied to the roof using long-handled, rubber-bladed squeegees.

Prior to application, the roof surface must be free from contaminants. Liquid membranes depend upon a bond to the surface, so all traces of dust, grease and oil must be removed. Concrete surfaces are usually primed with a suitable asphaltic solution.

Cold-applied liquid membranes

These membranes are polymeric compositions with one or more ingredients, such as modified asphalt or coal tar pitch, or various resins or elastomers, such as polyurethane, dibromobutadiene, silicone or acrylic. The bitumen-based solutions are usually applied as emulsions, brushed or rolled in place.

Resin-based systems can often be supplied in different formulations to give 'guaranteed' life expectancies of up to 25 years. These materials can also be dressed with sand or mineral granules to provide slip resistance, and for this reason are often used for waterproofing car park decks where a degree of friction is desirable and where various colour pigments can be used to advantage.

Cold-applied systems tend to be used for remedial operations, with the clear advantage that heat producing appliances are not required, and the membrane can be sprayed over existing finishes without the need for a temporary roof. The ability to form complicated weathering details with the minimum effort places the materials at a distinct advantage over BUR systems. Like hot-applied systems, it is usual to reinforce the membrane with a polyester fleece sandwiched between two layers of waterproofing. Some coatings require periodic refresher coats.

Limitations

Whilst both hot- and cold-applied systems are relatively easy to lay, this does not mean that they are tolerant of lower levels of workmanship. Until recently, many systems could be supplied and laid only by licensed contractors using trained operatives. In recent years, the market has opened up and quality control standards have (in some cases) not met expectations. Most systems require trained operators for their proper installation whilst the European Liquid Waterproofing Association is working hard to introduce a skills card system to encourage appropriate levels of workmanship. Most systems require good substrate preparation – clear of sawdust, swarf, dirt, hydrocarbons or organic materials, whilst the maintenance of the correct dry-film thickness is important to ensuring future durability. Similarly, many products have only a limited shelf life before they deteriorate (six months or so).

From a designer's point of view, a failure to consider the usual principles of flat roofing design, rainwater disposal and the design of roof penetrations will lead to failure in much the same way as it would using more traditional methods. Similarly, because one of the great benefits of liquid membranes is their ability to bond to the substrate (and hence limit the propensity of water to travel through a sheathing layer) it is vital to ensure that the correct level of preparation is used and that the correct primers are employed. Compatibility with the substrate (and any likely contamination of the surface) must be established at the outset.

Generally speaking, all roofing materials must, for their service life, remain watertight, resist stresses arising from application and service and withstand weather factors such as rain, hail, thermal shocks, UV light, etc.

In particular, when selecting a material, specifiers should consider:

- ❖ the ability of the material to deal with tensile stresses at places of concentrated movement, initiated, for example, by shrinkage in low temperature or creep during hot weather;

- ❖ ability to bridge cracks – particularly those that open and close cyclically as a result of changes in temperature or structural movements (if a membrane is fully bonded, the percentage elongation over say a 3mm crack is very high);

- ❖ ability to withstand heat and UV light;

- ❖ static and dynamic puncture resistance – the ability to withstand site damage due to an irregular substrate, construction traffic, falling loads (hail, dropped tools, etc.);

- ❖ compatibility with other materials; and

- ❖ risk of puncturing by plant growth (the roots of plants such as container grown bamboos can be highly invasive).

Health and safety

The generic precautions recommended in the *Health and Safety at Work etc. Act* and the *Control of Substances Hazardous to Health Regulations* (COSHH) apply to all liquid roofing materials. However, in some cases polyurethane resins can produce very unpleasant fumes, and if there is a danger of fumes being drawn into a building, one could well find that the occupants will protest volubly. In such circumstances, a solvent free membrane might be a safer option, although the life expectancy of these materials has yet to be proven by direct experience over, say, 30 years.

Where disposal is concerned, liquid waterproof systems must not be allowed to contaminate drains or water systems, or be buried where surface water may be affected.

Things to watch out for

Whilst the lack of obvious seams makes it easy to determine whether a liquid membrane has been installed, identifying the particular nature of the membrane is not always easy. Hot-applied systems are almost always protected against sunlight, whilst polyurethanes are usually of light, reflective colours with no additional protection. Look out for the following:

- ❖ adequacy of protection systems;

- ❖ evidence of chemical or biological attack – unusual colouring or mottling, softening and degradation;

- ❖ pinholing or mechanical damage;

- ❖ tearing;

- ❖ blistering;

- ❖ plant (root damage);

- ❖ adequacy of weathering details; and

- ❖ loss of adhesion.

Conclusions

Liquid applied systems offer real advantages over traditional asphalt membranes or built-up felt roofing. Good durability, flexibility and ease of detailing are attractive features, but in all cases they are no substitute for proper and considered good design.

Further information

The European Liquid Waterproofing Association (www.elwassociation.org.uk) publish a series of useful guidance notes on the various types of liquid membrane, their application and workmanship.

Canadian Building Digest 235, *Single ply membranes*, gives useful background information on performance characteristics and selection.

The National Federation of Roofing Contractors (www.nfrc.co.uk) publish several guides to the safe use of liquid materials.

The Flat Roofing Alliance (www.fra.org.uk) publish a code of practice for remedial works.

Flat roofs with continuously supported coverings – Code of practice, BS 6229:2003, BSI.

BLP Construction Durability Database www.componentlife.com

This section is based on an article originally written by Trevor Rushton for the RICS *Building Surveying Journal* (July 2006 edition), copyright RICS. Material is reproduced here with permission from RICS.

Building defects

Materials and defects

Common defects in commercial and residential properties

Period	Typical problem	Possible effects
Pre 1900	Failed or lack of damp-proof course	Rising dampness, penetrating damp, efflorescence on plaster, decay to skirtings and the like
	Poor ventilation of floor voids	Decay in wall plates, joists, etc.
	Poorly fitting sash windows, risk of decay within window reveals, water penetration beneath sub-sills	Draughty or dangerous operation, decay in concealed areas, lack of security
	Damp penetration through 225mm brick walls	Damage to plaster and finishes, decay to wall plates and bonding timbers
	Poor quality repairs to roofs and gutters	Risk of timber decay
	Roof covered with concrete interlocking tiles	Overloading of roof structure, bowing of rafters and purlins, roof spread
	Lack of restraint to flank walls	Bulging or instability, associated cracking on front and rear elevations
	Settlement of internal partitions	Plaster damage, distortion in floors and door openings
	Alterations to trussed (loadbearing) partitions	Removal of support gives rise to distortions in floors, reduction of loadbearing capacity and possible risk of collapse
	Failure of brick arches and timber lintels	Cracking and distortion of brickwork above window heads
	Defective rainwater goods	Risk of decay in built-in timbers
	Settlement of bay windows	Internal cosmetic damage, distortion in loadbearing elements
	Insect attack, particularly in poorly ventilated and damp areas such as floor and roof voids	Loss of strength if particularly badly affected
	Lead water mains	Hazardous to health – partly depends on plumbsolvency of the water
	Delamination of brick skins	Bulging of brickwork

Period	Typical problem	Possible effects
1900–1939	Wall tie failure in cavity brickwork	Bulging of brickwork, horizontal cracking or 'pagoda effect'
	Delamination of render finishes to walls	Cracking and bulging of render, detachment of same
	Corrosion of roofing nails	Slipping of tiles
	Lead water mains	Possibly hazardous to health
	Outdated electrical services	Possibly dangerous
	Corroded rainwater goods	Risk of decay in built in timbers, damp penetration
	Corroded galvanised steel or steel windows	Cracked glazing, high maintenance costs
	Timber joinery	Decay to cills and softwood frames

Period	Typical problem	Possible effects
1945–1970	Poor installation of lateral bracing to trussed rafters	Lack of restraint to gables, lateral buckling of trusses
	Poor cavity tray details	Water ingress
	Wall tie failure	Bulging of brickwork
	Poor quality jointing	Decay of external joinery

Period	Typical problem	Possible effects
All	Over notching of floor joists	Reduction in strength, sagging
	Removal of chimney breasts	Possible lack of support
	Provision of insulation, blocking ventilation paths	Condensation
	Blocking of airbricks	Lack of ventilation, risk of decay
	Removal of loadbearing walls or walls affording stability	Possible long term structural consequences
	Removal of, or planting of, trees or large shrubs	Possible desiccation or re-hydration of subsoil, damage to drains or foundations
	Replacement windows	Poor support to bay windows, distortion of brickwork

Problem areas with 1960s and 1970s buildings

The 1960s saw a frantic period of innovation and experimentation. The need for replacement housing following the Second World War gave rise to the development of numerous system types using innovative materials. Construction had started to drift toward an assembly process and away from traditional craft-based skills.

Some 1960s construction was appallingly bad, for example, some high rise social housing, but other schemes were of a very high standard using good quality and durable materials. Many buildings are now facing or have undergone major refurbishment or change of use (for example, office to housing or hostel accommodation), but many examples of good and bad construction remain.

Rather than look at typical problems associated with each style of building, this list overleaf is intended to give a very brief introduction to a number of common or typical materials or construction faults. The list is not exhaustive.

Brief résumé of some problems

Key to common building types – these are indicative only:

> W = warehouse or industrial
> O = Office or commercial developments
> H = Housing
> A = All types.

Item, element or material	Effects
Aluminum sash windows (O) A common type of window was the vertical sliding sash. Instead of the vision glazing being held in a frame, the glass ran in aluminium tracks, with horizontal top and bottom frame members clipped onto the glass. Spring balances were used to hold the windows open.	By now, these windows will be very worn. Defects in the springs or breakage of the glass can lead to the ejection of an entire sash window – clearly a health and safety issue. Treat these windows with caution.
Asbestos (A) Very common in 1960s buildings. Chrysotile (white) for some insulation boards, roof sheets, water tanks, cill boards, etc. Artex, floor tiles, partition wall linings, fire doors, etc. may also have a content. Amosite (brown) used as insulating boards, fire protection or fire breaks, behind perimeter heaters, partitions, etc. Crocidolite (blue) often paste-applied friable material in boiler rooms, pipework, calorifiers, etc.	Major health risks depending on type, location, risk of disturbance. Deleterious material – detection, management and control are highly regulated. Ask for a copy of the asbestos register.
Asphalt roofs (O) These could be of quite good quality and may have performed well if laid on a concrete deck.	The lack of insulation would have helped to reduce temperature ranges and so restrict thermal movements.
Calcium chloride concrete additive (A) Often used by manufacturers of precast elements or for concreting in cold weather. Enables rapid set and removal of moulds. Can also be found in brickwork mortar. Use of unwashed sea dredged aggregates may have led to chloride contamination.	Considered a deleterious material. Creates conditions of high electrical conductivity in the concrete with consequent high risk of corrosion of steel reinforcement. Very difficult to repair effectively. Look out for spalling concrete and very black, stained steel. Can result in severe pitting corrosion without disruption of the surface of the concrete. Tests should always be recommended. Since about 1978, this material should not have been used. In brickwork, risk of corrosion of wall ties. Exposure to de-icing salts, salt spray, etc. can also be very damaging. Watch out for coastal locations, car parks, road bridges, etc.

Item, element or material	Effects
Calcium silicate bricks (A) A smooth, often creamy coloured brick made from lime, sand and flint. Small particles of flint can sometimes be seen in cut bricks or weathered surfaces. Can be mistaken for concrete bricks (see below). Widespread use in 1960s and 1970s and still manufactured and gaining popularity again.  Flank wall of calcium silicate bricks – shrinkage cracking.	Prone to shrinkage (unlike clay bricks which expand after laying). If movement control joints are missed or badly spaced (which they often were) diagonal cracking can occur. Thermal or moisture cracking often visible at changes in the size of panels, eg long runs below windows coinciding with short sections between windows. Look out for thin bed cracks and wider cracks to vertical joints. Do not confuse with subsidence cracking or corrosion of steel frame. Use as a backing to clay brickwork likely to cause problems as a result of expansion of clay brick and contraction of calcium silicate brick.
Cold bridging and condensation (A) Poor insulation standards led to problems with severe cold bridging particularly in housing where humidity levels are higher. Polystyrene insulation was sometimes used but this was usually no more than 25mm thick. In the mid to late 1970s thermal insulation standards were increased, particularly in industrial buildings.	Watch out for cold bridging around balcony structures and precast lintels. Provision of insulation within industrial buildings resulted in a spate of condensation problems within roofs. Cold night sky radiation gave rise to condensation on the underside of metal roofing, while poor application of vapour control layers meant that problems were exacerbated.
Cold flat roof construction (A) Little thought was given to vapour control or for that matter roof insulation. It was common to provide sealed flat roof construction with minimal insulation and sometimes a foil backed plasterboard ceiling lining. Ventilation to the roof void was often ignored. Built-up felt roofs were often asbestos based, but had a life of around 15 years and no more. For this reason most felt roofs would have been replaced by now.	Risk of condensation occurring, with subsequent risk of decay to roof decking or to structure. 

Item, element or material	Effects
Concrete (A) Can be of mixed quality, sometimes poorly compacted and with lack of cover to steel reinforcement. Under codes, depth of cover for external work should have been circa 40mm.	Sometimes poor durability, corrosion due to the effects of carbonation or chloride content. Tests should be recommended. Poor curing methods could mean lack of durability. Calcium chloride added as an accelerator either in precast or in situ work.  Waffle slab showing the effects of chloride attack.
Concrete boot lintels (A) Concrete lintels designed to have a projecting nib to support the outer leaf, and built only into the inner leaf, to provide a neat appearance externally.	Rotation of the lintel under eccentric load, creating diagonal cracking to the brickwork above the window. Other signs are opening of the bed joint immediately above lintels and splitting of the reveal brickwork immediately beneath. Once rotation has taken place, brickwork will tend to arch over the opening, thus relieving some of the load on the lintel. Cracks can then be repointed.
Concrete bricks (A) Similar in appearance to calcium silicate brick but often used in dark brown, dark red or dark grey variants. Harder and coarser texture than calcium silicate bricks.	Suffer from similar shrinkage related problems. Can be hard to differentiate between these and calcium silicate bricks, but may be harder and contain small particles of visible aggregate.
Corrugated 'big six' asbestos cement sheet (W) Often found on industrial buildings and warehouses well into the 1970s. Name given as a result of the 6-inch profile, but in fact 'big six' was one of several different profiles of sheet. Often based on an asbestos content of around 12-15% chrysotile, (white asbestos) with profiled eaves and ridge pieces and hook bolt fastenings. By the end of the	Obvious health risks from fibre release. Friable surface, and very fragile – never walk on such a covering without crawling boards. Corrosion of hook bolts will cause sheeting to split. Often coated with bitumen or rubber solutions as a remedial treatment. Be very cautious of the effectiveness of these treatments.

Item, element or material	Effects
1970s insulation was being added to the roof construction and this brought about condensation problems.	
	Rigid foam spacers were sometimes used below cement fibre sheeting in order to create a void into which insulation could be placed. The rigid foam compresses with time and occasional traffic loads, leading to 'chattering' of the roof sheets and possible water ingress.
External ceramic tiling (O) See 'mosaic tesserae'. Tiles were often prism shaped or ridged in some way.	Similar problems to mosaic tesserae in terms of delamination of background materials.
Flat concrete floor slabs (Plate floors) (O,W) Fairly thin slabs with mushroom head thickening around column heads.	Very high shear stress around column head has been found to be cause of structural failure. Beware of flat slab car park construction – recent major collapse of car park of flat slab construction.
GRC Lightweight cladding panels, balustrade panels, permanent shutters, planters.	Early forms of GRC contained fibres that deteriorated in alkaline conditions. Loss of strength, cracking and bowing can result. Later alkaline resistant types (Cem-fil) perform better.
High alumina cement concrete (O,W) Often used in precast and prestressed work rather than in situ work. Mainly (but not exclusively) for roof and floor beams. X and I profiles were common. Some variants for precast factory units (portals and purlins). Sometimes used to form an in situ stitch between two precast beam members or column to beam connections. Developed high early strength. Can have a brownish tinge.	Loses strength with age. Susceptible to chemical attack in damp conditions and contact with gypsum plaster. Strength and durability assessments to be recommended. Since 1974 the material should not have been used in buildings. Considered to be a deleterious material. Several roof failures in the 1970s, but no known cases of flooring collapse. 

Item, element or material	Effects
Hollow clay pot floors (O) Quite common during the 1960s. Concrete poured between pots and in the form of a topping. Sometimes screed could be structural. In other case, non-structural screeds may have been removed to gain additional load or headroom. 	Watch out for clay spacer tiles between the pots. These can conceal honeycombing of the concrete rib, lack of fire protection, durability or strength. Removal of tiles and Gunnite repairs may be necessary. Concrete topping and rib  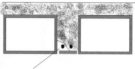 Risk of voiding
Lack of movement control joints (A) Cement masonry walls are prone to thermal and moisture movements. Cement mortar is less flexible than older lime mortars, and the stresses induced by thermal movement are relieved by cracking. Centres of joints depend on nature of brick, size and shape of panel, etc. Lack of joints was common in 1960s buildings.	Oversailing of brickwork on dpc, particularly in warehouses. Also watch out for joints that have been filled with Flexcell impregnated board, as this is not very compressible and can reduce the benefit of a joint. Early sealants were also resinous and could lead to staining of adjoining surfaces. Hardening and embrittlement of joint sealants to be expected now.
Large panel buildings (H) A number of different systems were constructed. Large panels formed the external enclosure and also supported precast floor planks or slabs. Connection details were made on site with wire hoops and in situ work. The design of joints in panel systems was critical in the success or failure of the system. A variety of types were often employed, in some cases using baffles in the form of open drained joints or face sealed joints using mastic or neoprene gaskets. The success of the building from a structural point of view relies on the connection between the individual panels The ability to withstand local damage by means of alternative load paths is critical.	Risk of disproportionate collapse – see Ronan Point disaster. Following this, high-rise blocks were strengthened. Some low-rise blocks may not have been checked. Poor quality control of structural connections led to weakness, poor fire stopping or corrosion risk. Possible lack of tying in of precast components. See 'Tying-in' later. Large panel systems suffer from many of the defects described previously; the more important being rain penetration, corrosion of reinforcement, poor thermal insulation, distortion or physical damage to panels. Calcium chloride was not used in most precast systems although in some types it was added on a batch by batch basis to aid manufacture perhaps where there were particular programming problems. Thus the inclusion of the material is unpredictable. The most common faults with these

Item, element or material	Effects
	types of systems relates to the gradual deterioration of either the baffle, particularly where butyl rubber was used, ageing of the sealants or ageing of gaskets in face sealed joints. Misplacement of baffles or insufficiently sized baffles in wide joints can lead to water penetration.
	It is quite common to find that quality control standards during manufacture were not up to scratch, with the result that reinforcement was commonly misplaced in the fabrication of the concrete panels. This later led to corrosion of the reinforcement and spalling of the concrete.
	In many cases dry packing used between infill concrete and the panel above is missing or poorly compacted, so that vertical loads are transferred only on the bolt fastenings, resulting in localised cracking around fixing positions.
	In the long term, panels can distort generally as a result of shrinkage in the concrete structure behind and as a result of normal thermal movements in the building as a whole. This can lead to damage at joints, displacement of seals and baffles and subsequent water penetration. Furthermore, smoke stopping between floors and compartments can be damaged with the result that in a fire, smoke can transfer rapidly between occupancies or zones.
Mineralite render (O) A thin (2-5mm) coating of fine grained minerals with a textured surface. Often applied to exposed concrete columns and beams or in larger areas such as spandrel panels. Variety of colours available.	Beware of adhesion failure – can be widespread. Difficult to match repairs.

Item, element or material	Effects
Mosaic tesserae (O) A common finish comprising small (25mm square) ceramic or glass tiles applied to a render background. Often supplied in paper backed sheets of around 300x300 to facilitate laying. 	Adhesion failure of tiles leads to individual tiles falling off and scattering over a wide area. Obvious health and safety risks. More often than not however, it is the render background that fails, losing adhesion to the concrete or brick substrate. This is potentially more serious as larger and heavier sections could collapse. A hammer survey is to be recommended to check for soundness and to identify hollow areas. Repairs are possible using vacuum injection techniques, but hacking off and repair of spalled areas can lead to peel back and cracking of adjoining surfaces and deterioration due to water ingress and freeze/thaw cycles.
Mosaic tesserae in overhead situations (O) Often used as a soffite finish to projecting balconies, shopping mall covered ways and the like. Tiles would be bedded on render or possibly applied over expanded metal lathing. 	Watch out for corrosion of the metal lathing or fixing screws as these may not have been protected against corrosion. Timber fixing battens behind the lathing can also be a problem. In severe cases, large sections of render and tile finish can collapse. If water penetration is suspected recommend further intrusive investigation.
No fines concrete (H) Used in the manufacture of large panels for housing and similar structures, intended to create slightly better insulation properties.	Very low level of resistance to carbonation, hence risk of carbonation and corrosion.
Panel joints (O,H) Panel joints in large panel systems often comprised a plastic or metal baffle sprung into grooves in the edge of each panel. To prevent leakage, it was common to provide a tape back seal to the rear face of the joint.	Baffles may be missing or dislodged. Back seals often missed with consequent risk of water penetration. Flat roof abutments often dressed under the bottom edge of panels, which makes them very difficult to repair. Often the need to modify the drained joint into a face sealed joint.

Item, element or material	Effects
Reconstituted stone (A) Often used as window cills or window surrounds, string courses or other projecting features in all types of buildings. Sometimes fixed with ferrous cramps rather than phosphor bronze. Contain light reinforcement.	Propensity to carbonate fairly rapidly with the result that reinforcement corrodes, causing the features to spall. Corrosion of cramps can lead to displacement of features such as projecting window surrounds.
Render backgrounds (A) Used in conjunction with tile finishes and mosaic tesserae. Often very strong Portland cement based mixes were used.	Possible adhesion failures on concrete due to presence of traces of mould oil on the surface. Sometimes used water based bonding agents (giving a white milky appearance when render is removed) when there was a poor mechanical key. Later bonding agents were of SBR, which were more durable. Inflexible renders, high vapour resistance and risk of water entrapment.
Reinforced aerated autoclaved planks Often used as roof decks – 'Sipporex' or 'Durox' or sometimes as vertical walling. Thin reinforcement, 300–750mm width. Made from a mixture of cement, blast furnace slag, pfa plus aluminium.	If designed before 1980 may deflect excessively, evidenced by transverse cracking on soffite. Some concerns over durability of reinforcement.
Sand faced fletton bricks (A) These were a popular and cheap brick type manufactured by the London Brick Company near Peterborough. Often found in 1960s housing or industrial applications. Often, but not always, a red/pink colour with a heavy textured wire cut type of surface. Rear face of brick is smooth with colour bands or 'kiss marks' arising from the burning process.	No problem in sheltered applications, but bricks in exposed situations such as parapets, chimney stacks and free-standing walls, where saturation is common, are at risk of sulphate attack. The bricks have a very high sulphate content. When wet, soluble sulphates react with Portland cement bedding mortars, causing the mortar to expand and so disrupting the brickwork. Once this occurs, the damage is terminal. Often rendered in mistaken belief that this will cure the problem, but this is a very short-lived solution and will only make matters worse.
Softwood joinery (A) External joinery was often of poorly seasoned sapwood with a low life expectancy.	Very poor durability, especially glazing beads, cills and horizontal rails. Further decay where timber has been pieced-in during repair.

Item, element or material	Effects
Steel windows and cladding (O,W) Typical single glazed windows were manufactured using a section known as W20 by Crittal Windows. Either casements or tilt and turn varieties. Larger curtain walled sections were manufactured by coupling window units together with galvanised steel tee bars.	By now, early windows may be paint bound or distorted. Ironmongery may be defective. Timber subframes were common and may be decayed.
Stramit roof decking (A) An insulation board often used as a roof decking. It comprises a rigid board about 50mm thickness of compressed straw sandwiched between two layers of building paper. The boards were about 1200x450 width and had a brown paper finish. Check in plant rooms, lift motor rooms, roof access housings and the like. Used in some domestic applications.	The material had a very low resistance to water and would decay easily. For that reason it is less usual to find it nowadays. The boards had a grain and needed to be laid correctly, with support perpendicular to the grain. Failure to do this could lead to distortion of the board and subsequent 'wave' effects in the roof line. This in turn could stress the covering and cause failure. Saturated Stramit board would turn into a brown silage-like mess. Beware of safety issues (risk of collapse) when walking on Stramit roofs.  Failed Stramit roof deck
System built housing (H) In general terms these types of buildings were prefabricated, based on either steel or concrete construction. Examples would be the British Iron and Steel Federation properties or, if concrete, Woollaway, Unity, Airey, etc. The form of construction was generally based upon the erection of a frame with cladding fitted to it or alternatively a panel system.	Problems have occurred as a result of carbonation in the concrete and initial lack of cover, use of unsatisfactory materials such as thin steel tube used as reinforcement, problems of interstitial condensation, damage to sealants, etc. In some cases the decay of structural parts has reached severe proportions and it has been necessary to contrive methods of reinforcing the frame or alternatively providing a new cladding system, possibly based on conventional brick and block cavity walling systems. In summary, the major problem areas are as follows: corrosion of reinforcement due to carbonation and/or chlorides,

Item, element or material	Effects
	resulting in expansion of the steel and disruption of the concrete;
	corrosion of metal ties securing cladding panels and the resultant expansion disrupting the cladding and compromising weathertightness;
	poor or uneven insulation, cold bridging giving rise to interstitial condensation;
	insufficient fire protection;
	poor wind bracing;
	deterioration of timber components such as window frames, particularly where they form part of the primary structure.
Trussed roof construction (H, O) Trusses were introduced into the United Kingdom during the mid-1960s and were primarily intended for the housing market, although gradual improvements in stress grading and timber engineering have now taken them into commercial, educational and leisure buildings. Commonly designed to pitches of between 20°–35°, with a span of around 3–10m, trussed rafters are usually jointed with factory fixed galvanised steel fasteners, although plywood gussets are sometimes used. With the use of stress graded timber, sizes can be reduced to as little as 35mm in width, with trusses arranged at 450mm or more, usually 600mm centres. Spans of greater than 10m can be achieved, although buckling of compression members can become a problem – and transport to site may be uneconomic.	The correct positioning of the connector plates is essential so that sufficient teeth engage in the timber to prevent the joint, particularly at the apex, from pulling apart. If this happens the truss will settle, or fail. The signs of this may be hogging in the roof and damage to internal finishes. Shrinkage of timber after fabrication can affect the adequacy of the truss as a whole. If the timber members cannot meet, all the joint forces will be taken up by the metal connections, which could buckle or pull out. Diagonal bracing was not a requirement of the Building Regulations before 1976. Corrosion of gang nails used in the manufacture of trussed rafters due to interaction with certain timber preservatives. Compression members may be subject to sideways buckling under load. Bracing is also needed to prevent buckling. Trussed rafter roofs are often clad with large interlocking roof tiles which, together with the tiling battens, tend to produce a relatively stiff plate. They are nonetheless vulnerable to long term vibrations which can lead, in an inadequately braced roof, to lateral buckling where the trusses adopt a sideways lean – domino effect – either in one or two directions towards gable walls. The structure will also be expected to afford support to gable walls and this is usually achieved by the use of

Item, element or material	Effects
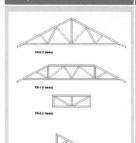	galvanised steel straps turned down into the cavity and fixed to at least two adjacent trusses. Lack of adequate restraint to gable walls or other unrestrained elements could allow an unacceptable degree of movement to take place.
Tying-in of precast concrete floor and roof slabs (O,H) Prior to 1972 (CP110) tying-in was left to engineering judgement. There is a need to form a connection between wall structures and internal precast floor planks. This can be achieved with continuous metal straps or structural toppings to prevent planks from gradually moving apart.	Failure to tie-in properly can lead to the elevation gradually parting company from the floors. Evidenced by a series of parallel cracks in the floors, gradually increasing in severity higher up the building. If neglected, collapse could occur under accidental loads.
Vitrilite panels (O) Used in conjunction with steel windows as above, these single glazed spandrel panels were made from annealed glass with a powder coating fused into the rear surface during manufacture.	Risk of failure due to heat build up in spandrel panels, bird strikes or mechanical damage from cradles. Water penetration can cause staining and deterioration of rear surfaces. Replacement panels no longer available and may have been made from painted glass with less life expectancy.
Wall ties (A) Often wire butterfly ties. Thin steel sections and poor galvanising standards. Cavity walls were rarely insulated and cavity tray detailing may be poor. During the 1960s it was common to use galvanised wire ties and, in some cases, vertical twist ties with sub-standard protection coatings. The life expectancy of bitumen and zinc coatings on these ties is frequently well under the 60 years that was originally predicted. In fact, in 1981,	Factors which could have an influence on the life of the tie are the steel alloy used, the quality of the protective coating and the mortar type – particularly if this was contaminated with chlorides or if the building was in an exposed location. Research work undertaken by the Building Research Establishment suggests that average zinc loss is about 2.1 microns a year. For pre-1981 ties, this results in a predicted coating life of 12–26 years for wire ties and 25–46 years for vertical twist ties. On the inner leaf, where the circumstances are less aggressive, the zinc coating can be expected to last much longer.

Item, element or material	Effects
BS 1243 tripled the minimum allowed zinc coating thickness on wire ties.	If wire ties have been used, these have the unpleasant tendency of corroding away without any substantial physical disruption to the brickwork. Damage becomes manifest by the sudden collapse of an outer leaf particularly in conditions of high wind.
	With the thicker, vertical twist ties the amount of metal is significantly more and if corrosion occurs it is likely that the thickness could increase by as much as four times. The cumulative effect of this corrosion will be the creation of horizontal cracks in the brickwork and eventually the lifting of the roof covering at eaves level to give the so-called pagoda effect.
Woodwool as permanent shuttering (W,O) Often used in basement car parks where additional insulation was required, or in some office buildings.	Risk of poor compaction of concrete during placing, or grout loss leading to honeycombing around re-bars. This could prejudice fire protection, durability or in extreme cases strength. Intrusive investigation required to determine if steel is covered properly.
Woodwool slab roof decks Often with galvanised steel tongue and grooved edge strips and with a pre-screeded finish, or an applied finish reinforced with chicken wire. Size about 1200x 450 or 600mm. (See for use in permanent shuttering.) The material offered some thermal insulation qualities. Often used in plant room roofs, access housings and the like.	Reasonably durable and, contrary to popular belief, does not degrade rapidly when wet. However, failure of screed is probable during re-roofing operations, leading to need to renew the deck. 

Item, element or material	Effects
Cladding systems (O, W) Early curtain walling systems relied upon the use of galvanised steel window components coupled together or fixed within framed openings. These systems were often single glazed and incorporated Vitrilite spandrel panels. In the early 1970s more aluminium curtain walling systems were developed. Early systems were single glazed and face-sealed but, latterly, drained systems were installed, incorporating double glazed units.	Inspect opening sashes for signs of distortion – usually due to paint build up. Window fittings are usually worn or inoperable. Pay particular attention to the security of fanlight fixings. Early double glazed systems were fully bedded. Volatalisation of sealants is common, leading to voiding, leakage and deterioration of edge seals. Be suspicious of early face-sealed systems in terms of future durability. 
Concrete frame Expressed concrete frames were common in the 1960s, often with brick infill panels. In the 1970s there was a move away from this form of construction to brick cladding, with the frame concealed either by brick slips or by a brick outer leaf supported on steel angles.	In both cases, there is a risk that the brick panels can become stressed as a result of the normal shrinkage (axial forshortening) of the concrete frame. A failure to provide movement joints means that loads can be transferred to the panels with the result that the brickwork is disrupted.

Thin stone cladding

Since the advent of steel frames in buildings, the claddings used to conceal those frames have become progressively thinner and more lightweight. Whereas in the early 20th century, stone claddings were often 100mm or so in thickness, advances in saw cutting technology meant that from the second half of the century, it was possible to produce stone panels in thicknesses much less than this, with 30mm or so being the norm for many buildings constructed from the 1970s.

Thin stone panels could be fixed with dowels to concrete cladding panels or could be 'hand fixed' using restraint straps and gravity fixings fitted into the edges of the stone or slots cut in the back face of each panel.

Whilst many natural stones can perform satisfactorily if used in this way, certain types of marble, particularly calcitic marbles have been found to deteriorate, with very serious results. The Amoco building in Chicago is a notable example: here some 43,000 Carerra marble panels had to be stripped off the building within 18 years of its construction at a cost in the region of $80m (15 years is a common period of time for problems to become manifest).

At microscopic level, marbles are composed of a series of grains. The shape of the grains and the pattern of the bond vary according to type – and this effectively governs how the marble will perform in service.

Marble is usually made up of the minerals calcite and dolomite, with some having a higher proportion of either. Both exhibit an anisotropic tendency, that is they expand at different rates according to axis. Imagine rolling out a sheet of pastry – as pressure is applied, the size of the piece increases, but the thickness reduces. This form of movement affects calcitic marbles. On the other hand, dolomitic marbles expand in three directions, but at different rates. Such patterns of movement are initiated by changes in temperature. Whilst a metal component will expand and contract uniformly, marbles tend not to do this, and so a gradual and progressive movement occurs.

Thermal expansion of stone materials is inevitable, and temperatures of around 40–50 degrees are sufficient to initiate movement. Temperatures of this magnitude are often found on the facades of buildings in Europe. The change in temperature creates stresses within the body of the stone, allowing tiny micro-cracks to form around the body of each grain. In much the same way as soil bulks up when it is excavated (the volume of excavated material being much greater than the volume of the hole) the marble expands but is prevented from returning to its original volume.

In turn, micro-cracking increases the porosity of the stone making it more vulnerable to atmospheric pollution with decohesion of the fabric of the stone – termed sugaring – being the result. Flexural strength also decreases and the panels warp in either a convex or concave pattern. Such movements can be enough to dislodge fixings or break the panel away from the fixings with obvious results.

Once anisotropic expansion has occurred, there is probably no going back, bowing and cracking of the panels will be irreversible and progressive. For this reason, inspections of buildings clad in thin white marble panels should invite questions as to the nature of the stone and its propensity for movement.

Regent Street disease

Until the early part of the 20th century, substantial buildings tended to be constructed using load bearing masonry – at least for the external walls. Because of the massive nature of these forms of construction, the walls were able to accommodate movements due to temperature and moisture as well as small building movements without significant harm. With the advent of steel as a versatile construction material, the position changed dramatically. By 1910, steel framing was becoming very popular, and this meant that walls could be reduced in thickness with obvious benefits in terms of economy of material, weight and cost. The use of these construction methods in London's Regent Street has given rise to the common description of Regent Street disease, but it is a problem that is by no means confined to this location.

Typically of many new construction materials, the properties of steel were not fully understood, or at least if understood, ignored. From the early part of the century up to the Second World War, it became common practice to construct load bearing frames of steel, clad on the external faces with stone, brick or terracotta. The external cladding would be notched around the steel frame, with the void between the two filled with low-grade mortar.

As we now know, moisture, oxygen and steel do not make good bedfellows: corrosion cells are set up which can cause significant delamination and loss of strength. The main problem is that corroded steel has the propensity to expand to at least four times its original volume. Given that the voids around the steel were filled, the expansion of the steel would inevitably result in cracking of the stone, and in extreme cases the loosening or loss of support to horizontal stonework, which could then collapse.

Whilst some corrosion protection was common after about 1930, the methods used were unlikely to offer a long term benefit, and so it is now very common to find evidence of corrosion in many steel framed, brick or stone clad buildings. Evidence will take the form of vertical or horizontal cracks reflecting the location of the steel frame. Parallel cracks indicating a column position may be less serious than horizontal cracks, but nevertheless investigations are needed to determine the condition of the steel. Whilst early evidence of corrosion is reflected by hairline cracks, more significant problems (particularly in glazed brickwork) can indicate advanced corrosion or loss of section.

Dealing with corrosion using traditional methods is expensive and disruptive. The steel must be exposed, cleaned and protected – not an attractive proposition when dealing with a listed building or an important facade. It is usual to provide a corrosion barrier to the steel and then to create a void around it so that if further corrosion does occur, it will not result in cracking.

Because of the cost and disturbance of these forms of treatment, more attention is now being paid to the application of cathodic protection systems, which rely upon the concealment of discrete anodes into the stone joints, and electrical connection to the steel frame and the introduction of an electric current to reverse the corrosion current. These systems require very careful design and installation and it is imperative that the entire frame is protected in this way to prevent stray currents from having a harmful effect.

Further information

Gibbs, P., *Cathodic protection of early steel framed buildings*, Monograph No. 7, Corrosion Prevention Association

Corrosion in masonry clad early 20th century steel framed buildings, Technical Advice Note 20, Historic Scotland Technical Conservation Research and Education Division

Warland, E.G., *Modern Practical Masonry*, London, Sir Isaac Pitman & Sons Ltd, 1929

Defects in concrete

The failure of concrete is often revealed by cracking, spalling and corroded reinforcement. While the outward symptoms of a number of faults may appear similar, repair methods must be based on a sound analysis of the cause.

Cracking can be caused before hardening due to workmanship problems or after hardening due to physical, chemical, thermal or structural effects.

The alkaline nature of concrete protects steel reinforcement against corrosion, a feature termed 'passivity'. A reduction in the level of alkalinity gives a risk of corrosion in steelwork provided water and oxygen are present. A summary of common defects and consequences are identified in the following table.

Fault	Reasons	Results
Carbonation	Carbonation is generally of concern on exposed concrete surfaces and will take place very slowly with high quality dense concrete. Features such as poorly compacted concrete, cracks or other fissures in the surface and the type of aggregates used could all affect the rate of carbonation.	A reduction in passivity of concrete coupled with water and oxygen can lead to corrosion of steel reinforcement and subsequent spalling of concrete. Lack of sufficient cover to reinforcement may allow steel to fall within the carbonated layer and become at risk. It has been found that the depth of carbonation is roughly proportional to the square root of the time $d=k\sqrt{t}$ (d=depth, k=constant, t=time). The constant will vary with the properties of concrete. By examining the age of the concrete and the depth of carbonation it is possible to make a rough prediction of the depth of carbonation at a future date.
Rust stains	An indication of reinforcement corrosion but avoid confusion with staining ferrous sulphide inclusions in the aggregate or rusting of small diameter wires. Chloride attack is difficult to deal with effectively and needs careful diagnosis (see later). Chloride induced corrosion will often result in dark stains around corroded reinforcement.	Although unsightly, staining such as this is unlikely to indicate reinforcement corrosion unless cracking is visible.

Fault	Reasons	Results
Chloride attack		See separate section on chlorides on page 212.
Sulphate attack	Sulphates are present in varying levels in many substances including gypsum plaster, certain aggregates and subsoils.	Possible disturbance to foundations and walls due to expansion of floor slabs. Loss of strength, material becomes friable. Rate of carbonation increases, expansive reaction occurs in the concrete.
Alkali aggregate reactions, principally alkali silica reaction	As a result of chemical inter-action between alkaline fluids in concrete and reactive minerals in certain types of aggregates, a calcium alkali silicate gel is formed. This gel takes in water and expands.	Relatively rare fault in UK structures. In non-reinforced concrete this cracking often illustrates a random pattern of fine, almost invisible cracks bounded by some larger cracks. This cracking is easily confused with shrinkage cracking or even frost attack. Gel can sometimes be seen on the surface of the concrete, possibly coupled with spalling lenses.
Aggregate reactions	Alkali carbonate reaction and alkali silicate reactions have similar problems, but are much less common in the UK.	In reinforced concrete, cracks tend to run parallel with reinforcing bars or prestressing tendons. In particularly severe cases, gel may be visible. Microscopic examination of concrete is the only sure way of identifying attack. Although rare, ASR is often only found in structures exposed to water.

Fungi and timber infestation in the UK

Fungi and moulds

Fungi live on dead organic material and play a natural role in the breakdown of dead organic material, which includes timber. Most timber is too dry for fungal growth but timber decay can occur if the moisture content (MC) is increased.

Sporophores (fruiting bodies) are often the first indication of a problem.

Wood rotting fungi is familiarly classified as dry and wet rot. Serpula lacrymans is the only true dry rot – there are many wet rots. Serpula lacrymans can decay timber at a much lower MC than any of the wet rot fungi and can penetrate masonry/brickwork and behind plaster.

The accompanying table should aid identification of various fungi.

Fungi identification guide

Type	Usually found	Effect on timber
Wood rotting fungi		
Dry rot Serpula cuboidal	Inside buildings, mines, boats – never attacks timber outside	Large cuboidal cracking (brown rot)
Wet rots Conrophora Puteana (cellar fungus)	Most common of wet rots in buildings; associated with serious leaks – failed plumbing, etc.; also decays exterior	Cuboidal cracking – small cubes (brown rot); may leave thin veneer of sound timber; affected wood becomes dark brown
Fibrioporia Vaillanti (mine or pore fungus)	Associated with water leaks; most common species of poria group	Cubodial cracking – large cubes (brown rot); affected wood darkens
Phellinus Contiguous	Decay of external joinery (softwood)	Timber becomes soft (a white rot) Wood becomes fibrous
Phellinus Megaloporous	Attacks oak heartwood; presence often associated with death-watch beetle	
Corioius Versicolor (Polystictus)	Most common white rot decay of external hardwood	No splitting or decay but much weight loss
Lentinus Lepideus (Stag's Horn fungus)	Rare, but sometimes in flat roofs	Cuboidal cracking Darkens woods; wood feels sticky
Non-wood rotting fungi		
Peziza (Elf-Cup)	Occurs on saturated masonry or plaster, internally and externally; associated with leaks	
Moulds		
Aspergillus Penicillium Pullularia	Almost any damp surface in humid conditions	Superficial – easily removed

Mycelium	Fruiting body	Conditions for growth
Cotton wool-like if damp; greyish white with purple/yellow and lilac patches if dry	Reddish brown centre, white margins; flat plate or bracket shape; possibly red spore dust nearby	Timber MC 20–40% (slightly damp) Temperature 0–26°C
Brown branching strands on wood and masonry or brickwork; usually not in daylight areas	Rarely found inside; flat plate-like; greenish brown centre, yellow margin; knobbly surface	Timber MC 45–60% (very damp) Temperature –30°C to +40°C
Strands flexible when dry; white	Plate shaped – white pores; rare	Timber MC 45–60% (very damp) Temperature up to 35°C
Light brown masses	Plate-like with pores; dull brown	Timber MC 22%+ Temperature 0–31°C
Yellow	Large, plate-like, hard; various browns in colour	Timber MC 20–35% Temperature 20–35°C
Rarely seen	Up to 25mm across; hairy ringed zones to pores to underside	
Soft whitish needle shaped crystals on surface	Some resemble stags horns, others are inverted mushrooms on stalk – brown	Timber MC 26–44% Temperature 25–37°C
	Buff coloured and fleshy; distinctive	
Like coconut matting	Toadstool – white head – spores released in black ink type liquid Microscopic but spores show up as various colours: black, green, white, brown, yellow, pink	Very humid conditions

Various superficial coloured moulds, often seen affecting timber to buildings, are easily removed, but indicate a MC that might permit more serious fungal decay. Lowering the ambient humidity by increasing ventilation is generally the best course of action. The presence of non-wood rotting fungi also suggests conditions suitable for dry or wet rot.

Treatment

There are many specialist timber treatment companies who will carry out surveys, analyse samples and guarantee any eradication work they undertake.

Briefly, the traditional specification for treatment of dry rot will include the following:

❖   identify cause(s) of dampness and effect cure;

❖   cut out timber to 0.5m beyond decayed wood, remove and burn;

❖   hack off plaster, rendering and remove skirtings, architraves and other joinery from area to be treated to 1.0m beyond infection;

❖   remove surface mycelium from exposed masonry and wire brush;

❖   surface spray exposed masonry with fungicidal wall solution at manufacturer's recommended rate of application;

❖   consideration should be given to irrigating masonry, although it is unlikely that this treatment will be as effective as one might hope;

❖   replacement timber to be treated to BS 5268, 1977 and thereafter, treat with preservative to BS 5707; and

❖   existing timber to be cleaned and sprayed with organic solvent preservative and further treated by application of timber paste.

Treatment of wet rot is similar, although affected masonry need only be isolated from the source of the dampness. In some circumstances chemical treatments can be minimised and the outbreak controlled by environmental manipulation, but this may not always be practicable. Where chemicals are used, request specialists to provide COSHH assessments. Permitted fungicides include zinc acypetacs and tri (hexylene glycol) bioborate. All specified treatments should display an HSE number.

In recent years there has been a trend towards less intrusive forms of repair. If the source of moisture can be removed, the fungus will die. Thus, by managing the building environment the problem of decay can be minimised, and the extent of disruption and intrusive surgery kept to a minimum.

The importance of safety measures cannot be over emphasised and it is vital that current safety legislation is understood and complied with, including the *Control of Pesticides Regulations* 1986 and the *Control of Substances Hazardous to Health Regulations* 2002.

Under the *Wildlife and Countryside Act* 1981, it is an offence to spray roof spaces that may harbour bats without the approval of the Nature Conservancy Council.

Insect infestation

In this country wood boring beetles are the major group of timber attacking insects. The life cycle of the various beetle species is similar; adult female beetles lay eggs in cracks or the end grain of the timber, larvae emerge from the eggs and feed on the wood leaving frass in the tunnels they bore. The larvae enter the pupal stage and soon after emerge as adults leaving flight holes in infested timber. Some species cause only superficial damage.

Examples of most common wood boring beetle species are as follows:

- ❖ Common furniture beetle: very common, estimated that up to 80% of houses over 40 years old in rural areas are affected. Infestation often in damp areas of house, for example, beneath WC. Flight holes 1.5–2.0mm diameter. Adult beetles emerge May–September.

- ❖ Death-watch beetle: infestation uncommon, often found in ancient buildings and therefore more expensive to eradicate. Confined to south and central parts of England and Wales. Attacks elm, chestnut and oak. Adult beetles emerge in Spring through flight holes up to 3mm wide. Presence indicates fungal attack.

- ❖ Bark borers: found in timber where bark not completely removed. Larvae confined to bark areas and hence damage caused is superficial.

- ❖ House longhorn beetle: only found in Surrey, Berkshire and Hampshire. Regulations require new timber to be treated prior to use. This is a very large borer.

- ❖ Wood boring weevils: several species – only attack partially decayed timber, cause considerable damage.

- ❖ Powder post beetle: few flight holes, convert timber to powder leaving veneer of 'sound' timber.

Troublesome plant growth: Japanese Knotweed

Japanese Knotweed was introduced into the UK in the 19th century. It grows vigorously and can cover large areas to the exclusion of most other plant species. It has been known to grow through bitumen macadam, house floors and sometimes through foundations.

Japanese Knotweed is a highly invasive plant and is not easy to control due to its extensive underground rhizome system, which enables the plant to survive when all above ground parts of the plant are removed. It grows to a height of about 3 metres and is formed from stiff purple speckled stems or canes resembling bamboo. The canes grow densely in the summer and die back in the autumn with white flowers appearing late in the season. The costs incurred in control of the plant are significant.

In the UK it is a criminal offence under section 14 of the *Wildlife and Countryside Act* 1981 to cause the growth in the wild of, among other things, Japanese Knotweed, (other plants include giant hogweed, Japanese seaweed and giant kelp).

Anyone found guilty of an offence can face up to two years in prison and/or an unlimited fine. Any waste material arising from attempts to control this plant should be disposed of in accordance with the *Environmental Protection (Duty of Care) Regulations* 1991 as controlled waste. Landowners can also face civil actions for allowing the weed to spread to neighbouring land if it can be shown that the owner knew or ought to have known of the weed and the problems that it can cause.

Soil from a site contaminated with knotweed must be disposed of at a suitably licensed landfill site at a depth of at least 5m. On site treatment is an alternative, but this is not an easy option. Detailed guidance has been published by the Environment Agency. For more information go to www.environment-agency.gov.uk

Key issues:

- ❖ Typical habitats include brownfield sites (which may be contaminated as a result of tipping of contaminated soil or knotweed cuttings), railway land, riverbanks, verges and the like.
- ❖ In winter, the leaves of the plant die off to leave tall, antler-like hollow stems with regular nodes in dense strands.
- ❖ In summer, the plants have green elongated heart shaped leaves with clusters of small white flowers. Young plants are often red stemmed with flower shoots spreading from the tip (not dissimilar to the appearance of bamboo, but more red than green).
- ❖ The rhizomes are yellow/orange when cut and snap rather like a carrot.
- ❖ The plant can be killed with the correct herbicides, but this is not a one-off treatment and can take up to three years.
- ❖ Controlled burning may destroy the plant at ground level, but the rhizomes can extend to 3m and may not be killed.
- ❖ Burial and covering with geotextile matting at a depth of at least 5m is possible, but very great care must be taken to avoid the spread of small fragments by mechanical diggers.
- ❖ Similarly, removal of contaminated soil carries the risk of spreading the plant; disposal must be under controlled conditions and transport off site could cost between £30 and £80 per ton.

Troublesome plant growth: Giant Hogweed

In contrast to the equally vilified Japanese Knotweed, Giant Hogweed not only creates serious environmental problems but also possesses the ability to create very unpleasant skin conditions in humans.

Like Knotweed, it is not a native species, having been originally introduced as an ornamental plant in the 1890s. Needless to say, the plant 'escaped captivity' to become common within the United Kingdom. Once established, it can dominate other plants rapidly and damage the natural habitats of insects and other animals. It is often found growing along railway land, footpaths, roads, rivers and wasteland. Seeds can be transported along waterways to infect areas further downstream.

During the winter, the plant dies down, leaving bare patches which can result in soil erosion. Carrot fly can inhabit Giant Hogweed infestations making it a very undesirable plant to have around.

Identification

As its name suggests, Giant Hogweed is characterised by its size, often growing to 3–5m over four years or so. The plant has a purple to red stem and furry, spotted leaf stalks. Leaf and flower growth is also large, 1.5m width is not unknown for leaves, whilst the flower heads (which resemble Cow Parsley) can be around 250mm wide.

Aside from the environmental problems associated with Giant Hogweed, the health risks can be serious. Brushing against the leaves, or breaking the stem releases sap. The sap contains a substance that reduces the ability of the skin to resist ultraviolet light. Burns can result: these often develop into large watery blisters after 20 hours or so of contact and exposure to sunlight. The condition can lead to a more serious and difficult to treat form of dermatitis called Phytophotodermatitis, a reoccurring skin condition that can persist for many years.

Under the *Wildlife and Countryside Act* 1981 and the *Wildlife (Northern Ireland) Order* 1985 it is an offence to 'plant or otherwise cause Giant Hogweed to grow' in the wild. Thus, a landowner could commit an offence by moving contaminated soil from one location to another rather than treating it as controlled waste.

As with the eradication of Japanese Knotweed, the control of Giant Hogweed is difficult. Unlike Knotweed, plant propagation is by seed, with a single flower head producing upwards of 1,500 seeds and a large plant producing up to 50,000 seeds. Treating the active plant growth with the herbicide Glyphosate is effective, but unless retreatment is undertaken regularly, and over a period of several years, it is unlikely to be effective as the seeds can remain dormant for up to seven years. If spraying is to be undertaken it is vital that this is done early in the growing season, before the flower heads have time to develop and produce new seeds.

The alternative treatment is to dig up the plants and dispose of them as controlled waste. This treatment will often be coupled with spraying, although because of the health effects outlined above, great care is needed to minimise the risk of exposure to sap. If this does occur, the affected area must be well washed and protected immediately after contact.

When removing specimens, some of the seeds will fall to the ground, usually within a four metre radius of the plant. Care is needed not to distribute these seeds, particularly where tracked or wheeled equipment is likely to be used.

Further information

Natural Environment Research Council: www.nerc-wallingford.ac.uk

NetRegs: www.netregs.gov.uk

Royal Horticultural Society: www.rhs.org.uk

Rising damp

Research by the BRE and others suggests that rising dampness is often misdiagnosed by surveyors and so-called damp specialists, with the result that costly and unnecessary remedial treatments are specified.

In many cases, diagnosis is undertaken by means of electrical resistance or capacitance meters, but these can give very misleading and unreliable results in materials other than timber. Surveyors should not diagnose rising damp without first having undertaken a proper study. When rising dampness is suspected, do not automatically recommend a specialist inspection – more often than not the specialist will use exactly the same resistance equipment to make his diagnosis. A more reliable method has been prepared by the BRE and may be found in BRE Digest 245, 1989.

Symptoms

Typically these may include:

- ❖ damp patches;
- ❖ peeling and blistering of wall finishes;
- ❖ a tide mark 1m or so above floor level;
- ❖ sulphate action;
- ❖ corrosion of metals, for example, edge beads;

- ❖ musty smells;
- ❖ condensation; and
- ❖ rotting of timber.

The above symptoms do not of themselves indicate the cause of dampness. Common causes could be lateral rain penetration, condensation or entrapped moisture. High external ground levels, bridging of damp-proof courses, defective rainwater goods and the like should all be self-evident and could give rise to similar symptoms.

Soluble salts are present in many building materials. The salts can be dissolved and moved to the surface of the element as evaporation takes place. Hygroscopic salts (typically, nitrates and chlorides from groundwater) can be present in some materials. These salts absorb moisture from the atmosphere, and can in certain circumstances cause extensive staining and disruption of finishes.

Other possible sources of salt contamination include chemical spillage, splashing from road salt, etc.

Equilibrium moisture content

Many building materials absorb moisture, and when exposed to damp air will attain an equilibrium moisture content. This hygroscopic moisture content (HMC) will vary according to relative humidity. Typical relationship curves can be plotted for different materials, and although these can only establish general indications it is possible to compare readings from different materials in the construction of a wall. For example at 75%RH the MC of yellow pine would be 13% while the MC of lime mortar would be 2% and 0.5% in brick.

Some materials possess an HMC of as much as 5% without the introduction of salts from external sources. This figure should be regarded as an appropriate threshold as to whether or not remedial action is likely to be required.

Measurement of moisture content

Resistance or capacitance meters can give misleading results.

The presence of soluble salts on the surface of a wall will cause an electrical resistance meter to indicate a high reading, even if the wall were otherwise dry. Deep wall probes may give a more accurate picture, but will still be affected by soluble salts, as these are generally highly conductive.

A Speedy Moisture Meter will give a much more accurate reading of MC in all materials. (Resistance meters are usually calibrated for use in timber and can give an approximation of MC in that material.)

The Speedy meter comprises an aluminium flask fitted with a pressure gauge and a removable lid. Using a 9mm drill on slow speed, a sample of dust is taken from the brick, mortar or plaster. The sample is weighed and placed into the flask. A small quantity of carbide is then added and the flask sealed. Moisture in the sample reacts with the carbide to form acetylene gas. The pressure of that gas is then read off the pressure gauge, which is calibrated to read %MC. With care, the meter can give a very accurate reading, comparable with laboratory kiln dried tests.

Rising damp

Rising dampness within a wall is in a sensitive equilibrium. There must be a supply of water at the base of a wall and the height to which that water will rise depends upon the pore structure, the brick, plaster or other finish. Water will also evaporate from the surface of the wall at a rate dependant upon temperature and humidity.

During wet weather, evaporation may decrease and ground water tables may rise, giving rise to an increase in the severity of the dampness. The reverse may happen during dry spells, and evaporation will be increased by central heating.

Soluble salts derived from groundwater or building materials will complicate the situation. Salts will increase the surface tension of the water and so draw it further up a wall. Furthermore, as evaporation occurs, stronger salt solutions are drawn towards the surface and may eventually crystallise out. This process reduces the amount of evaporation and so may raise the height of the dampness. The soluble salts are often hygroscopic and absorb moisture from the atmosphere. If this occurs, the situation will appear worse during wet weather and better during dry.

As noted above, the presence of hygroscopic salts does not necessarily indicate rising dampness.

Diagnosis of rising damp

BRE Digest 245 sets out a method of diagnosis. The method involves drilling samples from the wall to measure both their moisture content and hygroscopicity (HMC). Samples are taken from mortar joints from 10mm to a depth of 80mm every two or three courses from floor level up to a level beyond that which damp is suspected. While the carbide meter can be used to measure moisture content (MC) it will be necessary to send samples to a laboratory to measure HMC – to see if the samples could have absorbed the quantity of moisture from the atmosphere.

By subtracting HMC from total MC, it is possible to determine the value of 'excess' moisture, which could result from capillary action or water from other sources. The comparison of HMC and MC gives an indication as to which is controlling the dampness at any position. If MC is greater than HMC, then moisture is coming from some other source. If the reverse applies, then moisture is coming from the air. Plotting the results graphically can then assist in gaining an accurate picture of what is happening.

Surface damage arising from hygroscopic salts can be significant. The HMC of contaminated wallpaper or plaster can be as much as 20%. It follows, therefore, that contaminated plaster will need to be removed. BS 6576 deals with this subject in more detail.

Subsidence

Much of the UK's housing built on what are known as shrinkable clays has quite shallow foundations, usually less than 1m deep. Such clays are generally strong and able to support a building of four storeys on a single strip or trench-fill foundation. These soils shrink when their moisture content decreases and then swell when it increases. Slight movement of houses on foundations is therefore inevitable as a result of seasonal changes in moisture content resulting in downward movement or subsidence occurring during the summer and upward movement or heave during the winter.

Greater movements may occur during long periods of dry weather and may lead to sticking of doors and windows. Severe movements are almost always associated with localised subsidence caused by trees whose roots extract moisture from the soil. Conversely, removing a tree tends to cause heave as moisture gradually returns to the soil. Large broad-leaved trees of high water demand are notorious for causing damage.

Before World War II, it was common practice to use shallow foundations no more than 0.45m deep. Houses built within the past 25 years should comply with guidelines issued by the National House Building Council (NHBC) and the British Standards Institution (BSI). The former requires foundation depths often well in excess of 1m, while the latter requires a minimum depth of 0.9m for any buildings founded on clay and deeper foundations where there are trees nearby.

Because of the link between clay shrinkage and the weather, insurance claims for subsidence damage increase in long dry periods. There is an upward trend in claims and presently the background level of subsidence and heave damage in the UK is about £350M annually. Analysis of insurance claims indicates that of those cases involving foundation movements caused by the shrinkage or expansion of clay soils, 75-80% are exacerbated by moisture abstraction by trees.

Subsidence may also be a consequence of mining activity. The extent of subsidence due to mineral extraction depends on the method used for winning the minerals from the ground, whether by mining, pumping or dredging. The main problems in Great Britain arise from coal mine workings.

In many coal fields in Britain the presence of old workings remain as a constantly recurring problem in foundation design where new structures are to be built over them. If the depth of cover of soil and rock overburden is large, the additional load of the building structure is relatively insignificant and the risk of subsidence due to the new loading is negligible. If however the overburden is thick, and especially if it consists of weak crumbly material, there is a risk that the additional load imposed by the new structure will lead to local subsidence.

The risk of subsidence associated with coal workings may be obtained via a Coal Mining Report obtained from the Coal Authority.

It is important to differentiate between subsidence and settlement.

- ❖ Subsidence is vertical foundation movement caused by failure or shrinkage of the sub-soil.
- ❖ Settlement is vertical foundation movement caused by an increase in applied load.

Building into the basement

At a government-sponsored conference held on 24 January 2005, the government called on the UK house building industry to increase the provision of domestic basements. This is a complete reversal of previous policies, based on the perception that a basement area as living, working or storage space represented a poor relation to housing the same functions above ground. It also represents considerable challenges for both new and adaptive construction in providing dry, warm and decent environments below ground level.

Basements for Dwellings Approved Document 2005

The conference was the launch pad for the private sector *Basements for Dwellings Approved Document* 2005. This was also approved by the Secretary of State, under section 6 of the *Building Act* 1984, as practical guidance on meeting the requirements of the relevant paragraphs in Schedule 1 to the *Building Regulations* 2000 (as amended 2001 and 2002) as they apply to the incorporation of basements to dwellings. It has the same standing as HMSO Approved Documents.

The Approved Document brings into one text all of the relevant Building Regulations for dwellings that are affected by the inclusion of a basement. The sections covered are:

Part A – Structure

Part B – Fire safety

Part C – Site preparation and resistance to contaminants and moisture

Part E – Resistance to the passage of sound

Part F – Ventilation

Part J – Heat producing appliances

Part K – Stairs, ramps and guards

Part L1 – Conservation of fuel and power

Part M – Access and facilities for disabled people

Part N – Drainage and waste disposal

The sections are laid out in order of construction, rather than in the strict alphabetic order of the Building Regulations.

A consultation was undertaken in Autumn 2005 as to certain amendments in respect of structural design of plain masonry and in situ concrete basement walls. The outcome as regards DCLG (ODPM as was) enabling the incorporation in a revised Approved Document is as yet not known.

Keeping water out

Where basements are concerned, whether for new build or alterations and adaptations, the key issue is that of water resistance. The Approved Document details four grades of construction to achieve various levels of water resistance:

Grade 1 – which allows water seepage and is almost certainly going to be inappropriate for any dwelling use;

Grade 2 – which is the reasonable minimum for garages;

Grade 3 – which is the reasonable minimum for accommodation; and

Grade 4 – which is for totally dry conditions or for premises which require a very controlled environment. This is unlikely to be appropriate for housing except in very exceptional circumstances.

The Approved Document also details different types of wall construction. Typically, there are three:

Type A – which is geared around total reliance on waterproofing;

Type B – where the structure provides the main resistance; and

Type C – where the structure provides some resistance but the principal reliance is on an internal system which intercepts moisture ingress, controls it and carries it away so the internal environment is not affected. In simple terms, the moisture is intercepted by a drainage layer on the internal face of the wall directing the moisture downwards to gutters which, in turn, direct the water into a sump from which the water is pumped away into the drainage system to the outside.

Environmental exposure

On reading the Approved Document in detail, you will come across the phrase 'acceptability of construction types'. You start with the three forms of construction (A, B and C given above) and then you introduce different levels of severity, or environmental exposure, to the construction types. A key factor is where the water table lies in relation to the proposed, or existing, basement. This is referred to as 'low', 'variable' and 'high'. A pertinent observation here is that water tables are almost invariably 'variable' on a seasonal basis – higher in winter and lower in summer, unless you have water tables that are high all year round, particularly as a result of proximity to river or sea coasts.

Adapting existing basements

Without a doubt, the most complex cases will be where existing basements are being considered for refurbishment. Almost without exception, Georgian, Victorian and Edwardian houses had basements varying from limited storage and coal cellars to complete basements. These were either fully below ground level or semi-basements originally designed to provide storage, kitchens and servants' accommodation.

Houses built pre-1914 and some constructed pre-1939 should be dealt with cautiously. The brickwork of such properties will have been constructed using lime-based mortars rather than Portland or similar cements. Such mortars are hygroscopic and take up water readily, with the result that the mortars can decay and, in the worst conditions, can crumble away completely. Their ongoing stability and the retention of the strength of the mortars relies on their being able to release the moisture into the internal environment through plaster facings into the rooms. In other words, such construction has to be able to release moisture inwards. The last thing one would want to do in dwellings constructed in this way is to lock moisture into the brickwork by means of waterproof renders on the internal face of the walls.

Moisture ingress into basements of buildings such as these should primarily be dealt with by the Type C wall construction described above. Any use of Type A internal waterproofing to the building should be thought through very carefully to ensure the lime-based brickwork is not compromised.

Condensation and toxic moulds

Without question, surveyors do visit properties where black or green, or indeed other coloured, moulds exist on the walls, ceilings, floors, furnishings and fittings of the premises. Fungal mould spores exist in the air around all of us and when they alight on parts of the building that provide the right substrate and conditions for the mould spores to propagate and grow, they will.

Everyone will be familiar with dry rot, the product of one family of mould spores. There are many thousands of different moulds and they all occur naturally in our environment.

Condensation mould describes not a 'mould' but a set of conditions whereby various moulds can propagate. Moisture is a key requirement for propagation and if you have surfaces on which moisture is condensing then you are providing the conditions for moulds to grow.

There has been concern in the construction world in recent years over 'toxic mould'. This term is used for the discovery of either Strachybotrys chartarum or Aspergillus fumigatus in buildings, both of which can affect the health of people living or working in individual properties. Particular concerns surfaced in the United States and indeed the City of New York has an excellent website which gives useful guidance and advice, see www.nyc.gov/html/doh/html/ epi/moldrpt1.shtml.

Such moulds also appear in the United Kingdom. Strachybotrys is a black or greenish-black mould that grows on material with a high cellulose content, including building materials such as the paper facings of plasterboard, chip and particle boards when these materials become water damaged. This mould requires very wet or high humidity conditions for days or weeks in order to grow. Excessive indoor humidity from water vapour condensing on walls, plumbing failures, splashes from bathing or taking showers or water ingress from outside may lead to the growth of many varieties of mould including Strachybotrys or Aspergillus.

If you do observe mould that you believe might be one of these two, then there are UK laboratories that can identify whether they are present by means of testing from swabs taken from the moulds. Searching the web with keywords such as 'toxic mould analysis' will lead to appropriate organisations.

The best option for buildings and their occupants is to ensure that conditions do not exist whereby moulds of any variants can propagate. This is best achieved by keeping the buildings warm, dry and free from external water ingress into the fabric of the building.

If you do find you have problems arising from mould of any variety then the following documentation and guidance will help you understand why you have it and how to get rid of the underlying causes.

The BRE's *Walls and ceilings: remedying recurrent mould growth*, Defect Action Sheet (DAS) 16 (1983) states the following:

'Mould growth requires sustained high relative humidity but is unlikely to start unless surface water is present. Persistent surface condensation is the commonest, though not the only, cause of such conditions ... This occurrence of surface condensation depends on the relationship between, on the one hand, heating, ventilation, insulation, etc. and, on the other, the pattern of occupants' activities. The predominant cause can therefore either be in the design provisions or in the occupants' usage. There is no point in treating the symptoms unless the predominant causes have been identified and cured, since mould growth will otherwise recur.'

The BRE's *Controlling mould growth by using fungicidal paints*, Information Paper (1995) states the following:

'Removing the source of moisture

There is no doubt that the best way to achieve long-term control of moulds is to eliminate, or at least reduce, the incidence of dampness on the surfaces of buildings. Repair work to the structure will be necessary if the dampness is caused by rain penetration, plumbing leaks or rising damp. If it is due to condensation, the dampness can be reduced by improving the quality of insulation of the affected building surface, by increasing the level of heating and by improving ventilation (for example, by fitting humidistat-controlled extract fans in the kitchen and bathroom and trickle ventilators in the bedrooms). The occupants themselves can reduce condensation by a variety of measures, such as:

- ❖ Not drying washing indoors, or restricting it to rooms with open windows and closed internal doors.
- ❖ Ventilating rooms to the outside during and immediately after cooking, washing and bathing, or whenever the windows show signs of misting.
- ❖ Avoiding the use of flueless gas and oil heaters.'

The BRE's *Treating condensation in houses*, Good Repair Guide 7 (1997) states the following:

'What causes condensation?

Every day the average UK household puts about 12 litres of moisture into the air in their home, through normal activities such as cooking, washing clothes and bathing; breathing alone contributes about 1 litre per person every 24 hours. In homes where clothes are dried indoors, or which use paraffin or bottled gas heaters, the total can be over 20 litres a day.'

'The mechanics of condensation

There is always moisture in the air in the form of water vapour, although usually it cannot be seen. However, there is a limit to how much vapour the air can hold at any particular temperature: the higher the temperature, the more vapour the air can hold.

Therefore, when warm moist air comes into contact with a cold surface and is cooled, it can no longer hold so much vapour and the excess condenses as liquid water on the surface. A typical example is moist air from a warm kitchen which drifts to unheated rooms, such as bedrooms. The moist air cools when it reaches the walls and other cold surfaces, and the excess water is deposited as condensation. Another common experience is condensation on the surface of a solid floor when the weather turns warm and humid after a cold spell.'

'What's the cure?

There are two main factors involved in condensation in the home – the amount of moisture in the air, and the air temperature. To reduce the risk of condensation occurring, either the moisture content of the air must be reduced or the home must be made warmer. In practice it is usually necessary to do both.'

'Reducing moisture generation

The amount of moisture generated in a home depends on the size and lifestyle of the household. Most of the steps needed to reduce it can be carried out by the occupants themselves, including keeping lids on saucepans, drying clothes outdoors, and not using paraffin or flueless gas heaters.'

'Providing ventilation

High moisture production in homes need not be a problem if there is enough ventilation. The single most important step is to ensure good ventilation in kitchens, bathrooms and shower rooms, where most household moisture is generated, often in large amounts during a short period. This moisture must be vented to the outside to prevent it drifting to other parts of the house which are often colder and more likely to suffer from condensation.'

'Providing adequate heating

Condensation is almost bound to occur in rooms which are cold. The best remedy is to provide low background heating all day in cold weather, even when there is no one at home. It is far better to do this than to rely on a high level of heating for short periods, and the overall costs are often quite similar.

Background heating is particularly important in bedrooms, especially in bungalows and flats, where they are not above heated living rooms. If possible install a small, thermostatically controlled heater in each bedroom and in hallways. A minimum air temperature of 10°C is recommended, day and night.'

BRE material is reproduced with permission from Building Research Establishment Ltd. BRE publications are available from www.ihsbrepress.com.

A most useful paper, *Toxic Moulds and Indoor Air Quality* by Jagjit Singh of Environmental Building Solutions Ltd, describing the relationship between toxic mould and indoor air quality may be found at www.aspergillus.org.uk/secure/articles/pdfs/singh.pdf (Indoor Built Environment Review Paper, 2005, 14;3–4:229–234, accepted 21 February 2005).

Testing

Materials and defects

Chemical and physical testing requirements

The following are some of the more common requirements for specific tests, although it is better to discuss the quantity or type of sample required with the testing laboratory before sampling to ensure that a suitable and representative sample is provided.

Testing laboratories should be provided with an outline of the location of the sample and the nature of the element inspected. This is often critical in evaluating results and the possible level of risk involved.

Primary rules

- ❖ avoid contamination of sample
- ❖ label clearly
- ❖ inform laboratory of purpose of test
- ❖ consider health and safety aspects when dealing with hazardous substances; seek expert advice first
- ❖ for comparison, 10 grammes = a sugar cube.

Chloride ion content

About 30–50 grammes (enough to fill a 35mm film canister) of sample material is required. Drilled dust is preferred obtained using a 10mm percussion drill bit. Discard first 5mm depth of material to avoid contamination from paint, plaster or other surface effects. Take samples from two adjacent holes drilled to the depth of reinforcement. As chloride levels will vary, many samples should be taken for analysis. For chloride profiling to identify ingressed chlorides then take incremental samples at depths typically 5–25, 25–45 and 45–65mm.

Carbonation

Best carried out in situ. Drill two 10mm diameter holes and break out concrete in between. Treat freshly exposed concrete with phenolphthalein. Concrete will turn pink if uncarbonated. This is not a precise test and carbonation should be recorded to the nearest 5mm.

If you find the depth of carbonation by testing and you know the age of the building, then the rate of carbonation increase in the future can be predicted according to the following formula: $d = k\sqrt{t}$ where d = depth of carbonation, k is a constant and t = age of concrete (years).

Refer to BRE Digest 405 (1995), *Carbonation of concrete and its effects on durability*.

High Alumina Cement (HAC)

Dust samples taken, as for calcium chloride ion, to determine aluminium content and assess 'proof negative' the presence of HAC. Differential Thermal Analysis (DTA) required on lump samples for 'proof positive' confirmation. Phenolphthalein test for carbonation is not applicable to HAC. It is necessary, therefore, to remove a lump sample of sufficient size to enable a thin slide to be made for petrographic laboratory analysis. This test is very expensive.

Refer to *HAC concrete in the UK: assessment, durability management, maintenance and refurbishment*, BRE Special Digest SD3, by A. Dunster, BRE, 2002 (also BRE Digest 392, *Assessment of Existing High Alumina Cement Construction in the UK*, which has now been withdrawn).

Sulphates in concrete

As for calcium chloride ion (30g sample should be sufficient for chloride sulphate and HAC).

Plaster/mortar

To determine mix proportions including, for mortar, cement content. Take dust or preferably solid sample as for chloride ion content.

Asbestos

Air monitoring and bulk sampling by specialists only. Samples must be taken with due regard to health and safety. Seal loose material after sampling. Sample of loose insulation may be taken with corer. About a thumbnail size sample is sufficient for analysis. Laboratory to be UKAS accredited. Seal remaining material after sampling. Laboratory to report on asbestos type, % content and density.

Ground water

Approximately 1,000ml of water should be sufficient to determine chemical signature of ingressed water. A similar quantity of mains tap water should also be taken simultaneously so that the results may be compared. Results of laboratory analysis sometimes are not conclusive.

Leaks may also be identified by 'sounding' by placing listening rods on pipe valves, covers, etc. This work is done by specialists often when quiet at night.

Decayed timber

Provide sample large enough to indicate pattern of cracking and/or mycelium growth. Powder material is not sufficient except in cases of insect attack, where frass may give indication of type of beetle.

Non-destructive tests

See BS 1881: Part 201, *Guide to the use of non-destructive methods of test for hardened concrete*, and information supplied below.

Non-destructive testing

There are a range of non-destructive testing (NDT) techniques which may avoid the requirement for large scale costly and disruptive opening-up. Often the findings of non-destructive testing survey may allow opening-up to be targeted in specific locations. Non-destructive testing techniques are particularly useful to establish construction details and the condition of the structure and fabric of a building, in particular relating to building defect analysis.

A summary of the more common NDT techniques are as follows:

Impulse radar

Radar is a widely accepted non-destructive technique for establishing details of the construction and condition. Radar is effective through most building materials including concrete, asphalt, brick, stone and also through soil. Defects may be mapped without damage or disruption to surface finishes.

Radar is an echo sounding technique where pulses of radio energy are transmitted into the structure by an antennae moved over the surface.

Where material boundaries are encountered the different electrical properties reflect part of the energy back to the surface where it is detected by a receiver. Sampling is rapid and collected data effectively forms a continuous cross section enabling rapid assessment of thickness, arrangement and condition over large areas.

Thermography

Infrared thermography is a non-destructive testing method involving precise measurements of surface radiation to reveal changes in thermal performance caused by hidden changes in the construction or in a physical condition. Recent improvements in imaging and processing technology has enabled improved and compact handheld thermographic cameras to undertake surveys of large areas relatively quickly.

Modern thermo-imaging cameras are able to detect variations in surface temperature as small as 0.10°C. A major limitation of this method is that sufficient heat differential is required between the inside and outside of the building fabric. Environmental conditions favourable for thermographic surveys are therefore restricted to, for example, cold still winter nights when heat flows from the inside to the outside of walls. A major benefit of this technique however is that a great deal of work can be conducted some distance from the subject.

Ultrasonic pulse velocity

Ultrasonic pulse velocity is a non-destructive technique used in testing a wide range of building materials to determine properties including compressive strength and to investigate defects, such as the presence of delamination and the depth of cracking. The method can be applied to materials such as concrete, ceramics, stone and timber. The main advantage of this method is identifying general changes in condition such as areas of weak concrete in a generally sound structure. The technique involves the measurement of the compression wave velocity from a transmitter to a receiver.

NDT investigations

Often one or more of the above techniques may be required. Information may be provided relating to:

- ❖ debonding and delamination;
- ❖ compaction and voidage;
- ❖ spalling or micro-cracking;
- ❖ general details of construction, material types and layers;
- ❖ moisture content;
- ❖ reinforcement or other embedded ferrous metal; and
- ❖ brickwork details and conditions.

It is rare that NDT techniques will themselves tell the whole story. It is essential that NDT is considered as an investigation tool as part of a wider engineering assessment.

Cladding

Materials and defects

Mechanisms of water entry

Ways rainwater can penetrate

❖ kinetic energy
❖ surface tension
❖ gravity
❖ capillarity
❖ pressure differentials
❖ any combination of these.

Kinetic energy

This is the direct action of the wind carrying a droplet of rainwater with sufficient momentum to force it through a sealed joint. Prevention or drainage overcomes this. Prevention can be by baffles, by a durable seal or by a labyrinthine shape within the joint. Drainage collects the penetrating water and diverts it back to the outside.

Surface tension

This can cause water to adhere to and move across surfaces. It is guarded against by drip edges or throatings along leading edges, and horizontal surfaces should slope down and out. Connecting components can also have appropriate grooves or ridges.

Gravity

This can take water through open joints that lead inwards and downwards. Reversing the slope overcomes this.

Capillarity

This occurs in fine joints between wettable surfaces. It is only severe when other mechanisms persist – for example, wind-assisted capillarity. In metal components it is resolved by capillary breaks within the joint surfaces.

Pressure differential

This frequently is the main mechanism. It is overcome by maximising the outer deterrent and minimising the pressure differentials. This is achieved by self-contained (compartmentalised) air spaces behind the outer skin, which are well ventilated to the outside.

Composite panels

There has been some speculation of late that the use of metal faced sandwich panels is unsatisfactory, and that while buildings constructed from these materials can satisfy Building Regulations, there is an increasing reluctance on the part of building insurers to effect cover at reasonable commercial rates.

Given parallel concerns over fire safety and risks to occupiers and fire fighters it is clear that there is considerable potential for bad or misleading advice and unjustified criticism of composite panels in general.

In 1993, two firemen lost their lives tackling a serious blaze at the Sun Valley Poultry fire in Hereford. The fatalities were due to the early collapse of plastic foam cored sandwich panels, which contributed to the fire and generated significant quantities of thick black smoke and noxious fumes.

Sandwich panels are of a composite construction comprising two outer layers of steel or aluminium sheet with an inner core of an adhesive bonded lightweight core material. The resulting product is lightweight yet strong and able to span greater distances than would be possible with the individual component parts in isolation. Flexural strength is attained by maintaining the bond between the layers. One side will be in tension, the other in compression. Remove the bond to one face and integrity is destroyed and the panel will fail.

There are broadly four types of core:

   ❖   foamglass (fairly rare);
   ❖   polyurethane (PIR or PUR);
   ❖   polystyrene (EPS); and
   ❖   mineral wool (machine made mineral fibre).

If subjected to fire, polyurethane cores (which are thermosetting) will undergo localised charring, although flaming can take place if flammable vapours are released. The charred material will shrink and can lead to delamination of panels.

Polystyrene materials may burn fiercely, give off thick black smoke and allow burning droplets to fall.

Some of the adhesives used in mineral wool products can be combustible.

Foamed glass is generally non-combustible.

The two main issues are:

   ❖   instability of the panel facings in the event of a fire; and
   ❖   combustibility of the panel core material – method statements for fighting fires in composite panel buildings talk about 'fires of the building', rather than fires within the building.

Issue 1 was a contributory factor in the fire at Sun Valley, and could affect composite panels that are not properly supported or restrained. In the case of roof and wall cladding, there are usually additional supports in the form of purlins and sheeting rails and primary fasteners, which serve to tie the two leaves together and prevent them from becoming detached. However, in internal situations such as food processing plants, cold storage facilities, etc. the quantity of insulation required will often lead to panels of 200mm thickness or more. Such panels require less support and so present a greater risk of delamination. It is these panels which cause the greatest levels of concern – particularly as the core materials are often no more than EPS.

There will be a conflict between the requirements of the Building Regulations and the requirements of insurers. Building Regulations are aimed essentially at ensuring the health of users and neighbours of the building (and of course visitors as emergency services). Insurers may want higher standards of protection, fire suppression and/or more reliance upon non-combustible materials.

The relevant standards for composite panels were originally set by the Loss Prevention Council but are now administered by BRE certification under LPS 1181. Generally, materials with a PUR or EPS core will almost certainly not satisfy the requirements of LPS 1181, whereas PIR or stonewool products can be engineered to comply.

The Association of British Insurers has produced a report on the issue and it is hoped that insurers will now take a more relaxed view of buildings have been constructed using materials certified under LPS 1181 Part 1 (for external systems) or Part 2 (for internal applications). However, many buildings have been constructed (and still are constructed) using materials that do not satisfy these standards and, in these circumstances, it is important to consider the overall level of risk rather than the mere existence of the panels.

Whether or not sandwich panels constitute a risk is a matter of judgement and scientific fire risk assessment. A reasoned approach may involve the consideration of the following:

- ❖ Is there a sprinkler installation in the building?
- ❖ Are there any specific fire risks – use, storage of inflammable materials, arson, etc?
- ❖ Are the panels in the vicinity of battery charging areas?
- ❖ Are the panels perforated such that the cores are exposed?
- ❖ How are the panels fixed – are they properly restrained?
- ❖ What is the nature of the insulant?
- ❖ What is the extent of the material and to what extent could it contribute to fire load?

Many manufacturers keep records of consignments and can often, given the nature of the contractor, identify the nature of the material supplied to a specific site. More modern trends have included a small identifier that can be marked on the panels and revealed by exposure to a small UV light source.

Curtain walling systems

Curtain walling is a weatherproof and self-supporting enclosure of windows and spandrel panels in a light metal framework which is suspended right across the face of a building, being held back to the structure at widely spaced joints.

Types of curtain walling system

Stick system

Stick construction is the traditional form of curtain walling, comprising a grid of mullions and transoms into which various types of glass and/or insulated panels can be fitted. Most of the grid assembly work is done on site. The advantages include relatively low cost and the ability to provide some dimensional adjustment. The disadvantages are that performance is workmanship sensitive. It is not unusual to find systems failing initial waterproofing tests during erection.

Unitised system

Unitised systems comprise narrow width storey height units of aluminium framework containing glazed and/or opaque panels. The entire system is pre-assembled under factory controlled conditions. Mechanical handling is required to position, align and fix units on site onto pre-positioned brackets attached to the floor slab or the structural frame. Modern installation techniques increase the speed of erection and often minimise the requirement for scaffolding. Unitised systems have higher direct costs and are less common than stick system. Nowadays the curtain walling to most prestige buildings is of this type.

Panellised systems

Panellised curtain walling comprises large prefabricated panels of bay width and storey height which are connected back to the primary structural columns or to the floor slabs. Panels may be of precast concrete or comprise a structural steel framework which can be used to support a variety of stone, metal and masonry cladding materials. The advantages of these systems are improved workmanship as a consequence of factory prefabrication, allowing improved control of quality and rapid installation with the minimum number of site sealed joints. Panellised systems are less common and more expensive than unitised construction. Panel systems often appear similar to unitised systems.

Variations

Structural sealant glazing is a form of glazing that can be applied to stick or unitised curtain walling systems. With structural sealant glazing, the double glazed units are attached to the grid framework with factory applied structural silicone sealant rather than by pressure plates and gaskets in a more traditional system. The attraction of this form of glazing is that it provides relatively smooth facades which are visually attractive.

Structural glazing typically comprises large thick single panes of toughened glass assembled with special bolts and brackets that are supported by a secondary steel structure. This form of glazing is often referred to as `planar' glazing and is commonly used to form the enclosure to atriums and entrances.

Weather tightness

There are various methods of preventing rainwater ingress and these are discussed as follows.

Face sealed systems

Early curtain walling systems tended to be face sealed relying on a weatherproof outer seal to prevent water penetration. The seal must remain completely free of defects to prevent leakage paths occurring. Where there is no provision for drainage, any water that bypasses the outer seal could result in internal water ingress. With drained systems any water within the glazing rebate can then drain away within the framing system. There are also a small number of proprietary systems incorporating front zipper gaskets containing a large rubber gasket with a central press-in segment or zip which, when pressed into place, forces the gasket out onto the surface of the glass. This system does not normally have provision for water drainage.

Fully bedded systems

The systems are now largely obsolete and were utilised on the early forms of curtain walling. Fully bedded glazing is a face sealed system relying on the glazing rebate being completely filled with glazing compound to prevent the passage of water. They are therefore 'undrained'. Any voids within the bedding are a potential weak link for water ingress and early failure of the double glazed units.

Drained and ventilated systems

Most cladding designers now accept that it is difficult to exclude water and therefore provision for a small amount of leakage can be made within a drained system. Typically these dry glazed systems comprise an outer decorative cover plate, and an aluminium pressure plate with two narrow rubber oyster gaskets either side clamped against the glass or insulated infill panel. The pressure plates are screw fixed through a thermal break into the mullion or transom member. A further inner gasket between the glass and the mullion or transom provides a further seal.

In drained and ventilated systems the front gaskets provide an initial barrier. The rebates and cavities are drained and ventilated to the exterior to prevent the accumulation of any water that bypasses the outer seals. Drainage is usually via small holes or slots in the underside of transoms that drain water down through the mullions.

Some systems also incorporate a foil faced butyl adhesive tape applied over the transom and mullion nosings directly beneath the pressure plate to serve as a secondary line of defence.

While these systems will accommodate a small quantity of water within the glazing rebates, it is important that the pressure plate is fixed to the correct torque so that the outer gasket seal forms a good seal against the glass.

Pressure equalised systems

Pressure equalised systems are an improved variation of drain and ventilated systems. Here the ventilation openings in the pressure plates are of an increased size to permit rapid equalisation of pressure in the glazing rebates with the external pressure thereby preventing water penetration of the outer face. Consider the following diagram:

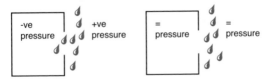

The rectangular box may be considered as the area around the glazing in a cladding system. If the pressure inside the box is less than the pressure outside, the water will be drawn in. If we can equalise the pressure in the box then the probability is that water will stay on the outside. In curtain walling systems we must provide a perfect seal around the inside of the window and must also provide the number of slots around the perimeter of the glass to enable pressure within the glazing rebate to equal that of the external air pressures almost instantaneously. Fundamentally therefore, with pressure equalised systems the outer face is sealed as tight as possible against rainwater while the inner face is sealed as tight as possible against air inflow. Nearly all modern curtain walling systems are designed utilising the principles of pressure equalisation.

It is very difficult to identify the differences between a drained and ventilated system and a pressure equalised system. However for pressure equalisation to work properly, the various zones of pressure must not be too large. Thus it is common to consider the area around one glass pane as one zone and therefore drainage must be made from the transom members and not from the mullions. In practice it is very difficult to provide full pressure equalisation and there is some doubt in the industry as to whether it is fully effective.

Double glazed units

Double glazed units are often referred to as 'insulating glass units' comprising two or more panes of glass spaced apart and hermetically factory sealed with dry air in the unit cavity. The air may then be flushed out and replaced with a range of other gases to improve thermal or acoustic performance.

The perimeter edge sealant prevents moisture from entering the unit cavity and holds the unit together. Two forms of edge seal configuration are single seal systems and dual seal systems. Single seal systems rely on the edge sealant to act both as the vapour barrier and as an adhesive bond to hold the panes of glass together. Dual seal glazing units rely on two seals, an inner seal to control water vapour transmission and an outer secondary seal to hold the glass tightly against the spacer bar. The combined properties of primary and secondary sealant provide high quality glass units. Nearly all units are now of this type.

The appropriate British Standard for Dual Seal Systems was BS 5713: 1979 and although this remains current it is now obsolescent.

There is a wide variety of glass types that may be used.

Annealed glass is untreated glass manufactured from soda lime silicates. It is the least expensive and most readily available type of glass. Annealed glass breaks into sharp edged shards and is therefore considered to be unsafe in all fire and breakage situations.

Low e coatings reduce the omission of long wave thermal radiation from the glazing and increase the reflection of this radiation. In the winter, solar radiation can be trapped within a room and reduce the need for heating. In the summer however heating can also occur and so low e glass needs to be used in conjunction with adequate provision for ventilation. Most Low e glass can be toughened and laminated.

Thermally toughened glass is formed by heating and then rapidly cooling or quenching annealed glass. Differential cooling and hardening across the thickness of the glass generates a compressive stress in the surface layer of the glass. Toughened glass is always a safety glass and compared with annealed glass is four to five times stronger in compression and bending. In failure, toughened glass shatters into small, relatively safe fragments. All annealed glass contains nickel sulphate impurities and as the glass is heated during the toughening process these impurities change state. Spontaneous breakage of the glass may follow. The failure of toughened glass in service can be reduced by heat soaking to encourage reversion of the impurities to the low temperature state before installation. Poor design and careless handling of glazing are much more common reasons for spontaneous breakage of toughened glass than nickel sulphite inclusions. As a minimum requirement, toughened or heat strengthened glass located at height or overhead should be heat soak tested.

Heat strengthened glass is formed by heating annealed glass and then cooling it under controlled conditions. Heat strengthened glass offers some of the strength of toughened glass but a reduced risk of failure due to nickel sulphite inclusions because of the reduced tensile stress in the glass. This glass is often also referred to as 'partially toughened'.

Laminated glass is formed by bonding together two or more panes of glass using a plastic interlayer. Any of the above forms of glass may be used in any combination. Upon failure, laminated annealed glass breaks into shards which are held together by the interlayer. Laminated glass may include one or more panes of toughened glass. If all panes are of toughened glass then the broken glazing will lose all structural integrity and may pull free from the pane unless properly secured. Laminated glass is recommended for the inner pane of overhead glazing and is considered to be safety glazing.

Surface finishes

The metal components of a curtain walling system will nearly always require finishes to provide protection against corrosion or for appearance.

To preserve the decorative and protective properties of any metal finishing, it is essential that atmospheric deposits are removed at frequent intervals, particularly those surfaces which are not exposed to the washing effects of the rain.

Quality of workmanship is particularly important and it is therefore essential to choose a reputable applicator preferably covered by a quality insurance scheme. Independent acceptance inspection testing can be undertaken to ensure compliance with the specification.

Organic coatings

Organic coatings are normally applied to either steel or aluminium and include polyester powder, PVDF, PVC, Plastol, and polyester. The most common organic finish for windows and curtain walling is polyester powder coating, however a range of wet applied finishes is widely used for opaque cladding panels. Polyester powder coatings may be applied to either galvanised steel or aluminium and are available in a wide range of colours. Polyester powder coatings are tough and abrasion resistant. Manufacturers often provide a guarantee for 15 to 20 years.

Anodising

Anodising is an electrolytic process that produces a dense, hard and durable oxide layer on the surface of aluminium. The oxide layer is porous and must be sealed to prevent staining but can be coloured by introducing dyes or chemical treatment before sealing. Anodised finishes are generally harder and more abrasion-resistant than organic coatings with an expected life of 50 years or more. However, anodised surfaces are susceptible to alkaline corrosion from contact with fresh concrete or mortar and rainwater run off from concrete surfaces.

Testing

Many standard and bespoke curtain walling systems are tested in laboratory conditions to determine the resistance to wind load, air tightness and water tightness. These tests are undertaken on a very small number of test panels assembled in factory conditions. By necessity they are a test of the design rather than on-site workmanship.

It is therefore critical that all installed curtain walling systems are subject to on-site testing to establish that the fabrication and installation has been undertaken to a satisfactory standard.

Water tightness on site is typically assessed using sprayed water from a hose in accordance with the AAMA Standard 501-94 or CWCT test methods. Ideally, the first areas to be tested should be among the first areas of each type of curtain wall to be constructed on site. Typically, the test areas are at least one structural bay wide and one storey in height, providing that all horizontal and structural joints or other conditions where leakage could occur are included.

Water is applied via a brass nozzle on the end of a hose that produces a solid cone of water droplets with a spread of 88°. The nozzle is provided with a control valve and a pressure gauge between the valve and nozzle. The water flow to the nozzle is adjusted to produce 22 +/− 2 litres per minute, producing a water pressure at the nozzle of 220 +/− 200 Kpa. Water is directed at the joint perpendicular to the face of the wall and moved slowly back and forth over the joint at a distance of 0.3m from it for a period of five minutes for each 1.5m of joint. There should be an observer of the inside of the wall, using a torch if necessary, to check for any leakage.

Glazing – windows and doors satisfying the Building Regulations

Amendments to Part L of the Building Regulations have brought about important changes in the specification of windows and doors. Essentially, compliance with the regulations will involve improving the insulation value of the frame (perhaps by reducing its size and increasing the extent of the better insulated glass panel) or by using more advanced glazing specifications such as low e coatings.

Specifically, measures could include the following:

✦   increase the width of the thermal break;

✦   utilise an alternative type of thermal break;

✦   provide alternative gasket design;

✦   increase the air gap in the double glazed unit;

✦   provide a gas filling to the glass;

✦   provide an alternative spacer (warm edge technology);

✦   utilise low e glass (either hard or soft coatings);

✦   triple glazing; and

✦   dual double glazing.

Increase the width of the thermal break

The width of the thermal break will have a significant impact on the thermal performance of the frame. Pre-April 2002 designs were often in the order of 12mm or less, but widths of 36mm are also realistic. Even with low e glass and an argon gas filling, a standard 4mm thermal break in a metal window will not meet the requirements.

Utilise an alternative type of thermal break

There are broadly two types of thermal break: those comprising a strip or 'web' of nylon 66 (polyamide) or glass fibre reinforced polypropelyne inserted into locating channels in the aluminium sections.

There is also those of resin which is poured into a single extrusion. When the resin has set the aluminium is then cut out.

By replacing a polyamide break with one made of polyurethane, one can reduce the u-value from say 3.95 W/m²K down to 3.72 W/m²K. However, polyurethane is not capable of accommodating the wider break designs.

Provide alternative gasket design

The thickness and positioning of gaskets, particularly those types which also compartmentalise the glazing rebate, can influence thermal performance to a comparable degree.

Increase the air gap in the double glazed unit.

Many domestic DGUs are of 12mm width, with some timber window frames being only able to accommodate a 6mm air gap with two panes of 4mm glass. By increasing the width of the gap to 16mm, thermal performance is improved. Beyond 16mm there is little thermal benefit to be gained.

Provide a gas filling to the glass

Conventional DGUs are air filled, although the substitution of air with argon or krypton gas will lead to a marked improvement:

❖ Air filled low e double glazed unit U=1.9 W/m²K.
❖ Argon filled low e double glazed unit U=1.6 W/m²K.
❖ Krypton filled low e double glazed unit U=1.35 W/m²K.

If the gas filled unit is well made it is possible that the gas will remain contained for many years. Estimates suggest that after manufacture, about 90% of the volume will be the specified gas with the remaining being air. A good unit should not lose more than a further 5% of gas over the next 25 years. However, there are no established test methods for establishing how much gas has been lost in service. The quality and effective life of gas filled units is therefore unknown at the present time.

Provide an alternative spacer (warm edge technology)

A high performance DGU such as those described above would not function as effectively as it could because standard aluminium spacer bars have a high thermal conductivity. By replacing the spacer bars with systems of low conductivity, it is thought that improvements of as much as 10% can be achieved. However, there are some concerns over the long term durability of these units. Additional types of warm edge spacers such as silicone foam cannot be tested under the methods described in prEN 1279-2 and this could restrict their use in the future.

Utilise low e glass (either hard or soft coatings)

Low e or low emissivity glass is made by coating one surface of a pane with a special metal coating. The treated pane is then encapsulated into a DGU, with the treated pane on the inner or room side. The coating reduces the amount of light that can pass through in the infrared spectrum, thus more heat is trapped on the inside of a room.

There are two types of low e glass:

   ❖   pyrolitic hard coat; and
   ❖   post applied soft coat.

Pyrolitic hard coat (for example, Pilkington k and SGG EKO Plus) is applied while the glass is being made. Thus the coating is very resilient, meaning that the glass can be toughened, cut and assembled without the need to remove the coating at the spacer bar contact point.

Soft coat (for example, SGG Planitherm) is applied post manufacture. Very high thermal properties will be dependent upon the type of coating used, but most soft coats cannot be toughened and are easily damaged. DGU's must be assembled within a short time of being cut. For these reasons, soft coatings tend to be more expensive, but some manufacturers will claim that they can provide improved thermal performance over hard coatings.

Triple glazing

A triple glazed window using float glass is not as effective as a DGU with low e glass, and is much thicker, resulting in heavier frame sections. However, a triple glazed unit with two low e panes can achieve 1.0 W/m^2K, while if the voids are filled with krypton, 0.7 W/m^2K can be achieved.

Dual double glazing

As its name implies, this involves setting two DGUs within a frame. However, the system would be very heavy with associated handling and cost implications. Thermal bridging at openings might be reduced because of the increased width of these systems.

Spontaneous glass fracturing

Nickel sulphide is one of several chemical contaminants that can occur during the manufacture of glass. There is some debate as to its origin, but it is thought that it is due to the mix of nickel and sulphate impurities within the glass batch materials, the fuels or even the furnace equipment, and this creates polycrystalline spheres which vary from microscopic to 2mm in diameter.

All glass has some of these inclusions present; they are impossible to eliminate entirely and therefore they are not considered a product defect.

In untreated (annealed) glass they are not a problem. But when glass is heat treated (toughened or tempered), the inclusions are modified into a metastable state which transforms with temperature and time and which is accompanied by an increase in volume.

In a majority of cases this has little effect but dependent on size and proximity to the centre of the pane where the forces are greatest, this can eventually cause the glass to break.

There is a theory that for an initial period of approximately one year after manufacture there are relatively few breakages. After this, the number increases for up to several years, thereafter decreasing in frequency. There have been reported incidences where fractures have occurred more than 20 years after the installation of glass.

Prior to pr EN 14179, a breakage rate of 1 per 5 tonnes of glass was thought an average level. However, this corresponds to only 200m² of 10mm glass. This, on a glazed roof of say 6000m², could be expected to have a failure rate of 30 breakages.

Panes in external situations are at greater risk. However, there have been a small number of cases where spontaneous breakage has occurred in internal glazing, remote from external influences, for example, panels to a staircase balustrade or an internal partition.

Although the safety risks are very small, because of the risk of falling debris, some companies will not recommend or supply and glaze toughened glass for sloped overhead applications where it will be used either as a single pane or as the inner leaf of a sealed unit.

In 'heat strengthened' glass, nickel sulphide inclusion is not generally regarded as a source of fracture. The difference between this and toughened glass is the rate of cooling. In the former this is less rapid, reducing surface compressive strength and making it much less susceptible to the transformation of nickel sulphide inclusions. Offering 5.5 times the strength of annealed glass, in many circumstances it is a useful replacement for tempered glass. However, it is not a suitable substitute where safety glass is required.

'Heat soaking' is a quality controlled process which gives increased reassurance against the presence of critical nickel sulphide inclusions by subjecting the glass panels to accelerated elevated temperatures to stimulate the transformation of the crystals and thus initiate immediate failure. It is thought that this process identifies 90% or more glass, which might have subsequently failed after installation. The heat soaking process could be used either as a sampling method or as an additional treatment, which in the case of clear toughened glass could add up to 20% to the cost.

Heat soaking does not change any of the physical properties of toughened glass and therefore there is no means of distinguishing whether or not this process has been carried out. Current best practice dictates that specifiers should ensure that they specify 'heat soaked toughened glass to pr EN 14179. This standard reduces the anticipated failure rate to 1 per 400 tonnes of glass used.

Identification

When toughened glass is broken, the tensile stress is spread out from the source causing the pane to crack into small fragments (dicing). These fragments tend to be slightly wedge-shaped, emanating from the source of the fracture and are often held into position wedged against the frame due to their increased volume.

If the fracture is as a result of expansion of the nickel sulphide inclusion, those fragments immediately adjacent are more hexagonal and at the epicentre of the breakage the two larger particles form a distinctive butterfly shape linked by a central straight line crack. If large enough, the inclusion may be seen in the form of a black spec, or its presence may be confirmed by optical microscopy.

When carrying out an investigation, all possible causes of failure should be considered, including poor glazing tolerances and insufficient allowance for subsequent movement of the frame and any supporting structures. Possible causes may include deflection or rusting of steel frame, shrinkage of concrete frame, thermal movement, normal air pressures and even sonic booms. If the fracture is a result of impact or of local point loading, there should be evidence of local crushing.

The chances of installing a toughened glass pane, which may later fail due to the expansion of nickel sulphide inclusions, are very small.

Where it is essential, for reasons of accessibility or safety, that the pane should not fail, alternative forms of glass should be considered. One particular example would be in overhead situations – say in a shopping mall.

Testing

Samples should be sent intact with the epicentre protected with clear film to a suitable testing laboratory. Microscopic analysis will be sufficient for an initial diagnosis, but a scanning electron microscope will yield more information.

Glazing – ten things to look out for

Modern curtain walling systems are complex, and glass failures can be misdiagnosed easily. This section describes ten questions to consider when making an assessment of a commercial building.

What is the glass specification? Reference to operating and maintenance manuals may help in identifying glass type, the configuration of double glazed units and whether they are coated, gas filled, toughened, laminated tempered or annealed glass. Identify the age of manufacture if possible, either by reference to drawings, or sometimes, if you are lucky, by reference to a date stamped on the inside of an aluminium spacer in the double glazed unit (DGU). Such stamps commonly have the month and year of manufacture and can be a good guide as to the possible future life expectancy of the unit. Estimating the life of an edge seal is very difficult because of the wide range of service conditions that could apply.

What is the glazing method? Is the glass gasket glazed or 'wet' glazed with glazing compound? Is there a mechanism for allowing water to drain out of the glazing rebate? If not (and this is particularly the case with fully bedded systems) there is an acute risk that the edge seal to the DGU will deteriorate and become vapour permeable. When this happens, the pane will mist up with condensation. Typically, in fully bedded systems, a life expectancy of 10-15 years is common for DGUs – sometimes even shorter if the edge seals are in permanent contact with moisture.

Even if the glazing system is drained and ventilated (most modern buildings will be) it is best to check to make sure that the drainage system is not obstructed, that drainage slots line up or are present and that sealing tape (where present) has been cut in appropriate locations to allow drainage blocks to function – unfortunately, this is more than a straightforward visual check as the cover plates and pressure plates need to be removed.

Check gaskets for fit, particularly at corners and by pressing the back gaskets determine whether there is sufficient clamping pressure – they should not be able to be pushed inwards easily. Defects in either could allow water penetration into the system.

How is the glass supported? The way in which glass is fitted and supported in a frame can be critical to its future performance. Aside from the visual indications of failure (cracking or shelling), poorly located or incorrect setting blocks may not be immediately apparent unless glazing beads or pressure plates are removed. Block dimensions should be equal to the sum of the glass thickness and the back face clearance to maintain proper support. Look out for blocks that are positioned incorrectly – if the glass panel is obviously out of square with the frame it could mean that the setting blocks are defective – too soft perhaps, or poorly positioned.

Is the glass coated? There are a variety of different coatings that can be applied to glass – most adding some degree of reflectivity or solar control. Some low emissivity glasses are coated with soft coatings – these are effective but vulnerable to damage during manufacture. Is there evidence of deterioration? Will it be possible to source replacement tints of the same colour or will they need to be specially made at high cost?

Is there a history of breakage? If toughened glass has been used, has there been a history of failure due to nickel sulphide inclusions? Although research in Australia has identified a photographic method of identifying installed glass at risk of breakage, the system is not available commercially in the UK and there are no practical tests that can be undertaken to assess the risk.

If the glass is toughened, is it likely to be restrained if failure occurs?
Vertical glazing, whether this be obscured or vision glass, can be contained as it cracks and expands and will not necessarily fall out so long as it is contained within a rigid frame. However, if the frame is inclined to the vertical, or if the glass exists in an overhead situation, the glass will fall out. Whilst toughened glass breaks into small individual dice, it can clump together, particularly if the glass has a fritted finish. Larger clumps of glass could cause serious injury to occupants or passers by. Similarly, if the glass is not contained – say, for example, a glass balustrade, sudden failure will inevitably lead to collapse – the effects of this happening should be considered.

Is the glass damaged? Glass is a strong material, but surface defects can weaken it significantly. The stress at which a material fractures depends on the size of the largest flaws present, the larger the flaw, the lower the fracture stress. Invisibly small cracks can cause stress concentrations, which allow cracks to propagate. Poor handling causing edge damage can be material, and deep pointed shells on the edge of a pane can be critical to its performance. Look for evidence of handling damage – this may not be apparent unless cover caps and pressure plates are removed. Examine the glass for evidence of scratching – this can happen with cleaners using abrasives or wearing diamond rings.

Can the glass cope with service temperatures? Thermal stress can result in failure – particularly where the centre of the pane is heated to a higher temperature than the edges. Solar controlled glass and DGUs containing 'warm edge' spacers are also susceptible to thermal stress. In this type of failure, cracks will usually propagate from one or more small defects in the edge of the glass. Coloured glass spandrel panels can be susceptible to high temperature ranges, and unless the glass is able to cope with this, failures can occur. Toughened or tempered glass is usually better able to cope with temperature than ordinary annealed glass, but the manufacturing methods can give rise to optical distortions known as roller wave.

Is the glass located in an area that is 'at risk' within the meaning of regulation 14 of the Workplace (Health, Safety and Welfare) Regulations 1992? The provision of suitable safety barriers, safety film or replacement glass may be required if it is. Glass testing kits are available to help determine whether toughened, laminated or annealed glass has been used. Remember that wired glass is not necessarily safety glass and that, depending upon the size of the panel and its thickness, ordinary annealed glass may be sufficient to satisfy the Regulations.

Is the building located in an area that could attract terrorist activity? Consider the risk of blast damage. the primary aim of the facade should be to transfer the pressures generated in a blast back to the structure, so that the overall inertia of the building can absorb lateral forces.

Ordinary annealed glass is not a safety glass, and if it breaks, dangerous shards of glass can and often will cause the most severe injuries. Laminated glass offers the most advantageous properties, as the glass is held together by the action of the polyvinyl butyl (pvb) interlayer. However, for the system to work properly, laminated glass must be securely bonded to the frame with silicone. The installation of anti-shatter film (ASF) can be a useful strategy, particularly if combined with special net curtains. However, if used in unsuitable situations it can actually make matters worse. For example, its use in conjunction with single point fixed glass will mean that the relative stiffness of the filmed panel will permit failure at fixing positions. Applying ASF to a window that already contains laminated glass is not to be commended since it alters the flexural properties of the original glass which may then show a greater propensity to rupture around its edge and fall out.

The above questions are not exhaustive by any means: if in doubt it is best to consult an experienced facade consultant for detailed help and advice.

Further information

See BS 6262 and BS 8000 Part 7 for recommendations on glazing practice. The Glass and Glazing Federation (www.ggf.co.uk) publish recommendations for glazing and inspecting glass, whilst hugely valuable material can be found at the Centre for Window and Cladding Technology (www.cwct.co.uk) and glassfiles.com (www.glassfiles.com).

This section is based on an article originally written by Trevor Rushton for the RICS *Building Surveying Journal* (May 2006 edition), copyright RICS. Material is reproduced here with permission from RICS.

Environmental

Sustainable development

What is sustainability?

The following summarises the meaning of sustainability, (source: the 1987 Brundtland report on sustainable development):

meet[ing] the needs of the present without compromising the ability of future generations to meet their own need.

Sustainability is essentially concerned with living within environmental limits, ensuring a strong, healthy and equal society and maintaining a sustainable economy.

Why do we need to be more sustainable?

The world, in particular the developed world, has discovered and exploited a wealth of mineral and natural resources such as oil, water, coal, gas, and other natural resources. The increasing world population, mass consumerism and mass consumption has contributed to climate change and the rapid depletion of the natural resources relied upon to sustain our way of life.

It has been estimated by the World Wildlife Fund for Nature that the average person in the UK has an ecological footprint of 5.4 global hectares. A global hectare is the equivalent amount of land needed to produce the food, clothing, energy, water and other materials each person consumes throughout their life!

We must therefore give serious consideration to how we may conduct our personal lives and business in their operations, to ensure we are not unduly consuming the earth's limited resources in an unsustainable way that could compromise the health, wellbeing and survival of current and future generations.

Current generations must take immediate steps to be more sustainable now to protect future generations.

Climate change has been identified as the biggest threat to our existence on the earth, therefore the buildings we design and construct today need to be of low carbon intensity or ideally 'carbon neutral' and must be adaptable for our future climate.

'Sustainability' has become something of a buzz-word in recent years, a term which has been over-used, misused, or plain misunderstood, and often means different things to different people.

Sustainability is commonly referred to in terms of the 'triple bottom line': optimising the three key elements of **economic**, **social** and **environmental** sustainability.

Businesses are recognising the increasing importance of green credentials as a key part of corporate responsibility reporting and maintaining reputation. By engaging in sustainable practices, business organisations have peace of mind in the knowledge that stakeholder interests are managed and, additionally, new business opportunities can be realised.

Sustainable development

Sustainable development is primarily concerned with environmental sustainability, however the economic and social elements must also be considered in unison to measure the entire impact of development. The breadth of what sustainable development entails is vast. It covers waste reduction, recyclable materials and water, energy efficiency, renewable energy and water efficient delivery, to name a few key areas.

The guidance document *Constructing for Sustainability*, produced by the Construction Industry Council, points out that sustainable development:

| aims for synergy, rather than compromise, between economic, social and environmental factors. It secures a profitable project that functions well financially and for all stakeholders, whilst maintaining economic, social and environmental costs.

The above text is reproduced from *Constructing for Sustainability – a basic guide for clients and their professional advisors*, with permission from the Construction Industry Council.

The journey to achieving sustainable development is challenging. The process begins with a series of intentions and a firm commitment followed by the implementation stages and then continuous improvement and reporting.

The solutions to achieving sustainable objectives will demand an holistic and often innovative approach. It must be recognised that many construction activities and buildings will not always achieve total sustainability, as it will not always be practicably or feasibly possible. However, by demonstrating a positive commitment to environmental 'damage limitation', surveying professionals can collectively contribute to providing a more sustainable built environment.

When a development is being proposed, fundamental questions that should initially be considered are:

❖ Is development necessary? This is a key question to establish what factors are driving the need and what is the benefit of development, other than financial.

❖ What economic, social and environmental benefits would development create?

There are a number of assessment tools available, the most common being BREEAM, which can rate the sustainability impact of a development, particularly with regard to the environmental impact of development.

The environmental impact of construction activities and the built environment

Everyday modern activities within business or domestic life have an impact on the environment and therefore it is up to every individual or business to take responsibility and accountability for taking action to minimise the impact we humans have.

The increase on landfill taxes, costs of hazardous waste disposal, the climate change levy and Building Regulations, for example, are designed to encourage more resource efficiency. This by implication will have an effect on the sustainability bottom line, and stimulate improvement in efficiencies.

The construction industry and the built environment have an important contribution to make in supporting long term sustainability objectives associated with the effective management of:

❖ materials and natural resources;

❖ energy;

❖ water;

❖ emissions, effluents and waste;

❖ transport;

❖ ecology; and

❖ land use, urban form and design.

Developments must be designed and procured (from client inception) to embrace all of the environmental, social and economic issues associated with immediate and long term sustainability objectives.

Creating a sustainable built environment

The following guiding principles should be followed to design for sustainable developments:

- ❖ Make existing buildings more energy efficient.
- ❖ Use less energy.
- ❖ Use energy saving materials.
- ❖ Recycle more in order to save the energy used to manufacture, transport and dispose of materials.
- ❖ Consider use of renewable energy sources and alternative technologies.
- ❖ Physically orientate buildings to maximise their capacity to exploit solar energy.
- ❖ Consider how existing materials could be reclaimed, recycled and reused in construction.
- ❖ Minimise the energy consumption in the transport of materials.
- ❖ Utilise prefabricated components.
- ❖ Incorporate natural building materials where practical into construction.
- ❖ Specify low maintenance materials in order to reduce further energy and resources use during the future life of the building.
- ❖ Dispose of ozone depleting substances responsibly.
- ❖ Use materials that do not emit harmful gases, radiation or dust.
- ❖ Recycle rainwater and grey water and specify water efficient devices.
- ❖ Reduce transport needs by procuring local materials, manufacturing and labour when practical.
- ❖ Use more sustainable resources where possible, such as timber.
- ❖ Design buildings to be sympathetic with their local environment and encourage ecology and habitat restoration.
- ❖ Design to minimise waste generation and consider the long-term impacts of design decisions.
- ❖ Adopt 'just-in-time' ordering where possible to prevent the wastage of unused materials.
- ❖ Educate all personnel, especially on site, to enhance their understanding and their capacity to reduce waste and increase recycling.
- ❖ Specify energy efficient mechanical and electrical installations.
- ❖ Encourage occupiers to purchase only energy efficient electrical equipment and appliances.

The above guiding principles are by no means comprehensive. They simply provide a flavour of the scope that environmental sustainability might encompass.

Sustainability and risk

A sustainable approach to development has also become an exercise in risk management and risk avoidance. For example, the exposure to the high costs of green taxes can be mitigated by taking the time to include sustainable design solutions at inception. Another example, in respect of planning applications, is a development which focuses on sustainable objectives, thereby increasing its chances of gaining planning permission, thus minimising opportunities for stakeholder objections.

The current UK Government has become reliant upon policies, regulations and legislation that penalises unsustainable practices and will reward those who actively promote sustainability. Therefore, compliance with these policies, regulations and legislation is imperative to mitigate and manage business risk, particularly with respect to prosecution for breach of regulations, public relations, business survival and cost exposure.

The cost of being sustainable

Consideration beyond capital costs alone must be made and more emphasis put on the analysis of life cycle costs together with the tangible and intangible investment for the life an asset. Payback periods and life cycle can be a compelling argument when proposing sustainable design.

Many individuals or businesses would not typically undertake a payback analysis for the purchase of a car or flat screen TV, yet these same individuals or businesses may baulk over capital cost of solar water heating, for example. However, when the life cycle and payback costs are compared, the benefits become obvious. Therefore, more objective and alternative value assessments need to be considered to demonstrate the entire benefits and not just the capital costs in isolation.

Sustainable development may inevitably cost more to implement, however it can provide longer term investment benefits to building owners and occupiers, particularly when the life cycle and payback costs are factored into any calculation. A long term view must be taken with buildings as assets because in the future, buildings that are more sustainable and energy efficient will become more sought after and may command higher market and rental values.

Establishing the appropriate sustainability objectives

There are numerous opportunities for adopting sustainable practices. However, these opportunities cannot always, without qualification, be implemented in all circumstances for reasons of practicality, feasibility or cost. The key here is to target sustainable objectives that will have the most beneficial impact on a development. The decision, therefore, must be based upon a structured evaluation process. The most obvious method of analysing and adopting sustainability objectives is to set SMART targets, that is:

> **S**pecific
>
> **M**easurable
>
> **A**ffordable
>
> **R**ealistic
>
> **T**ime-related

A structured approach provides a focussed application for construction teams to deliver sustainable performance. Without such an approach there is the risk of attempting to do everything and not actually achieving anything!

As surveying professionals we can make a significant contribution to making the built environment more sustainable.

Further information

Construction Industry Council, *Constructing for Sustainability – a basic guide for clients and their professional advisors*

Our Common Future, Report by Brundtland in 1987

The British Land Company PLC, *Sustainability Brief*, November 2004 (developed with the assistance of Arup).

Contaminated land

Environmental due diligence is now commonplace in property transactions. The presence of contaminated land can adversely affect site value and rental income and can hinder transactions if not properly managed. With an increasing move away from greenfield development, it is no longer possible for the majority of investors or tenants to avoid owning or occupying some land affected by contamination, whether as a city centre property that has had a variety of past uses, or a new out of town development constructed on an old industrial site.

Documentation

Documentation is the key to ensuring a smooth property transaction. Documentation should be in place to demonstrate the site condition has been adequately assessed. This can be undertaken by commissioning an Environmental Audit and/or an intrusive ground/groundwater investigation. These assessments, which are discussed in further detail below, should ascertain the following:

- ❖ the site condition has been adequately assessed by an environmental assessment or review (commonly known as either an Environmental Audit or Phase I) and/or an intrusive site investigation (Phase II) and there are no significant information gaps;
- ❖ whether contamination is present (or is likely to be present), and the types of contaminants;
- ❖ where contamination has been identified, it does not represent a risk to the existing or proposed use of the site;
- ❖ contamination is not migrating off-site within groundwater;
- ❖ contamination does not represent a significant risk to groundwater and surface water resources or other sensitive receptors (e.g. sites of special scientific interest);
- ❖ contamination does not represent a risk of regulatory authority action (e.g. under Part IIA of the *Environmental Protection Act* 1990);
- ❖ contamination does not represent a risk of third party action (e.g. from adjoining land owners); and
- ❖ whether any potential liabilities may exist from any forthcoming business transaction.

Environmental Audit

An Environmental Audit (also known as a Phase I or an Environmental Assessment) is based on background research and should include a site walkover. An Environmental Audit Desktop does not include a site walkover. A walkover would normally be advised to ensure all present day site issues are appropriately assessed. The research will normally include a review of:

- ❖ current site uses;
- ❖ historical site activities;
- ❖ environmental sensitivity;
- ❖ regulatory authority records; and
- ❖ a risk assessment and environmental risk rating.

Intrusive ground/groundwater investigation

An intrusive ground/groundwater investigation (also known as a Phase II) is based on a physical assessment of the underlying site conditions, and usually comprises chemical analysis and/or monitoring of ground, groundwater and ground gas.

If an Environmental Audit or existing knowledge identifies a potentially significant contamination issue, then it may be necessary to conduct a Phase II investigation, to gain an understanding of whether contamination is actually present and whether it is likely to represent a significant risk.

A Phase II investigation will normally include:

❖ a summary of the Environmental Audit findings;
❖ a description of the Phase II investigation methods;
❖ data and observations recorded during the site work, including field evidence of contamination;
❖ data from chemical analysis of ground/groundwater/ground gas samples;
❖ interpretation of the results and an assessment of risk; and
❖ recommendations for remediation (if required) of the underlying ground and/or groundwater.

The Phase II investigation should be designed to address the specific issues raised by the Environmental Audit, such as the range of contaminants highlighted as possibly being present (for example, petrol on a petrol station, landfill gas on a landfill site, etc.).

The majority of sites undergoing development will require a Phase II investigation, particularly where the previous use was industrial. Phase II investigations can often be combined with geotechnical investigations for foundation design. Sites that are not being developed may also require Phase II investigations (for example, during transactions). This may depend on whether a significant pollutant linkage has been identified or if the local authority may investigate the site in the near future.

Remediation

Remediation of sites can be achieved by removing sources of contamination, reducing levels of contamination or modifying the 'pathways' between the source and the identified sensitive receptors. The main approaches include:

❖ excavating and removing contaminated material off site to landfill (dig and dump);
❖ encapsulating or separating contaminated material on site, by severing contaminant pathways with barriers (e.g. underground bentonite walls); and
❖ treating the contaminated material, either in situ or after removal.

Remediation can often be combined with the redevelopment of the site, for example, by excavation. Remediation strategies should be approved in advance by the local authority and the Environment Agency. Post-remediation validating sampling (e.g. of ground/groundwater) should be undertaken to document that the remediation has been effective.

The latest available Environment Agency figures claim two thirds of land identified as being affected by industrial contamination in England and Wales is estimated to have undergone some form of remediation.

Environmental insurance

Environmental insurance is increasingly being used in property transactions to cover risks associated with contaminated land. Environmental insurance can be obtained directly from specialist underwriters, or through an insurance broker. A broker will normally obtain quotations from a number of different underwriters, in order to negotiate the best insurance cover and premium for a client.

The most common type of environmental insurance covers regulatory and third party claims due to land contamination. Other types of insurance can provide protection against unpredictable costs should site remediation expenses prove difficult to quantify at the planning stage.

When taking out environmental insurance, one of the most important aspects is to understand what circumstances the policy will not cover. Furthermore, as with many insurance policies, environmental insurance policies are often written in a language that is sometimes not at all clear.

Common exclusions from policies are:

- ❖ known contamination;
- ❖ business disruption costs;
- ❖ remediation costs on change in use; and
- ❖ loss in value.

Key contaminated land legislation

The government believes that the planning process provides the best means of remediating sites. In most cases the planning system is capable of handling such issues, for example by requiring Phase II investigations or by requiring remediation to be approved by the local authority prior to development. A new contaminated land regime was introduced in 2001 in the UK (as Part IIA of the *Environmental Protection Act* 1990). This is intended to deal with problem contaminated sites that are not being developed and which would therefore not be dealt with under the planning system.

Definition of contaminated land under Part IIA

For the purposes of the Part IIA legislation 'contaminated land' means land where substances are present in, on or under, the land that are causing, or are likely to cause, significant harm or pollution of controlled waters. Many sites that are contaminated will not fall within the definition and will not be classified as 'contaminated land' under Part IIA. However, such contamination could still have implications for owners and occupiers (for example, in terms of affecting the saleability and marketability of a site) and may still require a Phase II investigation.

Land is only defined as 'contaminated land' if there is a 'significant pollutant linkage' present. There must be evidence of a 'source – pathway – target' relationship. This means there should be a source present, a receptor that could be harmed by the source, for example humans, and a pathway linking the two.

Enforcing authorities

The local authority is duty bound to provide a public register containing information about land that has formally been identified as potentially contaminated, and the action which has been taken to remediate it. Any land that has satisfactorily been remediated prior to a remediation notice being served will not appear on the public register. Furthermore, if land is to be redeveloped in the near future it is unlikely that a notice will be served.

The cost of any clean up will normally lie with the person (or 'appropriate persons') who knowingly caused the contamination. The local authority will ensure the clean up is carried out either through the planning process, via voluntary remediation, or if necessary by serving a remediation notice requiring them to clean up the site. In the case of an emergency the council will remediate the site and recover the costs afterwards.

The local authority has primary responsibility for the identification of contaminated land, although the Environment Agency will respond to requests for information from the local authority on land that it is considering to prioritise for inspection. Where a site has been determined as contaminated land, they must take into account any information held by the Environment Agency on issues of water pollution.

Special sites

Land may also be categorised by the local authority as a 'special site'. This definition includes sites which may be affecting underlying water supplies or major aquifers such as military land, oil refineries and nuclear plants.

Once the local authority has made this designation then the Environment Agency takes over the enforcing role. The Environment Agency would then maintain full responsibility for the site including both the cost of enforcement and also any testing and monitoring required. Should the site become an 'orphan site' (when no knowing polluter is found) then they will also be responsible for the cost of remediation. The disadvantage from the local authorities' perspective is that they do lose control of what can be politically sensitive sites. If there is a dispute as to whether or not the site is a special site the matter can be referred to the Secretary of State for determination.

Remediation notice

The local authority cannot serve a remediation notice until three months have elapsed since the person or persons were notified of the designation of their land as contaminated. If the local authority finds, in the course of the consultation period, additional appropriate persons, it must notify them of the designation of the land as contaminated, and then wait three months before serving any remediation notice on them.

Although the local authority is under a duty to serve a remediation notice, it may wait for more than three months before doing so. This may well be the case where discussions about voluntary remediation are ongoing. It is vital that time limits be set for the actions that are going to be required otherwise it will not be possible for the local authority to initiate enforcement proceedings on the basis that the action has not been carried out. Any remediation notice must effectively be justified with reference to the statutory *Contaminated Land (England) Regulations* 2000 guidance by including the following:

- ❖ the remediation scheme proposed;
- ❖ any exclusion from liability; and
- ❖ any apportionment of costs.

The remediation notice may, therefore, have to be a fairly lengthy document. It should be carefully drafted, so as to attempt to avoid an appeal being made against it. It should be remembered that there might be several remediation notices for each site. Copies should be provided to all the people that were consulted about remediation, and to the Environment Agency. Where there are several appropriate persons for a given action, a single remediation notice may be served on all of them. Details of the notice must be included in the register.

Appeals

There is a right of appeal against a remediation notice. Where the local authority serves a remediation notice the appeal is heard in the local Magistrates' Court. An appeal is made by way of a summary application to the Court. If the Environment Agency serves the remediation notice because it has taken over regulation of a site and it is now the appropriate authority an appeal will be heard by an inspector appointed by the Secretary of State.

The time limit for bringing an appeal is 21 days beginning with the first day of service. A remediation notice, on appeal, can be modified, confirmed or quashed. The remediation notice may be quashed if there is 'a material defect' in the notice. The grounds for appeal are set out in the *Contaminated Land (England) Regulations* 2000. There are a large number of grounds of appeal including:

- the appellant is not the appropriate person;
- the authority failed to exclude the appellant;
- there has been an improper apportionment of costs;
- there is some error with the notice;
- the requirements of the notice are unreasonable having regard to the costs and benefits; and
- the period of time for compliance is insufficient.

Who is liable under Part IIA?

- Remediation notices are served in the first instance on 'Class A' persons, i.e. polluters or knowing permitters of contamination. If these responsible parties cannot be found, the current owner or occupier may be responsible (although for a more limited range of liabilities) – 'Class B' persons. Several parties may be implicated.
- Sellers can avoid liability where there are payments for remediation, with an explicit statement in the sale contract that a purchaser is being paid to clean up land or that the purchase price is being reduced to reflect the contaminated state of the land.
- Sellers/landlords can also avoid liability by selling with information – giving the purchaser (or tenant under a long lease) the necessary information to identify contamination before buying. Where transactions have occurred since 1990 between large commercial organisations, the granting of permission by the seller for the buyer to carry out its own investigations as to the condition of the land, is normally sufficient to indicate that the buyer had the necessary information.

Progress with Part II implementation

The latest available Environment Agency figures indicate that of the estimated 100,000 contaminated sites UK wide, local authorities have formally designated only 406 sites as 'contaminated' under the Part IIA definition, of which 22 have been designated as 'special sites'.

Furthermore, the number of remediation notices served by local authorities remains very low. In most cases remediation is undertaken by site owners via the planning system with infrequent use of remediation statements. Local authorities have so far served only four remediation notices.

Radon

Radon is a radioactive gas that occurs naturally in the earth. It has no taste, smell or colour and detectors have to be used to test its presence. When concentration levels rise within buildings, it can pose a serious risk to health.

Radon occurs when uranium decays and becomes radium. When radium decays, it becomes radon. Uranium is found in small quantities in all soil and rocks. It can also be found in building materials derived from rocks.

Radon rises from the soil into the air. Outdoors, radon is diluted and the risk it poses is negligible. Problems occur when it enters enclosed spaces, such as buildings, where concentration levels can build up.

Radon is everywhere but usually in insignificant, variable quantities. There are some areas in the UK where geographical effects result in higher levels.

The Health Protection Agency (HPA) has produced maps of radon affected areas, which include Derbyshire, Devon, Cornwall, Northamptonshire,

Bristol, Somerset, Yorkshire and the Lake District in England, Grampian and Highland regions in Scotland and County Down and Armagh in Northern Ireland, and Newport and West Cardiff in Wales.

The HPA has set threshold levels for both commercial and residential properties. Detectors should be installed to ascertain the level of radon present.

If the readings exceed the threshold level, remedial works will be required in order to reduce the effects of radon. They offer a search service and report, which specifies whether a property is in a radon affected area and the probability that radon will exceed the action level. However just because a property lies within one of these areas it does not necessarily mean that it will have a problem with radon. The British Geological survey also states whether radon is likely within a particular area as part of its Address Linked Geological Inventory.

Identification of radon

Radon levels vary appreciably with time, so prolonged measurements are required for reliable results. Short measurements can be misleading, low or alarmingly high. The government recommends that people in affected areas test their property for a period of three months using passive monitors in order to provide a reliable estimate of the average radon level. Passive monitors are easy to use, inexpensive and available from Defra. A good rule of thumb is one detector per 100m² of floor area. In larger open planned work areas such as a production area in a factory or an open plan office, the number of detectors may be reduced to one per 500m² of floor area.

Remedial action for high radon levels can be quite straightforward. The best approach is to prevent radon entering the building from the ground by altering the balance of pressure between the inside and outside.

This can be achieved by carrying out the following:

❖ Install a small sump pump below the floor and connect to a low power fan in order to extract the air and reduce the pressure under the floor. This is known as an active sump (a passive sump relies on natural forces to drive air through the system). To minimise inconvenience, the sump may be outside the building with a pipe through the wall. A sump is a reliable and effective remedy that can reduce radon levels by at least a factor of ten. Multiple sumps can be used in large buildings.

❖ Improved ventilation under suspended timber and concrete floors. New airbricks are installed, sometimes together with a fan. This system again limits the amount of radon entering the property.

❖ Increase the pressure in the building by blowing air (called positive pressurisation) from the roof space with a small fan. Best results are in buildings with low natural ventilation. This is a reliable remedy that can at least halve radon levels. Secondary benefits may include a reduction of other indoor pollutants such as carbon dioxide, reduced condensation and a 'fresher' indoor environment.

❖ Alternatively, one may seal ducts, joints and cracks in the floors although this is rarely effective by itself and always laborious. It is helpful to close large openings when a sump is used.

❖ Ventilation (other than positive ventilation).

❖ Install a membrane barrier. This is very difficult to successfully achieve in an existing building.

For domestic properties the DETR recommend six main ways to reduce indoor radon levels to significantly below the action level of 200 Bq/m³.

Remember that it is the average exposure to radon that matters. Short exposure at high levels is not important if over the long term your average exposure is low. This means that you should have time to plan for the solution that is best for the client, property and the radon level. But having found the best solution, it should be implemented as soon as it is practical.

It is best to stop radon entering a house or, if that is not possible, to try and remove it if it gets in. Solutions are similar to those recommended for commercial properties, but with subtle differences:

❖ Install a radon sump pump. The system limits the amount of radon that enters the house and for a typical house it is by far the most effective method. Modern sumps are often constructed from the side of the house so there is no disruption inside.

❖ Improve ventilation under suspended timber floors.

❖ Use positive ventilation. This system is designed to change the air pressure in the house by blowing air in from the loft level. The system both dilutes the radon to acceptable levels and stops some of it getting in.

❖ Seal cracks and gaps in the floors.

❖ Change the way the house is ventilated. This solution is only suitable in quite special cases and has drawbacks.

❖ Install a membrane barrier.

When action has been taken and radon levels reduced, it is recommended to arrange routine checks on fans and other equipment. Periodic measurements of radon should also be made for overall assurance that levels remain low. These guidelines apply to all types of buildings.

Radon and the Building Regulations

With the new understanding of radon risk, the government legislated that houses built since 1988 in parts of Devon and Cornwall and 1992 in parts of Somerset, Derbyshire and Northamptonshire had to have radon protection measures built in. Additionally, the precise areas where radon protective measures should be taken are periodically reviewed by the DETR as new data is provided by the National Radiological Protection Board.

Two zones of risk were allowed for. First the primary zone (the area with the highest risk). Requirement C2 of Schedule 1 of the Building Regulations requires that each house has a radon proof area, together with other precautionary measures that can be upgraded if a risk shows high radon levels. In the secondary zone (where the risk is lower) only precautionary measures must be built in. If a house has precautionary measures, upgrading them (for example, adding a fan to a sump and pipe system) could solve the radon problem quickly and simply.

The BRE has published guidance on protective measures for new dwellings in support of the Building Regulations entitled BRE Report *Radon: Guidance on Protective Measures for New Dwellings*. Equivalent advice has been prepared by the HSE within a document entitled *Radon in the workplace*. The document recommends many similar measures are applicable for non-domestic buildings.

Energy conservation

Some of the ways in which energy efficiency can be enhanced are outlined below:

❖ **Greater thermal insulation.** This is one of the most cost-effective ways of increasing a building's energy efficiency. With new buildings, obviously the starting point is to meet the standards of thermal insulation set out in the current Building Regulations. However, there is a strong argument for further increasing thermal insulation and the level chosen will depend upon a variety of factors including the pay-back period required, the user's pattern of occupation and whether environmental concern outweighs strictly financial considerations. Our existing buildings offer great scope to increase insulation and this can be carried out during refurbishment or maintenance periods when better use can be made of access equipment and other site overheads.

❖ **Efficient lighting.** In commercial buildings, lighting costs usually run between 40% and 50% of total energy costs. Highly efficient lighting that can significantly reduce running costs is now available for both new and existing installations.

❖ **Efficient services.** These require preventative maintenance to ensure that all plant is operating at maximum efficiency. When plant requires renewal, consideration should be given to alternatives, such as condensing boilers or combined heat and power plant, or even whether the plant is required at all; many are re-evaluating the need for air conditioning.

❖ **Building management systems.** These monitor and control all service installations. Due to recent technological advances, these systems are becoming less expensive and can therefore be installed on smaller properties. Even where a full BMS is inappropriate, simple systems are available which control single services such as lighting management systems.

❖ **Using locally sourced materials.** This minimises energy consumption when transporting materials to site.

❖ **Building materials.** Those with a long life expectancy imply energy efficiency because they make good use of resources. The manufacture of building materials entails energy consumption and this varies widely depending on the product. Unfortunately, there is insufficient research into the energy consumed during the manufacture of building materials to allow choices to be made with a great deal of confidence. In the meantime, a useful rule-of-thumb is that the greater the degree of processing or manufacture, the greater the energy consumed.

❖ **Making use of solar gain.** Even with their humblest dwellings, our ancestors frequently designed their buildings to make use of solar gain. Generally this entails the use of large areas of glazing on southern elevations and minimal openings to the north. Increasing numbers of building designers are re-interpreting these techniques.

❖ **The use of soft landscaping.** Trees and other planting can conserve energy in buildings by minimising heat gains and losses. A screen of deciduous planting at the south of a building will filter strong summer sun but will allow for natural heat gain from weaker winter sun. Soft landscaping also has an important part to play in influencing the micro-climate around buildings by reducing wind speeds.

❖ **Out-of-town schemes.** Many of these schemes are built with high levels of thermal insulation and efficient building services. Nevertheless, because of the fuel used in transporting building users from their homes, the whole scheme may be very inefficient in energy terms.

Increased energy efficiency is available at little extra cost – it is just a matter of adopting an environmental train of thought. Increased awareness of these issues by players in the property market and pressure of legislation should be seen as an opportunity to create more energy efficient buildings.

Environment and specification

The environment does not lend itself to simple right-or-wrong selection criteria of materials. However, careful specification does play a part in a complete design and operating philosophy for environmentally responsible building. There are, of course, environmental aspects to the use of all materials but for reasons of space only two model specification clauses are included here: timber and chlorofluorocarbons.

Timber

All references to timber contained within the specification are to be obtained exclusively from sustainable sources. The contractor is to provide evidence, by a supplier's certificate and labelling for each consignment delivered to site, that the timber is from such a source.

The certificate and label should include the following information:

❖ the species and country of origin;
❖ the name of the concession or plantation;
❖ a copy of the forestry policy; and
❖ shipping documents confirming the source.

The Good Wood Seal of Approval by Friends of the Earth would suffice. Information on appropriate suppliers can be obtained from the Timber Trades Federation, Friends of the Earth and the International Timber Trades Organisation.

CFCs, HCFCs and halons

In line with current good practice, the following clauses relating to chlorofluorocarbons (CFCs) hydrochlorofluorocarbons (HCFCs) and halons, their removal and restrictions on use, shall be deemed to have been allowed for in any tender or estimate offered.

Existing plant

Where CFCs or HCFCs are identified as being contained within existing air conditioning or refrigeration plant, the contract administrator is to be informed immediately and instructions obtained.

Where the plant is scheduled, or instructed subsequently, for removal then under no circumstances is the gas to be dumped by venting into the atmosphere. The gas is to be collected for recovery/destruction by a specialist firm.

The contract administrator is to be informed in writing of the specialist undertaking the works, the date for removal and be provided with a copy of the recovery/destruction certificate.

New plant

The contractor shall receive and transmit to the contract administrator documentary evidence from suppliers, subcontractors and designers of all new installations that no new or reused plant contains refrigerants with an ozone depletion potential of more than 0.06 (or with any ozone depleting potential). Furthermore, compounds with the lowest possible ozone depleting potential are to be selected where there is a choice.

As an alternative, consideration can be given to the use of absorption chillers or ammonia chillers.

Halon fire fighting systems

The general requirements for decommissioning the systems shall be the same as for CFCs and HCFCs in plant.

If the system is to be tested, then compressed air or some other non-ozone depleting gas shall be used.

If the system is to be recharged, a leak detection system should be installed. However, the preference is for some other form of fire extinguishing system wherever possible. Depending on the circumstances options include inert gases (Inergen, Argonite, etc.), carbon dioxide and water fog/mist systems.

Hand-held fire extinguishers

All fire extinguishers on site supplied by the contractor, or specified to be supplied in the Schedule of Works section shall be either powder, foam, carbon dioxide, water spray or some other type without the use of halon.

Additional measures

CFCs and HCFCs are used in the manufacture of a variety of other products including insulating materials, carpets, furnishings and aerosol sprays. They must not be used unless specifically instructed by the contract administrator.

BREEAM

The Building Research Environmental Assessment Method (BREEAM) is the world's most widely used system for assessing, reviewing and improving a range of environmental impacts associated with buildings.

Since its launch in 1990 BREEAM has been increasingly accepted in the UK construction and property sectors as offering best practice in environmental design and management. Buildings are assessed against performance criteria set by the BRE and awarded 'credits' based on their level of performance.

The building's performance is then rated as pass, good, very good or excellent.

BREEAM covers a range of building types: offices, homes (known as EcoHomes), industrial units, retail and since January 2005, schools.

BREEAM 2002 was launched on 31 August 2002 by the Building Research Establishment and all new assessments are carried out under this scheme.

BREEAM for Offices is updated every year to ensure best practice and relevance to changing standards and regulations. The challenge to achieve the highest rating has increased as targets are being continually raised.

Developers and designers can utilise BREEAM for a range of reasons including creation of better environments for people to work in, increased building efficiency, improved marketability, increased value and rentals and also as a checklist for comparing buildings.

Clients and developers can use BREEAM as a tool to define and specify the environmental and sustainability performance requirements of their buildings at the briefing stage. Agents can use the rating to promote the environmental credentials and benefits of a building to potential owners and tenants. Designers can use BREEAM as a method to improve the performance, environmental and sustainability aspects of buildings.

A BREEAM Office assessment of the building fabric and services is undertaken plus, as appropriate, the quality of the design and procurement and also management and operating procedures.

The scheme requires a commitment to a number of areas, listed below, that are reviewed by independent assessors who are trained and licensed by the BRE.

- ❖ Management: overall policy, site management via the Construction Confederation Considerate Constructors Scheme and procedural issues.

- ❖ Health and well being: both internal and external issues affecting occupants health.

- ❖ Energy efficiency including operational energy and carbon dioxide issues.

- ❖ Transport: carbon dioxide and location related factors.

- ❖ Water consumption and efficiency.

- ❖ Materials: environmental implications and life cycle impact.

- ❖ Land use regarding greenfield and brownfield sites.

- ❖ Ecology including enhancement of the site as well as ecological value conservation.

- ❖ Pollution of air and water.

To achieve an excellent rating the most cost effective way is to address the main issues at the earliest point of the design process with input from the full project team. A design and procurement prediction checklist is available to assist with this process and it has been recently updated in line with BREEAM Offices 2005 Manual.

A BREEAM assessor can be used to coordinate and collate input from the team and to track the development of ideas. The assessor can also give advice about BREEAM to the entire project team at the start of the project.

As the scheme progresses, the assessor can provide specialist advice on the specification of products to achieve particular BREEAM credits, undertake preliminary BREEAM assessments to assess the predicted rating and provide a sustainability report inclusion with submission for planning approval.

At completion a certificate is awarded and this can be used for promotional purposes.

The European Directive on the Energy Performance of Buildings

The European Directive on the *Energy Performance of Buildings* (EPBD) took effect from 4 January 2006. In the UK, the Directive is being enforced through major changes to the Building Regulations (effective from April 2006) and the introduction of energy certification and will affect both domestic and non-domestic properties.

The Directive will play a vital role in delivering the government's energy objectives.

The Directive's key provisions are:

- ❖ minimum requirements for the energy performance of all new buildings (enforced through Building Regulations);

- ❖ minimum requirements for the energy performance of existing buildings more than 1000m² that are subject to major renovation (also enforced through Building Regulations – improvements must be undertaken but only where they are technically and economically feasible and with a 15 year payback. Historic buildings are not exempt. Improvements will also be required on buildings less than 1000m² through Building Regulations where, for example, parts of the building envelope are renewed, such as windows and doors);

❖ energy certification of all buildings (which on public buildings needs to be prominently displayed). Certification will be required to be in place prior to sale or lease of buildings which will need to be renewed every ten years; and

❖ regular mandatory inspection of boilers and air-conditioning systems in buildings (a practical inspection and assessment method is currently being developed at the time of writing).

It is anticipated that qualified and/or accredited independent experts will be required to carry out inspections and issue certificates. Details are due to be provided from the Department for Communities and Local Government (DCLG) in due course. The proposed implementation strategy has yet to be agreed (at the time of publishing). Energy performance certificates for dwellings will be compulsory as part of Home Information Packs from 1 June 2007. Energy certification for existing non-dwellings is still undecided at the time of publishing. It is expected that the proposed implementation strategy will be agreed at the early part of 2007 with commercial properties energy rated from 4 January 2009.

To help the government implement the Directive, a high level working group has been established called Directive Implementation Advisory Group (DIAG). This has been formed by representatives of more than 22 key professional bodies and trade associations.

For more information visit www.diag.org.uk or www.communities.gov.uk

Renewable energy

Renewable energy relates to naturally available sources that are constantly being replenished and capable of being harnessed for human benefit, such as energy from the sun, the wind and tides, and energy from replaceable matter such as wood.

Low or zero carbon energy (LZC), synonymous with renewables, is the term normally applied to renewable sources and to technologies which are more efficient than traditional solutions or emit less carbon. LZC technologies being applied to buildings include:

❖ solar thermal systems;

❖ photovoltaics;

❖ district heating and cooling;

❖ combined heat and power;

❖ ground source cooling;

❖ ground source heat pumps;

❖ wind power;

❖ biofuels; and

❖ fuel cells.

Solar thermal systems

Solar air or water collectors absorb solar radiation, which is transferred directly into the interior space or to a storage system to be distributed to the building later.

Photovoltaics

Photovoltaic (PV) systems use solar cells to convert sunlight into electricity. PV is usually installed in parallel with the grid, although stand-alone generation is not uncommon, particularly in isolated areas.

District heating and cooling

District heating, also known as community heating, provides heat from a central source to more than one building or dwelling via a network of distribution mains. Heat may be generated from LZC sources such as CHP or biomass boilers, or heat that would otherwise be dumped to atmosphere can be used.

Combined heat and power

Combined heat and power (CHP), or cogeneration, refers to the simultaneous generation of electricity and heat in the form of hot water or steam. Electricity is generated using an engine or turbine, and useful heat is recovered from the exhaust gases and cooling systems. Tri-generation is a term applied to a CHP system that produces electricity, heating and cooling. The cooling output is generated from the waste heat feeding an absorption chiller.

Ground source cooling

Fluctuations in ground temperature reduce with depth and stabilise to around 9°C to 12°C at about 12m below the surface in the UK. This stored 'coolth' is suitable for directly cooling buildings. The two most common methods use either an 'open' or 'closed' loop circuit embedded within the ground. In an open loop system water is abstracted from the ground and then passed through a heat exchanger, before being discharged back into the ground or to a river. In a closed loop system a continuous loop of pipework is buried in the ground, with water circulated through the pipework network, which acts as a heat exchanger being in direct contact with the earth.

Ground source heat pumps

Ground source heat pumps (GSHPs) make use of refrigeration equipment to extract heat from the stabilised ground temperature and raise it to a more useful output temperature to heat the building. The heat is abstracted from the ground by either an 'open' or 'closed' loop circuit, as described under ground source cooling. The depletion of the heat source is matched by the rate of heat flow back from the surrounding earth and under these circumstances the technology is a renewable source of energy. Because the ground is at a constant temperature the refrigeration process can be very energy efficient. GSHPs can also be used as a means of generating cooling in a building by utilising reverse cycle heat pumps, with the recovered waste heat dissipated to the ground, similar in principle to ground source cooling.

Wind power

Wind power is used to turn a turbine and generate electricity, which is distributed in much the same way as for photovoltaic systems. In order to generate worthwhile quantities of electricity average wind speeds of more than 5–6m/s are typically required. There are essentially two basic kinds of wind turbine in use, defined as horizontal axis and vertical axis. Horizontal axis turbines are the more common comprising a central hub with evenly spaced blades, supported on a tower. Vertical axis systems can be installed without the need for a tower and may be easier to integrate with a building's structure.

Biofuels

Energy from biomass is produced by burning organic matter such as trees, crops or animal dung. The biomass is carbon-based so when used as a fuel it also generates carbon emissions. However, the carbon that is released during combustion is equivalent to the amount that was absorbed during growth, and so the technology is carbon-neutral. The bio-energy created may be in the form of electricity, heat, steam, and solid fuels.

Fuel cells

Hydrogen fuel cell technology, although still at an early stage of development, is starting to be used as a means of storage as opposed to a source of energy. The hydrogen fuel cells can produce heat, power and pure water without releasing any greenhouse gases.

Environmental Liability Directive

The *Environmental Liability Directive* came into force in all EU member states in April 2004. In the UK, although existing legislation already applies to many of the areas covered, the Directive will enforce some important changes, particularly in the area of remediation.

The Directive aims to establish a framework that would prevent 'significant environmental damage' or rectify damage after it has occurred, by forcing industrial polluters (or 'operators') to pay prevention and remediation costs. In this respect it is no different to the *Environmental Protection Act* 1990 and its accompanying Part IIA legislation dealing specifically with contaminated land, which was introduced in 2001.

For this reason, it is thought unlikely that the Directive will lead to an increase in the number of contaminated sites for which UK operators find themselves liable. However, at a more detailed level it does introduce a number of key changes. There will be new, specific criteria for determining environmental damage, as well as the two new categories of complementary and compensatory remediation, which will have implications for UK landowners and the property industry.

Determining damage

As described in the Directive, 'significant environmental damage' will be defined by reference to:

❖ biodiversity, whether protected at EU or national levels;

❖ waters covered by the Water Framework; and

❖ human health (including land contamination when it is a threat to human health).

The Directive provides specific criteria to assess when damage is 'significant'.

Member States will be under a duty to ensure that the necessary preventive or restorative measures are actually taken but will have the flexibility to decide when measures should be taken by:

❖ the relevant operator;

❖ the competent authorities; or

❖ a third party.

What are the implications for landowners?

Operators carrying out 'hazardous' activities will be held strictly liable (i.e. no need to show fault or negligence) for preventing or restoring any damage caused by those activities to land, water and protected habitats and species. In addition, operators carrying out other, less harmful, activities will be held liable when damage to protected habitats and species has been caused by their fault or negligence.

For UK businesses, the most significant changes that will be introduced by the Directive are the two new categories of 'complementary' and 'compensatory' remediation. Under existing UK legislation, operators are only held liable for what the Directive calls 'primary remediation'. This means remedying the particular damage caused in order to return the damaged natural resources and/or impaired services to or towards 'baseline' condition (or that which would have existed had the damage not occurred). However, in the future liability will be extended to include:

- ❖ complementary remediation – any remedial measure taken to compensate for the fact that primary remediation does not result in fully restoring the damaged resources and/or services; and

- ❖ compensatory remediation – any action taken to compensate for interim losses of natural resources and/or services that occur from the date of damage occurring until primary remediation has achieved its full effect.

Operators will automatically be exempt from having to compensate for damage caused:

- ❖ by war or an act of God; or

- ❖ by a third party, despite having taken all safety measures.

Damage from nuclear and maritime accidents falls outside the regime's scope and remains subject to existing treaties.

Opportunities

The Directive is expected to provide opportunities for environmental and property consultants to advise their clients on:

- ❖ whether or not significant damage has occurred to the environment as a result of their business activities;

- ❖ whether or not they can be held liable;

- ❖ what type of remediation will be required and at what cost; and

- ❖ when successful remediation of the site has been achieved.

Timescale

Member states have until 30 April 2007 to incorporate the Directive's provisions into national law. The Directive will not apply to contaminating emissions or incidents prior to this date. Nor will it apply to emissions or incidents resulting from activities that ended prior to this date. As the UK already has wide-ranging environmental legislation in place, it now remains for the government to ascertain whether or not existing law satisfies the EU requirements and whether changes to that law are necessary.

Water Framework Directive

Water quality in England and Wales has improved dramatically in recent years. Building on progress to date, the Water Framework Directive sets out to enforce sustainable water use and promote a range of ecological objectives.

The *Water Framework Directive* (WFD) is the most substantial piece of EC water legislation to date. The Directive came into force on 22 December 2000 and was transposed into law in England and Wales in 2003, with implementation from December 2006. The WFD requires all inland and coastal waters to reach 'good status' by 2015. This new standard is far more rigorous than existing water quality measures, with an estimated 95% of water courses at risk of failing to meet the criteria set out by the Directive.

The key environmental aims of the WFD are to:

❖ prevent deterioration of aquatic ecosystems;

❖ protect, enhance and restore polluted waters and groundwater to 'good status', which is based on ecological and chemical factors for surface water and water quantity and chemical status for groundwater;

❖ comply with water-related standards and objectives for environmentally protected areas established under other EU legislation;

❖ progressively reduce pollution from priority substances (pollutants that represent a significant risk to the aquatic environment) and cease or phase out discharges from priority hazardous substances (those that are the most polluting); and

❖ prevent or limit input of pollutants into groundwater and reverse any significant or sustained upward trends in the concentration of groundwater pollution.

These demanding new environmental objectives will be set within an integrated river basin district structure. Each river basin will have its own management plan (RBMP) for surface and groundwater; all with common objectives and principles. The first RBMPs are to be published by December 2009, with the aim of avoiding the difficulties that can arise from a piecemeal approach. Issues such as the availability of water supply, maintaining water quality in rivers and managing flood risk will, in future, be considered as a whole, not addressed in isolation.

For planners and developers the WFD has far-reaching implications. However, according to the Royal Town Planning Institute (RTPI) many planners remain unaware of the impact it will have on the planning process. As a result, a report has been produced jointly by the RTPI, the Environment Agency, the Local Government Association and the Welsh Local Government Association, to provide advice for planners in advance of the final details of the WFD. The report, *The Water Framework Directive and Planning: Initial advice to planning authorities in England and Wales*, outlines the key elements of the Directive and focuses strongly on its future ramifications.

Spatial planners are increasingly aware of the fundamental need to manage development pressure against a background of challenging water-related issues and constraints. The report recognises the additional requirement on planners, who now need to balance the need to provide water and to treat waste water with a requirement to maintain/improve the water environment.

In some parts of England, major growth is proposed in places where water resources and the ability to handle increased volumes of sewage are already stretched. Implementation of the WFD means that future development will have to be carefully planned so that it does not result in further pressure on the water environment.

However, new development can provide an opportunity to tackle existing pressures on water, through imaginative, high-quality project design and planning as well as the use of planning conditions and obligations attached to planning permissions. The RTPI makes the point that these positive impacts can be linked to the remediation of contaminated land and hence improvements to ground and surface water quality, river habitat restoration, water-use efficiency and protection of natural ecosystems. Where waste or a legacy of contaminated land or mine water is causing pollution, intervention by a range of authorities and agencies will be needed to clean up or at least mitigate these problems. All this will add a new element to both the planning and development processes and therefore it is important that client organisations are aware of the implications for their future projects.

And it is not only at planning stage that property and construction will be affected by the Directive, there may be more technical issues to deal with. For example, the Building Research Establishment (BRE) is in the process of undertaking research into the use of recycled and secondary aggregates (RSA) in structural concrete in the context of the WFD. There is a perception in the construction industry that use of RSA may lead to hazardous materials leaching into the soil from foundations and resulting in drinking or groundwater pollution. BRE is keen to determine whether or not this is the case and is working with the Waste and Resources Action Programme (WRAP) to research the issue. It seems inevitable that other building materials and techniques will also be called into question in future.

At present, a great deal of the detail of the WFD is still to be finalised. However, as it becomes clearer what the full impact of the Directive will be, developers and the construction industry will gain a fuller understanding of its implications.

Recycled materials

In May 2004, the government's Sustainable Buildings Task Group report, *Better buildings – better lives*, recommended that 'revised Building Regulations should specify a minimum percentage by value (at least 10%) of reused/reclaimed/recycled materials in building projects' (see www.dti.gov.uk/sectors/construction/sustainability/sbtg/page11919.html). The group went further to add that a single national code be drawn up for sustainable building (CSB) and that the CSB should be based upon the BRE Environmental Assessment Method (BREEAM), set at a higher, more demanding level than national building regulations.

Recycling makes sense: it enables organisations to deliver on sustainability with no additional cost and stimulates local markets. Removing materials that would otherwise go to landfill has positive benefits on the environment. Current initiatives include analysis of the uses of old car tyres (disposal of which is being restricted) and the recycling of gypsum plasterboard materials, to name but two.

Recommendations for recycled content are based upon a percentage of the value of materials in a building excluding labour costs, with the expectation that the 10% minimum be achieved at no extra overall cost. The recommendations are such that the target could be achieved by using a large amount of low-grade material such as hardcore or recycled aggregate or in the alternative a much smaller amount of a higher value material.

The Waste and Resources Action Programme (WRAP) created by the government in 2000 (www.wrap.org.uk) as part of its waste strategy, has identified a series of what it calls 'quick wins' – options with a higher recycled content that are cost-effective (or at worst cost-neutral) and which offer comparable performance and quality, and are readily available in the marketplace. Both WRAP and BRE consider that using good practice it should be perfectly possible to increase the value of recycled products to well above the 10% minimum.

Recycled materials can be defined as any materials that have been redirected from landfill. Primary materials are those with no recycled content (see BS EN ISO 14021:2001 *Environmental labels and declarations*).

Whilst one might be tempted to believe that the case for recycled materials is the product of recent concerns for the environment, the reality is that for many years, recycled materials, particularly aggregates, have been commonplace. For example, pulverised fuel ash and ground granular blast furnace slag have been covered by British Standards for at least 15 years.

WRAP has identified some 3200 recycled products in the UK – these can be traced from a number of online sources including:

- ❖ www.recycledproducts.org.uk – listing of recycled products available in the UK
- ❖ www.aggregain.org.uk
- ❖ www.bremap.co.uk
- ❖ www.ciria.org/recycling

WRAP also publish online tools to assist in the selection of recycled content in buildings: www.wrap.org.uk

It is important to distinguish between reclaimed and recycled materials. Reclaimed materials may be defined as materials that have previously been used in buildings without reprocessing. The materials may be cleaned or adjusted in size, but essentially they retain their original form. Examples might include timber joists or floorboards, refabricated structural steelwork, reused glass or windows.

By contrast, recycled materials are any materials that have been removed from the waste stream and modified or reprocessed in some way to form an entirely new product. Examples of recycled products include crushed glass as an aggregate, crushed concrete for hardcore, sheet materials containing recycled timber, paper, etc.

The National Green Specification (www.greenspec.co.uk) contains a wealth of information on the use and specification of recycled materials.

Maintenance management

Primary objectives of maintenance management

It is essential that property owners and managers allocate sufficient time and resources to maintenance. Managers need to be aware of the full extent of maintenance liabilities and how much money should be spent and when. Maintenance management requires a systematic approach to ensure high standards, value for money and management control.

Buildings comprise a number of elements. Their constituent materials and components have a range of life expectancies that in most cases will be shorter than the life of the building as a whole. Maintenance is therefore inevitable and arises from failure at this component level.

The primary objectives of maintenance are:

Protection of the investment to ensure high utilisation of the building and its long life

Maintenance affects the profitability of a commercial organisation in a number of ways. First there are the direct costs of labour, plant, materials, and management. The second category is indirect where inadequate maintenance of buildings prevents the organisation from functioning properly.

Safeguarding the return on the investment

Poorly maintained commercial buildings fare unfavourably in the market when compared with their well maintained equivalents. The run down of an investment from lack of maintenance will discourage tenants from wishing to remain in occupation. This will have an effect on rent levels and encourage assignments and vacations on termination of leases.

The control of costs

Timely, planned maintenance enables efficient use of resources.

Establishing a safe working environment

The safety of the building and establishing a safe working environment must be the first priority of the maintenance manager.

Maintenance closes the gap between the actual state of the building and the acceptable standard. The acceptable standard will be dependent upon a number of factors, which may include:

- ❖ statutory requirements (health and safety);
- ❖ tenant or occupant satisfaction;
- ❖ minimising loss of production;
- ❖ morale of users, employers and customers; and
- ❖ public image.

A systematic approach to maintenance management

A systematic approach to maintenance management has a number of elements.

Policy

A building may be an asset to an investor or a resource to the user. The maintenance policy defines the objectives that maintenance of the building sets out to achieve. It is a dynamic concept, subject to change just as the plans and objectives of the user or organisation will change.

Standards have to be defined. The use of 'normal standard' is inadequate. The acceptable range of performance of any element of a building will depend upon the relationship between each of its functional requirements and the use of the building as a whole.

The policy must therefore contain objective criteria to define what constitutes failure or non-conformance in each category. The policy must identify those activities that are sensitive to the physical condition of the building and those building elements that play a significant role in providing the necessary conditions.

Once these components are identified, the acceptable delay time in correcting any failure can be assessed.

The statement of policy constitutes the brief for the maintenance manager. It should cover future requirements of the buildings, changes of use, statutory and legal conditions, maintenance cycles, required standards and acceptable response times for breakdown or failure.

The policy must be regularly reviewed and amended as necessary. Consideration of a maintenance policy often shows that there may be some conflict between parties with different interests, for example, between landlord and tenant.

Survey and data gathering

In order to measure how the buildings compare against the policy, and how to close the gap, it is essential to review all existing maintenance information and to undertake regular condition surveys. These identify the condition of the asset and record the status of the building at any one time. A condition survey has the specific purpose of:

- ❖ identifying maintenance needs;
- ❖ recording the priority of the need;
- ❖ recording proposed remedies and quantities of items requiring attention before the next survey; and
- ❖ predicting the scale of items requiring attention after the next survey.

Planning of work

Having agreed a policy for the organisation and identified work to be done, the first function of the maintenance manager is to formulate a maintenance plan. The objective of planning is to ensure that work is carried out with maximum economy. A key function of maintenance management is to achieve positive control over the work and to avoid overloading or inefficient utilisation of resources. Planned maintenance consists of preventive and corrective work.

❖ **Preventive maintenance**

   That which is carried out at predetermined intervals and is intended to reduce the probability of failure.

❖ **Corrective maintenance**

   That which is carried out after failure has occurred and is intended to restore an item to a state in which it can perform its required function.

Generally speaking, the most economic plan in direct cost terms would be the one that maximises preventive maintenance. However, by definition, this form of maintenance takes place before failure has occurred and some degree of useable life has been wasted. This wasted life has a value that can be costed and must be added to the direct cost of the maintenance resource used. The split of work between preventive and corrective maintenance is a management decision. The actual proportion of each will be determined by reference to the maintenance policy.

Plans must take into account practical considerations and the availability of resources. They are prepared with different time horizons for different purposes:

- ❖ Long term – for strategy, to establish general expenditure levels and to profile the maintenance demands of a property or portfolio over an extended time horizon.
- ❖ Medium term – addressing demands that are predicted within the next five years and to refine budgeting and the assessment of workload.
- ❖ Annual – for work and resource allocations.

Organising

The construction of an organisation and a control system capable of ensuring the implementation of the plan.

The main constituents of a maintenance organisation:

- ❖ Resources – i.e. labour, materials, plant and management. These may be either directly employed or obtained through contracts with outside contractors.
- ❖ Administration – a staff structure for coordinating and directing resources.
- ❖ Work planning and control – the system for work, budget, cost and condition control. At its heart lies a documentation procedure, an information base to support effective decision making.

  The documentation system will include a number of elements such as an asset register, a property information base, and preventive maintenance documentation together with a system for initiating and controlling works: works orders, work request forms, etc. These systems are generally computerised. There are a number of proprietary computer programs available. Such programs revolve around relational databases that can be tailored for strategic work, planning and budgeting right through to processing of day-to-day orders for reactive maintenance.

Procuring

A contract and procurement strategy must be established. The strategy will be driven by the nature of anticipated and known workloads and the need to achieve maximum efficiency of operation.

The workload may include the need to provide reactive maintenance cover for unforeseen or accidental repairs, 24 hour emergency call-out cover, planned maintenance contracts and small items of maintenance work packaged into cost-effective contracts.

The decision about which contract and procurement strategy to adopt will depend on a number of factors including the geographic spread of the portfolio in question; the preferred type of model arrangements to be implemented; and the number and type of resources available to the maintenance manager.

Monitoring

Monitoring and auditing is essential to ensure that the maintenance management system is functioning properly and achieving the requirements of the policy statement and if not, to record deficiencies and initiate corrective action.

The maintenance manager needs to monitor the system and organisation to ensure that quality and value for money is being achieved. The audit is a post examination of maintenance work and procedures, not dissimilar to a financial audit. The audit can be condition, technical, systems or design based.

The condition audit involves the checking of planned maintenance schedules against the actual condition of the building.

The aim of the technical audit is to examine a sample of maintenance activities to investigate how each task has been approached and dealt with.

The systems audit will analyse maintenance management practices. It will establish the true nature and extent of the database being used and how this is stored and accessed. It will look at overall policy and whether or not there are realistic plans and programmes in existence, at the method used for budget preparation, budget control, and for feedback of information to assist managers in future decision-making.

The design audit concentrates on the interaction between design and building performance. In most cases it is a question of lessons to be learned for the future.

Condition surveys

Property assets are extremely important to owners, investors and occupiers and therefore need to be properly maintained and managed (see also 'maintenance management'). Research indicates that UK business fails to understand the importance of its property assets, an important aspect of which is building condition which deteriorates with time, reducing value and utility.

Condition surveys represent an essential means of collecting data and ultimately reporting on the physical condition of a property or portfolio of properties, as well as addressing performance and statutory compliance issues if required.

The RICS guidance note *Stock Condition Surveys* (2nd edition) defines a condition survey as follows:

▌A survey of property assets to collect information about the ▌condition of stock for a defined purpose.

Condition surveys are of benefit to everyone involved in the ownership, occupation and investment in property. For owners, occupiers and managers, these surveys can provide a database of information identifying maintenance and repair work as well as the timescale for undertaking that work allowing budgeting, assessment of compliance and strategic planning. This information may be essential for some clients, particularly public sector, where, for example, there will be a requirement for asset management of education buildings, and for housing, this will form an essential component of a decent homes methodology. For investors, it represents an audit to measure the condition of their asset, while for purchasers it assists in asset valuation by identifying repair and dilapidation liabilities. At strategic/policy making level, it will enable both a view of policy effectiveness, and allow implications of regulatory change to be established.

Briefing, format and content

The agreed brief should define the number of properties to be inspected; for example, for portfolios of large numbers of similar types of property, a sample is often taken rather than surveying the full portfolio. It should confirm whether the surveys will include the internal and external building fabric, building services, infrastructure items such as roads and main services; hard and soft landscaping and boundaries; and the extent and detail of statutory compliance items. Agreement should be reached on the depth of the survey and the approach to complex defects which will often need to be noted as requiring further investigation, as well as whether any specialist tests and surveys form part of the requirement. The method of costing items should also be established.

The format and content of the reports will inevitably vary across clients and will relate to how they will aim to use and present the data, how they wish to prioritise the works identified, and what type of timescale the condition surveys are considering. Typically, condition surveys tend to consider the condition and works required over five to ten years but may address much longer periods.

The format and content of the surveys will also depend on how the data is to be collected and stored. With the availability of powerful computerised databases, and hand-held computer technology for gathering data, clients may not in fact require much in the way of traditionally written reports, while others would prefer to have a textual report with a basic chart or spreadsheet indicating building assets, building description, condition, priority of remedial works, along with a time frame and budget cost.

It is recommended that there should always be a written report summarising the findings of the survey in addition to confirming the limitations and the brief. It should include a summary of the results, possibly with easily understood graphics, as well as suitable cross reference to electronic files that may have been provided in the process.

Priorities

The classification of repair priorities will also vary but, typically, items affecting health and safety will have the highest priority, while works necessary to maintain an element in repair, or those maintaining civic/corporate standards may be less important. For example:

❖ **Priority 1/serious/unavoidable** – Typically relating to health and safety compliance; items requiring immediate attention to avoid a major breakdown, serious hazard or critical deterioration leading to possible closure of the building.

❖ **Priority 2/poor/essential work** – Typically works that if neglected might lead to damage to the value of the property, and premature replacement.

❖ **Priority 3/fair/necessary work** – Where neglect might affect rental income, the condition of the element is less than adequate and defects need to be remedied within two/three years.

❖ **Priority 4/adequate/desirable** – Works necessary to maintain an element in repair but probably not in the immediate short term. Might include items that would improve working conditions or generate financial benefits such as energy conservation.

In order to avoid ambiguous interpretation of repair items, it is wise to keep the number of categories to a minimum. Whatever categories are adopted should be clearly defined with the survey team appropriately briefed and trained.

The subsequent use of data collected depends very much on how it is stored. It is essential to use spreadsheets or preferably databases that allow data to be filtered and sorted with enquiries run as appropriate to the beneficiaries of the surveys. Prioritisation of condition should, preferably, be undertaken using computers as this enables items to be evaluated with more than one factor, typically not only physical condition but also consequential effect on the asset and the building occupant, as well as management factors and policies.

Frequency of surveys

It is unfortunate that often expensive condition survey exercises are undertaken providing what effectively results in a 'snapshot' of the condition at the time of the survey but thereafter the data is not used or updated. In the case of a property transaction, this 'snapshot' assessment of repair liability is appropriate but to ensure cost effective long term maintenance of building assets, the condition data should be periodically updated. British Standard 8210: 1986 suggests in-depth surveys on a five-year programme, supplemented by two-yearly inspections on a more superficial basis. Clients may choose a different profile but generally the view is that, for maintenance purposes, intervals of a maximum of five years are acceptable. Whether to survey entire portfolios in one go, or to perhaps undertake surveys on a rolling programme on a five-year basis, will depend on many factors, not least the funds available to commission the survey in the first place. Arguably, mass condition surveys of entire portfolios required in a short period may suffer in terms of quality, but if carried out correctly will give an earlier fuller picture than a rolling programme.

Further information

Royal Institution of Chartered Surveyors guidance note, *Stock Condition Surveys* (2nd edition), 2005.

British Standard 8210 (1986), *Guide to Building Maintenance Management*.

'Best value' in local authorities

What is 'best value'?

The government has defined best value as:

> A duty to deliver services to clear standards – covering both cost and quality – by the most economic, efficient and effective means available.

This clearly has a direct bearing on construction-related services provided by local authorities. The government will require local authorities to publish an annual best value performance plan (BVPP) covering the entire range of the authorities' services. This is intended to be a public document and will include an assessment of the authorities' past and current performance against nationally and locally defined standards.

The performance plan will be the main instrument by which local authorities will be held accountable to the local community for delivering best value.

How are best value studies carried out?

The Audit Commission appoint an external auditor to undertake an audit of the authorities' BVPP. In the case of construction related services this is likely to be a professional consultant in the relevant field. The audit will cover:

- ❖ compliance with legislation and guidance;
- ❖ performance information; and
- ❖ continuous improvement strategies (the 4 Cs – see below).

'The 4 Cs'

Authorities are required to carry out a Best Value Review as part of the BVPP this includes putting in place strategy for continuous improvement implementing the '4 Cs':

- ❖ **Challenge** – why and how the service is being provided.
- ❖ **Compare** – with others' performance (including organisations in the private sector) across a range of relevant indicators.
- ❖ **Consult** – with local taxpayers and service users with the view to setting new performance targets.
- ❖ **Compete** – as a means of securing efficient and effective services.

More detail regarding the methods of inspection can be seen on the Audit Commission website www.audit-commission.gov.uk or at www.localregions.detr.gov.uk

Continuous improvement for construction and property services

A Service Improvement Plan (SIP) is one which identifies areas of potential improvement from:

- ❖ those services already subjected to a Best Value Review;
- ❖ advice from the Audit Commission inspection service; or
- ❖ advice from an external consultant by way of a best value 'healthcheck' (commonly termed a 'critical friend').

Depending on the particular service, the following core issues will be included in the SIP:

- ❖ Description of action – to be taken to improve service.
- ❖ Target – either qualitative or quantitative.
- ❖ Target and timescales – timescale for achieving the improvement(s).
- ❖ Likely effect – impact of the improvement identified.

Other issues which are likely to be included in construction related services could be:

- ❖ current performance;
- ❖ national benchmarks;
- ❖ resource requirements; and
- ❖ monitoring and review strategies.

This overview of best value is intended to give some insight into government efforts in improving services to the taxpayer. When considering the detail of Service Improvement Plans for construction and property related services it is recommended that consultancy advice be sought.

Material and component life

The life expectancies of common building components and materials need to be understood when carrying out building surveys, planned maintenance schedules, life cycle costing exercises and other surveying tasks.

Life expectancies of components or materials are impossible to accurately predict, depend on many criteria and, in this case, are based on a number of basic assumptions:

- ❖ it has been handled and installed correctly;
- ❖ it is of reasonable quality;
- ❖ it is not subject to extreme weather conditions; and
- ❖ it is subject to a reasonable amount of maintenance.

Estimated life spans will need to be altered if the above do not apply and common sense should prevail. The life expectancy figures below take into account both physical and increasing maintenance cost factors but components may be replaced earlier, for instance, for reasons of appearance or style, or in order to meet contemporary technical standards. It should be noted that guarantee durations offered by companies are (for precautionary reasons) usually less than the average life span.

The information in the following table is a guide only and has been taken from a number of sources with a typical life span used.

Material/component	Life span (years)
Clay tile covering to pitched roof	70–80
Fibre cement slates to pitched roof (integrity not coating life)	30–35
Slate covering to pitched roof	75–90
Liquid organic coatings to profiled steel cladding to pitched roof (light colours)	20–25
Asbestos-cement corrugated covering to pitched roof	35–45
Bitumen felt covering to flat roof (highly dependent on felt quality)	15–25
Asphalt covering to flat roof: exposed asphalt, insulated deck	25–30
Asphalt covering to flat roof: exposed asphalt, uninsulated deck	30–35
Asphalt covering to flat roof: concealed asphalt, inverted roof	40–50
Flexible PVC covering to suitable flat roof	30–35
Cold applied liquid overcoating to suitable flat roof	20–30
Cast iron rainwater goods (pipework usually more durable than gutters)	40–50
Plastic rainwater goods	20–25
Aluminium framed curtain walling	30+
Double glazed units (before misting in glazing void): undrained framework	10–15
Double glazed units (before misting in glazing void): drained framework	25+
Softwood/aluminium/PVCu framed windows	25–35
Steel framed windows	50+
Liquid organic coatings to window frames	20–30

Sources

BMI Guide to Life Expectancy of Building Components

HAPM Component Life Manual

Building Research Establishment

Watts

Sources of information in maintenance management

BMI/BCIS

Building Maintenance Price Book, published annually

SR 338 *The Economic Significance of Maintenance*, Feb 2006

SR 341 *Review of Maintenance Costs 2006*

SR 343 *Review of Occupancy Costs 2006*

BSRIA

AG1/87.1 *Operating and Maintenance Manuals for Building Services Installations 1990*

AG4/89.2 *Maintenance Contracts for Building Engineering Services (2nd edition) 1992*

AG24/97 *Operation and Maintenance Audits 1997*

AG1/98 *Maintenance Programme Set-up 1998*

AG20/99 CD *Cost Benchmarks for the Installation of Building Services* Parts 1-3 1999

AG4/2000 *Condition Survey of Building Services 2000*

AG1/2003 *Condition-based Maintenance: Using Non-destructive Testing 2003*

BG2/2004 *Computer-based Operating and Maintenance Manuals – Options and Procurement Guidance 2004*

BG7/2004 *Business-focused Maintenance Toolkit 2005*

NJCC

Procedure Note 16, *Record Drawings and Operating and Maintenance Instructions and the health and safety file* (2nd edition), June 1996, RIBA Publications

Note: NJCC no longer in existence, but guidance notes still in general use.

RICS

Building Maintenance: Strategy, Planning and Procurement, RICS guidance note, 2000, RICS Books

Computerised Maintenance Management Systems, A Survey of Performance Requirements, May 1999, RICS Research Paper

Miscellaneous

Building Maintenance Management, Chanter & Swallow, (2nd edition) August 2000, Blackwell Science

Building Maintenance and Preservation, Mills, 1996, Butterworth-Heinemann Ltd.

Lee's Building Maintenance Management, P. Wordsworth, (4th edition) November 2000, Blackwell Science

Maintenance Management – Its Auditing and Benchmarking, A. Kelly, 2005

British Standards in maintenance management

BS 3811	Glossary of Terms in Terotechnology	1993
BS 3843	Guide to Terotechnology	1992
	Pt 2 Introduction to techniques and applications. Pt 3 Guide to the available techniques	1992
BS 6150	Code of Practice for Painting Buildings	2006
BS 6270	Code of Practice for Cleaning and Surface Repair of Buildings Pt 3 metals (cleaning)	1991
BS 7543	Guide to Durability of Buildings and Building Elements Products and Components	2003
BS ISO 15686	Buildings and constructed assets. Service life planning. General principles	2000
	Pt 2 Service Life Prediction Procedures	2001
	Pt 3 Performance Audits and Reviews	2002
	Pt 6 Procedures for considering environmental impacts	2004
	Pt 7 Performance evaluation for feedback of service life data from practice	2006
BS 8210	Guide to Building Maintenance Management	1986
BS 8221	Code of Practice for Cleaning and Surface Repair of Buildings	
	Pt 1 Cleaning of natural stones, brick, terracotta and concrete	2000
	Pt 2 Surface repair of natural stones, brick and terracotta	2000

Cost management

Urban regeneration

What is urban regeneration?

As cities and urban conurbations grow they constantly change to respond to demand and supply according to prevailing economic, social and environmental factors. Many thriving communities lose their regenerative capacity over time and fall into decline. We know many examples from our own history such as the economic decline of the London Docklands and the pit communities in the north, or social decline in the major cities such as Manchester's Hulme district.

Sustainable urban regeneration requires a balanced mix of social, economic and environmental factors to enable each area to establish its own continuous regenerative capacity.

Urban regeneration projects tend to be large scale and multi-faceted; successful schemes incorporate mixed uses such as commerce, retail, industrial and of course residential. They also have a mixture of tenures including freehold and leasehold in both the public and private sectors. Projects often involve many different organisations such as local authorities, government bodies, private developers or house builders and social housing providers and more.

Key players

The key players in urban regeneration can be divided into the following groups:

- ❖ Government Departments and Agencies: English Partnerships is the national regeneration agency and reports to DCLG. Regional and local agencies include the likes of SEEDA, EEDA, London Development Agency, Sheffield One, etc.
- ❖ Local and regional authorities are often key landowners and major drivers of urban regeneration in their deprived areas. They also have land assembly powers.
- ❖ Housing associations, who are key to the provision of social and public sector housing and management.
- ❖ Private house builders are often essential to realising the economic value of many urban areas and providing initial capital investment.
- ❖ Private developers: many schemes require commercial, industrial, retail and other property essential to the initial and continuing regenerative capacity of an area.
- ❖ Private business and occupiers are essential to local economic welfare.
- ❖ Investors and funders are essential for raising the requisite capital.
- ❖ Infrastructure companies including transport, statutory supplies and services.

Types of regeneration

Urban regeneration can be classified into three main types:

- ❖ Urban centre renewal – town centre regeneration schemes like Lewisham High Street.
- ❖ Estate regeneration – generally housing based schemes in deprived and declining areas.
- ❖ Urban renewal and new urban villages – schemes like the Greenwich Millennium Village.

Key areas for growth

The DCLG has identified four key areas for growth to meet a massive predicted shortfall in housing provision in the South East. These include:

- ❖ Thames Gateway;
- ❖ Cambridge – Stanstead – London Link;
- ❖ Milton Keynes (and East Midlands); and
- ❖ Ashford.

The predominant focus in these areas will be to bring developers together with the central government agencies tasked to deliver government housing policy. This will be influenced by a switch of development responsibilities, particularly funding, away from RSLs direct to developers.

Procurement strategy

The projects associated with urban regeneration are large and activity is set to continue over the long term. Various forms of Public Private Partnership are essential in bringing together necessary resources and skills to undertake:

- ❖ land assembly and contamination issues;
- ❖ infrastructure development for transport and statutory services;
- ❖ social infrastructure development for essential schools, hospitals, affordable housing, etc.;
- ❖ planning and urban design for sustainable communities and buildings;
- ❖ construction industry supply chain management, standardisation and innovation in techniques; and
- ❖ funding and capital development routes.

New skills will be required in integrating development management with project management in the context of regeneration.

Each regeneration project will have its own unique and challenging dimensions across the economic, social and environmental factors that make for sustainable placemaking for the benefit of people today and future generations.

VAT in the construction industry – zero rating

VAT and construction works

VAT in relation to buildings and construction is a complex area but below are some of the fundamental issues to consider when building new or carrying out works on an existing property.

Building new property

All goods and services supplied for use in the construction of a building are standard rated (at 17.5% generally and 5% in specific situations) except in the following circumstances, when they would be zero rated:

Where the new building is a dwelling and it is:

- ❖ self contained;
- ❖ able to be sold as a single dwelling;

❖ has been granted planning consent; and

❖ entitled to be used as a dwelling throughout the year.

NB: Certain elements within a dwelling will always be standard rated (see later note). This zero rating only applies to goods and services supplied in the course of construction of a new building and to the first grant of a major interest, by the developer.

Relevant residential building fulfilling the following criteria:

❖ facilities shared by residents, for example, children's homes, old people's homes, hospices, living quarters for school pupils or armed forces; and

❖ an institution which is the sole or main residence for 90% of its residents.

NB: Flats and sheltered housing schemes made up of individual flats will be zero rated as dwellings rather than relevant residential buildings.

NB: Prisons, hospitals and hotels are specifically excluded from zero rating. This applies to goods and services and the first grant of a major interest.

Relevant charitable building is:

❖ a building used solely by a charity for the **non-business use** of the charity or as a village hall.

NB: The supply must be made to the person who intends to use the building for such purposes before the supply is made, then the person receiving it must give to the person making the supply a certificate that the intended use is for relevant residential or charitable purposes.

Works to an existing property

All goods and services supplied will be standard rated except in the following circumstances:

Relevant Housing Association (HA) converting a building from non-residential to residential use, to alllow zero rating the HA must:

❖ be a Registered Social Landlord within the meaning of Part 1 of the *Housing Act* 1996; and

❖ be a registered HA within the meaning of the *Housing Associations Act* 1985 (or Part II of the *Housing (Northern Ireland) Order* 1992).

NB: This applies to goods and services only.

Approved alterations to existing protected buildings – basic principles to allow zero rating are as follows:

❖ the work must be to a qualifying protected building as defined in VAT law and to the fabric of that building (for example, a listed building or scheduled monument);

❖ the work must require and be granted listed building consent;

❖ the works must not be of a repair or maintenance nature; and

❖ the works must be apportioned if there is an element of both repair and maintenance and approved alteration.

NB: Unlisted buildings in conservation areas do not qualify as protected buildings for the purposes of VAT relief. This applies to goods and services only.

Substantial reconstruction to existing protected buildings – basic principles to allow zero rating are as follows:

- ❖ definition of protected buildings as above;
- ❖ the work must require and be granted listed building consent;
- ❖ at least 60% of the cost is attributable to 'approved alterations'; or
- ❖ only the wall(s) remain along with the other features of architectural or historic interest.
- NB: This applies to the first grant of a major interest to the person carrying out the substantial reconstruction.

Conversion of buildings from non-residential use to dwellings or relevant residential use:

- ❖ from 1 March 1995 if you are the person converting a building the first grant of a major interest can be zero rated provided the building was neither designed nor adapted as a dwelling (or relevant residential purpose), or if it was designed as a dwelling and/or subsequently adapted, it has not been used as a dwelling for the whole of the previous ten years.

Residential conversions

From 12 May 2001 a lower rate of 5% applies to the following supplies of building services and related goods:

- ❖ a 'changed number of dwellings conversion', i.e. a conversion of a building (or part of a building) so that after conversion it has a different number of single-household dwellings (SHD) from the number before the conversion;
- ❖ a 'house in multiple occupation conversion', i.e. a conversion of a building (or part of a building) containing one or more single-household dwellings so that it contains only one or more multiple-occupancy dwellings; and
- ❖ a 'special residential conversion', i.e. a conversion of premises containing dwellings (single-household or multiple occupancy) for use solely for a relevant residential purpose or converting a care home into a single-household dwelling.

Renovation and alteration of dwellings

The lower rate of 5% also applies to supplies of:

- ❖ building services; and
- ❖ related goods.

In the course of the alteration (including extension) or renovation of a single-household dwelling that has been empty for three years. 'Empty' means unlived in, so use for another purpose, such as storage, is acceptable. The dwelling can remain a single household.

Specific conditions apply to both of these lower rate situations.

The reduced rate of VAT

The reduced rate of 5% VAT applies from 1 June 2002. The reduced rate is extended to the costs of:

- ❖ converting a non-residential property into a care home or multiple occupancy dwellings, e.g. bedsits;
- ❖ converting a building used for 'relevant residential' purpose into a multiple occupancy dwelling;
- ❖ renovating or altering a care home or other qualifying building that has not been lived in for three years or more; and
- ❖ constructing, renovating or converting a building into a garage as part of the renovation of property that qualifies for the reduced rate.

Charity annexes

Prior to 1 June 2002 all of an annexe had to be used or intended for use for a relevant charitable purpose in order to zero rate its construction. From 1 June 2002, there is a concession whereby minor non-qualifying use for example, use where the annexe or part of an annexe is not used solely for a relevant charitable purpose, can be ignored with there being no requirement to apportion these between relevant charitable purpose and alternative usage.

Supplies to handicapped people

Certain goods and services supplied to a handicapped person, or to a charity for making them available to handicapped people for their domestic or personal use, may be zero-rated.

DIY projects

For claims made on or after 29 April 1996, HM Revenue and Customs will refund any VAT chargeable on the supply, acquisition or importation of any goods used in connection with construction or conversion work where the following criteria are met: the work is not part of a business project; the work comprises the construction of a dwelling, relevant residential or charitable building; or is the conversion of a non-residential building into a dwelling.

All works, which fulfil the criteria set out above, can be zero-rated. However there are some items, within these categories, which will always be standard-rated:

- ❖ site investigations;
- ❖ temporary site fencing;
- ❖ concrete testing;
- ❖ site security;
- ❖ catering;
- ❖ cleaning to site offices;
- ❖ temporary lighting;
- ❖ transport and haulage to and from site;
- ❖ plant hire (without operator);
- ❖ professional services (architects, engineers, surveyors, solicitors, etc.);
- ❖ landscaping;
- ❖ furniture (other than fitted kitchens) – material only;
- ❖ some electrical or gas appliances – material only; and
- ❖ carpet and carpeting materials (including underlay and carpet tiles) – material only.

See the following notices issued by HM Revenue and Customs for further expanded information and definitions:

- ❖ Notice 708 VAT Buildings and construction
- ❖ Notice 742 Land and property
- ❖ Notice 719 VAT refunds for 'do it yourself' builders and converters
- ❖ Notice 701/1 Charities
- ❖ Notice 701/7 VAT reliefs for people with disabilities
- ❖ Notice 701/19 Fuel and power
- ❖ Notice 708/5 Registered social landlords (housing associations, etc.).

The primary legislation relating to this subject includes:

- ❖ Group 5 of Schedule 8 to the *VAT Act* 1994 as amended by Statutory Instrument 1995 No 280 and Statutory Instrument 1997 No 50 – buildings under construction
- ❖ Group 6 of Schedule 8 to the *VAT Act* 1994 as amended by Statutory Instrument 1995 No 283 – approved alterations to protected buildings
- ❖ Group 12 of Schedule 8 of the *VAT Act* 1994 – supplies to the handicapped
- ❖ Section 35 of the *VAT Act* 1994 – DIY scheme
- ❖ The *VAT (Input Tax) Order* 1992 as amended by Statutory Instrument 1995 No 281
- ❖ Schedule 10 to the *VAT Act* 1994.

Capital allowances for taxation purposes

The following provides a brief summary of the capital allowances that are available to UK property owners, occupiers and investors. It is intended as an overview at the time of publication and the authors would direct readers who require more detailed or specific advice to contact a capital allowances expert.

The UK taxation system has no general provision for tax relief for capital expenditure or for the depreciation in value of capital assets with the passage of time. Although there are numerous accounting standards detailing how the depreciation of capital assets must be dealt with for accounts purposes, there is no allowable deduction for tax purposes. Accounting depreciation is therefore added back to the accounting profits when computing the tax charge.

Capital allowances provide tax relief for at least some of this accounting and tax mis-match. Qualifying capital expenditure incurred on certain buildings, fixtures and chattels will attract specific rates or amounts of tax relief, which are available to be offset against taxable profits.

This valuable form of tax relief is, in most cases, either under-claimed or not claimed at all due to a lack of understanding or application of the legislation and case law governing the availability of the relief.

General scheme of allowances

There are certain hurdles that must be cleared before capital allowances can be claimed. The entity incurring the expenditure must be within the charge to UK tax, therefore local authorities, government departments, charities, pension funds, etc. will not be in a position to use the relief (although they may be able to pass the benefit on for consideration).

The expenditure must be capital in nature, i.e. there must be an enduring benefit to the trade of the entity incurring it, e.g. the initial acquisition of an asset, or the subsequent improvement of it. Expenditure on the maintenance or general upkeep of an asset or on the development of an asset held as trading stock is likely to be classed as revenue. Revenue expenditure will not qualify for capital allowances, but could still potentially be tax deductible in its entirety in the year it is incurred. It should be noted that the revenue deduction is dependent on the accounting treatment of the expenditure. Revenue expenditure that is capitalised for accounts purposes, e.g. to improve the balance sheet, will not qualify for the 100% deduction in the year it is incurred.

The capital expenditure must be incurred for the purpose of a qualifying activity, e.g. a trade, profession, vocation, etc. In some circumstances, the asset that is acquired or created must also be 'in use' for the purpose of the qualifying activity.

Finally, the capital asset that is acquired or created must be qualifying for capital allowances purposes, and in this regard many tests have evolved through statute and case law.

Types and rates of allowances

Plant and Machinery Allowances (P&MAs)

These are given at a rate of 25% per annum on a reducing balance basis, i.e. 25% of the balance of the qualifying expenditure carried forward year on year. There is generally little help from the tax legislation on what constitutes qualifying P&M and therefore there has been much litigation in this area. Specialist advice should be taken, but typical examples will include IT equipment, heating and ventilation systems and specialist mechanical and electrical installations.

Qualifying P&M that has a useful economic life, when new, of exceeding 25 years is deemed to be a Long Life Asset (LLA) by the capital allowances legislation. The test applies from when the P&M is first used, therefore a second hand asset with a useful economic life of less than 25 years at the date of purchase may still be a LLA in the new owner's business. LLAs attract allowances at a rate of 6% per annum on a reducing balance basis and are therefore less attractive than non-LLAs. Excluded from this is expenditure incurred on a dwelling house, hotel, office, retail shop or showroom.

Expenditure incurred on new (unused) qualifying P&M by a small or medium sized enterprise (SME) will attract a first year allowance of 40%. The balance will be relieved in subsequent years on the 25% reducing balance basis.

Specific legislation exists to give a 100% first year allowance for expenditure incurred on new P&M that satisfies defined energy saving or environmentally friendly criteria.

Hotel Building Allowances (HBAs), Industrial Buildings Allowances (IBAs) and Agricultural Buildings Allowances (ABAs)

These categories of buildings have been grouped together as they all attract allowances at the rate of 4% per annum on a straight-line basis, ie the qualifying expenditure is written off over a period of 25 years from when the building is first used.

The properties must satisfy certain criteria specified in the capital allowances legislation in order to be 'qualifying'. For HBAs, the property must be open for four months or more between April and October, have a minimum of 10 letting bedrooms and provide guest services of at least breakfast, dinner and room cleaning. For IBAs and ABAs the test relates to the use to which the building is put, therefore there has to be qualifying industrial or agricultural use for the relief to be forthcoming.

Research and Development Allowances (R&DAs)

Expenditure incurred on facilities used for qualifying R&D attracts allowances at 100% in the first year. Again, the accounting treatment of the expenditure is key and this is supplemented by published guidelines providing more clarity. The underlying test is innovation.

Capital allowances issues for property transactions

Except where it has already been identified that qualifying expenditure must be on 'new' P&M, capital allowances are available on the purchase of second hand assets. There are many tests and restrictions that apply to property transactions to ensure that a subsequent owner is restricted in its claim to the original cost of the asset. Where no previous capital allowances claim has been made, there may be an opportunity to 'step up' the new owner's claim to reflect the price that it has paid for the asset, where this is greater than the original cost.

The vendor and the purchaser must apportion the purchase price, on a just and reasonable basis, between the components of the sale, i.e. the interest in the land, the building and the qualifying P&M. These figures are then compared to the original cost to establish what restriction may apply to the subsequent claim and conversely what disposal proceeds the vendor must account for on sale. In some situations, it is possible for the parties to the transaction to agree and formally elect for a specified value to be attributable to fixtures qualifying for P&MAs. The effect of the election is that all, part or none of the allowances can be passed between the transacting parties. Tax aware parties may be able to negotiate an adjustment to the purchase price to reflect the agreed capital allowances position.

It is important to establish the capital allowances history of a property during the pre-acquisition due diligence. The information that will be relevant to the claim is generally more readily made available at this time, than post-transaction and the opportunity to obtain any additional benefit through joint elections may not arise once the deal is concluded.

The following table provides a guide to the expected levels of qualifying P&M that may be available on an unrestricted basis for differing property and transaction types. It should be noted that depending on the type of property, ABAs, HBAs or IBAs might also be available in addition to the expected P&MAs identified.

Property type	Acquisition / disposal Qualifying %	New build Qualifying %
Office	14% – 25%	15% – 45%
Office refurb/fit-out	–	40% – 100%
Retail	2% – 20%	5% – 35%
Retail refurb/fit-out	–	40% – 90%
Industrial	2% – 15%	5% – 20%
Hotel	10% – 40%	15% – 50%
Hotel refurb/fit-out	–	40% – 80%

Summary

The above is intended as an overview of the current availability of capital allowances. Specialist advice should be sought to maximise the availability and quantum of capital allowances.

Further sources of information

Capital Allowances Act 2001

Income and Corporation Taxes Act 1988

Finance Act 2004

www.eca.gov.org

Land remediation allowances

Various tax incentives have been introduced following the recommendations of the Urban Task Force set up by the government in 1998 to investigate causes of urban decline. Land Remediation Tax Relief is one such generous incentive that provides up to 150% of tax relief for expenditure incurred in remediating contaminated land or, where a company is loss making, a tax credit (payment from the Exchequer) of 24% of the qualifying cost.

Availability of tax relief

The qualifying expenditure must be incurred after 11 May 2001 on qualifying remediation works to land situated in the UK that was acquired for the purpose of a trade in a contaminated state. Land includes interests over land and buildings on the land.

The relief is available for companies but not for individuals or partnerships. A company in limited partnership can claim the relief in respect of its share in the partnership's expenditure on remediation. The relief is not available where the land is contaminated due to the actions of the acquiring company or someone connected with that company, or where the company has failed to prevent contamination.

Land is in a contaminated state if there are substances in, on or under the land that are likely to cause harm to people, property or ecological systems or is likely to pollute controlled waters. Nuclear sites are specifically excluded from the definition of contaminated land.

Qualifying expenditure

Expenditure must be incurred on the prevention, remediation or mitigation of the effects of the pollutant or on the restoration of the land to its former state. The expenditure must be directly linked to the remediation and as such, general site clearance will not qualify. Where in-house employees undertake the work, all of these costs are qualifying provided at least 80% of the time is spent on remediation tasks. Where employee time is less than 80%, some pro-rata adjustment will be necessary.

Preparatory works such as site investigations and incidental professional fees can be included in the claim for the relief. Where remediation work is subcontracted, then this cost will form the basis of the claim.

Claiming the relief

This relief is available to property owners, investors and developers. Any claim for the relief must be made within two years of the end of the accounting period in which the qualifying expenditure was incurred.

Interaction with landfill tax and aggregates levy

There are tax-planning opportunities to structure projects such that the waste from qualifying remediation works is exempt from landfill tax or the aggregates levy.

Summary

The above is intended as an overview of the principles and the current availability of land remediation tax relief. Specialist advice should be sought on the availability and to maximise the quantum of the tax relief.

Further sources of information

Income and Corporation Taxes Act 1988
Finance Act 2001
www.inlandrevenue.gov.uk

Tender prices and building cost indices

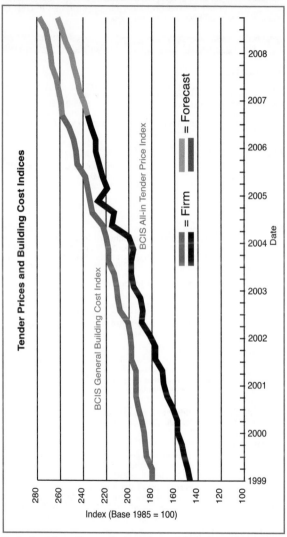

For further information on the breakdown of the indices, please contact the Building Cost Information Service.

The BCIS tender price indices and general building cost indices monitor the movement of tender prices and building costs. They can be used to forecast cost movement for the years to come by using the forecast indices based upon cost trends. The Tender Price Index measures the trend of contractors' pricing levels in accepted tender for new work (cost to client), whereas the General Building Cost Index measures changes in costs of labour, materials and plant (cost to contractor).

Rating revaluation 2005

Introduction

Since the introduction of the *Local Government Finance Act* 1988, rating assessments on business premises are subject to five yearly revaluations. The new 2005 Rating List came into effect on 1 April 2005. This covers England and Wales only and Rateable Values can be accessed at www.voa.gov.uk. Rateable Values for Scotland can now be accessed from the Scottish assessors at www.saa.gov.uk.

Basis of valuation

The 2005 Rateable Values are based on rental values on 1 April 2003, which is known as the Antecedent Valuation Date (AVD). The rating hypothesis as set out in the *Local Government Finance Act* 1988 forms the basis of valuation.

Right first time

The Valuation Office Agency (VOA) has approached the 2005 revaluation under a new modernised agenda to be 'right first time'. The government felt that past revaluations encouraged too many appeals and wanted to create a more efficient system to more accurately forecast budgets and to ensure that the Uniform Business Rate (UBR) is set at an appropriate level.

'Notice Requesting Supply of Information...'

In order to be 'right first time' the VOA have required the return of Information Notices setting out rental information on any given property. The proportion of forms returned is historically low and the VOA can issue a fine of £100 if the form is not completed and returned within 56 days of its issue, to be increased by £20 per day thereafter.

Uniform Business Rate

The uniform business rate (sometimes known as the multiplier) is an amount set by the government each year. There is a UBR for England and one for Wales. It is set to ensure that the overall amount collected in rates only ever increases by the rate of inflation.

England:
The standard UBR for 2006/07 in England is 43.3p
The small business UBR for 2006/07 in England is 42.6p

Transitional relief

Transitional relief is a government scheme which ensures that large increases or decreases in rates bills that are due to the revaluation are phased in gradually over a number of years.

The transitional arrangements spread the burden of increases and the benefit of reductions over the five year period of the List to avoid sharp increases over the first few years. Downward phasing of the transitional relief continues to apply to recoup the losses incurred by the government.

Small-business relief

This is a new relief that came into effect on 1 April 2005. Eligible businesses with rateable values of below £5,000 get 50% rate relief on their liability. This relief decreases on a sliding scale by an estimated 1% for every £100 of rateable value over £5,000 up to £10,000. Your local billing authority will calculate the exact decrease.

The relief is available to ratepayers with either:

❖ one property; or
❖ one main property and other additional properties, providing the additional properties do not have individual rateable values of more than £2,200 and the combined rateable value of all the properties is under £15,000 (or £21,500 in London). The threshold for the combined rateable value is dependent on the location of the main property. The main property is the only one that has the relief applied to it. The additional properties have their charges calculated using the standard multiplier.

For further information on rating valuation please refer to the following websites:

www.voa.gov.uk

www.mybusinessrates.gov.uk

Cost management

Predicting costs

Be mindful:

❖ of the level of information;
❖ of the perceived requirements for budget, time and quality;
❖ that the brief will inevitably change;
❖ that not all of your assumptions will be right; and
❖ that the initial assessment will stick in the client's mind.

Always:

❖ undertake a detailed assessment;
❖ set down clearly all assumptions and exclusions; and
❖ make provision for risk – in the market, in design development and in the client changing his or her mind.

Never:

❖ rely solely on blanket unit rates; or
❖ expect the client to remember anything other than your first assessment.

The procurement process

Be mindful:

❖ that the process of project delivery is dynamic; and
❖ of the inevitability of the design (in part at least) developing apace with construction and that if this design development is not managed, cost and time over-runs will result.

Always:

❖ assess the programme as part of the cost planning process;
❖ clearly describe the brief that you have assumed and are working to;
❖ select an appropriate form of contract and consider not just the value but the nature of the work;
❖ understand the budget and know where the uncertainties are;
❖ maintain projections of cost on an 'open book' basis;

> ❖ make the projections 'real time' and as soon as issues are suspected, make provision; and
> ❖ assess and reassess risk.

Never:

> ❖ avoid routine financial appraisals;
> ❖ proceed on the basis that things will turn out all right if left to their own devices – they never will; or
> ❖ proceed without adequate contingency.

Value for money

Be mindful that:

> ❖ value for money is not just the lowest price;
> ❖ it must balance time, cost and quality; and
> ❖ simply applying competitive tender procedures does not itself demonstrate value for money.

Life cycle costing

The life cycle cost of an asset may be defined as the total cost of that asset over its operating life including initial capital/acquisition cost, occupation costs, operating costs, and the cost or benefit of the eventual disposal of the asset at the end of its life.

Use

Life cycle costing is essential to effective decision-making in four main ways:

> ❖ It identifies the total cost commitment undertaken in the acquisition of any asset.
> ❖ It facilitates an effective choice between alternative methods of achieving a stated objective, recognising different patterns of capital and running costs.
> ❖ It is a management tool that details the current operating costs of assets.
> ❖ It identifies those areas in which operating costs might be reduced.

The use of life cycle costing techniques has seen considerable growth in recent years, driven predominantly by shifts in public sector procurement policy towards 'best value' rather than lowest cost. This policy change is demonstrated in publications such as *Construction Procurement Guidance, No 7 Whole Life Costs* (Office of Government Commerce) which states that 'all procurement must be made solely on the basis of value for money in terms of the optimum combination of whole life costs and quality to meet the user's requirements'. The increasing reliance upon PFI / PPP for the procurement of major capital projects has also contributed to the need to consider the whole life cost of an asset rather than simply the 'up front' capital outlay.

The benefits of life cycle costing should not be construed as being effective for the public sector alone – long term investment returns on property can be influenced significantly by future maintenance/operational obligations which were not considered at the outset of a project. Energy efficiency of buildings in particular, is considered to be a prime candidate for life cycle cost evaluation. In an era dominated by European directives, the Climate Change Levy, etc. the higher capital cost of energy efficient installations can often be more than offset by longer term savings. Adding the benefit of potential tax advantages, the value of effective whole life cost techniques becomes apparent.

As a result, life cycle cost planning should, wherever possible, form an integral part of the design development process, being implemented from project outset to achieve maximum benefit.

Implementation

Implementation of appropriate life cycle costing techniques must reflect not only the nature of the clients' needs but also their property specific objectives. The objectives of an owner-occupier client, retaining a long term interest, will be significantly different from an investor seeking to transfer maintenance risk to a prospective tenant.

The following major elements should therefore be considered:

❖ the overall time period;

❖ all costs and revenues attributable to the project, including initial investment, recurring costs and revenues, proceeds from ultimate sale or other disposal and tax benefits;

❖ only those costs and revenues directly attributable to the project;

❖ the effects of time, including allowance for the impact of inflation; and

❖ the fact that pounds spent or received in the future are worth less than pounds spent or received today.

Stages of life cycle costing

Life cycle costing techniques can be split into the following stages :

Life cycle cost planning (LCCP)

Objectives:

❖ to identify the total costs of the acquisition of a building or building element; and

❖ to facilitate the effective choice between various methods of achieving a given objective.

LCCP can be broken into seven basic steps:

Step 1 – Establish the objective.

Step 2 – Choose alternative options for achieving the objective (consider all realistic possibilities).

Step 3 – Formulate assumptions (e.g. discount rate, construction duration, asset replacement cycle, building life, basis of residual value).

Step 4 – Calculate all capital and recurrent costs over a defined period.

Step 5 – Compare costs and rank the alternatives.

Step 6 – Carry out a sensitivity analysis (i.e. when the results of step 5 are not demonstrably in favour of one choice).

Step 7 – Investigate capital cost constraints.

Applying the foregoing approach for each option under consideration will generate a life cycle cost plan, reflecting all costs and revenues over the selected time period. Recognising that monies spent in the future will be worth less than the same money spent today, the cash flows are discounted to a present day value. The total of all present day values over the life of the LCCP represent the net present value (NPV). Compared against alternative options, the NPV facilitates identification of the option which offers best value for money.

The sequence linking LCCA, LCCP and LCCM

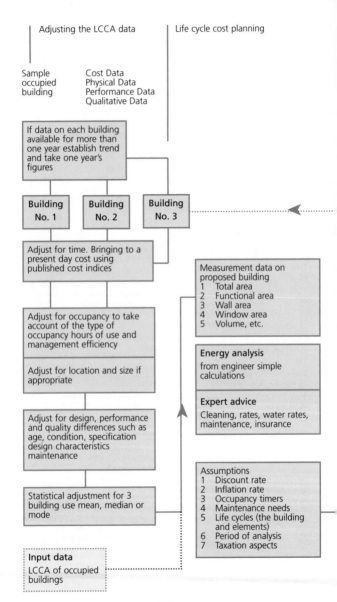

Adjusting the LCCA data | Life cycle cost planning

Sample occupied building

Cost Data
Physical Data
Performance Data
Qualitative Data

If data on each building available for more than one year establish trend and take one year's figures

| Building No. 1 | Building No. 2 | Building No. 3 |

Adjust for time. Bringing to a present day cost using published cost indices

Adjust for occupancy to take account of the type of occupancy hours of use and management efficiency

Adjust for location and size if appropriate

Adjust for design, performance and quality differences such as age, condition, specification design characteristics maintenance

Statistical adjustment for 3 building use mean, median or mode

Input data
LCCA of occupied buildings

Measurement data on proposed building
1 Total area
2 Functional area
3 Wall area
4 Window area
5 Volume, etc.

Energy analysis
from engineer simple calculations

Expert advice
Cleaning, rates, water rates, maintenance, insurance

Assumptions
1 Discount rate
2 Inflation rate
3 Occupancy timers
4 Maintenance needs
5 Life cycles (the building and elements)
6 Period of analysis
7 Taxation aspects

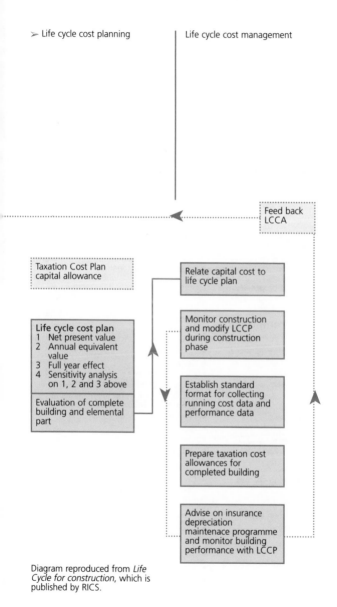

> Life cycle cost planning

Life cycle cost management

Feed back
LCCA

Taxation Cost Plan
capital allowance

Relate capital cost to
life cycle plan

Life cycle cost plan
1 Net present value
2 Annual equivalent
  value
3 Full year effect
4 Sensitivity analysis
  on 1, 2 and 3 above

Monitor construction
and modify LCCP
during construction
phase

Evaluation of complete
building and elemental
part

Establish standard
format for collecting
running cost data and
performance data

Prepare taxation cost
allowances for
completed building

Advise on insurance
depreciation
maintenace programme
and monitor building
performance with LCCP

Diagram reproduced from *Life
Cycle for construction*, which is
published by RICS.

Life cycle cost management (LCCM)

Objectives:

- ❖ to identify areas where running costs might be reduced;
- ❖ to establish where performance differs from the LCCP projection;
- ❖ to make recommendations on more efficient utilisation of the building;
- ❖ to provide information on asset lives and reliability factors for accounting purposes;
- ❖ to assist in the establishment of a maintenance policy for the building; and
- ❖ to give taxation advice on building related items.

LCCM therefore applies throughout the operational phase of a building's life, focused upon maintaining and/or improving the asset's efficiency. LCCM should be read in conjunction with maintenance management.

Life cycle cost analysis (LCCA)

Objectives:

- ❖ to provide a management tool which identifies actual operating costs incurred; and
- ❖ to relate cost and performance data to advisers about the running costs of occupied buildings.

LCCA is an ongoing operation, contributing to both LCCP and LCCM – in practice, one cannot take place without the other.

While each component can be viewed as a separate activity in its own right, there is a logical sequence that links them together. The sequence is demonstrated in the figure on the previous pages, where a life cycle cost plan for a proposed project is based upon three similar buildings for which life cycle cost analyses are available.

Main components

Consider the following when implementing life cycle cost techniques:

1 Capital costs	• Land (including cost of acquisition)
	• Demolitions
	• Construction costs
	• Fit-out expenditure
	• Decanting charges (including rental of temporary accommodation)
	• Relocation expenses
	• Professional fees
	• Statutory fees
	• VAT (and other taxes)
2 Financing charges	• Cost of finance for land/site acquisition
	• Cost of finance during occupational period
3 Operation costs	• Heating, electricity and other energy
	• Cleaning and caretaking
	• Rates
	• Insurance
	• Security and public health
	• Staff (building related)
	• Rent

	• Management charges
	• Land charges
4 Maintenance costs	• Life cycle asset replacement (specific)
	• Annual maintenance (general)
	• Annual grounds maintenance (general)
5 Residual values	• Disposal of existing buildings, land, etc.
	• Disposal of temporary decant accommodation
	• Retained value at end of evaluation period
6 Revenue	• Other income derived from the accommodation
	• Benefit of capital allowances or other incentive.

Other considerations

The discount rate and inflation

When compiling life cycle cost plans, it is important to distinguish between the interest rate and the discount rate. Where project cash flows include an allowance for inflation, the discount rate should make an equivalent allowance. Alternatively, where estimates are in current prices, they should be discounted at the real discount rate.

While there is no definitive approach, it is reasonable to state that if all cost estimates are expected to inflate at the same rate then it is not unreasonable to perform all calculations in current prices, applying a real discount rate. Alternatively, where cost estimates are likely to inflate at different rates (e.g. energy costs inflating significantly faster than construction prices) then it may be beneficial to account for the differing rates of inflation.

In the case of financing through borrowing, the discount rate will equal the long term cost of borrowing money in the market place (net of inflation). While the discount rate will vary with the source of funding, it is worth noting that HM Treasury apply a discount rate of 3.5% in public sector option appraisal.

Project life

An estimate of the probable life of the project should be made. When ranking projects with identical lives, the option with the lowest present value should be chosen. However, where the options have different lives, the cost of each alternative should be expressed as an annual equivalent and the option with the lowest annual equivalent chosen.

Reinstatement valuations for insurance purposes

Generally it is considered prudent to insure a property for the value of complete reinstatement following total destruction (including partial destruction that necessitates demolition and rebuild). However, some clients request that only a portion of less vulnerable elements of the building (for example, external areas such as car parking and hardstandings) are included in the valuation.

When compiling a reinstatement valuation the following points should be considered:

❖ Demolition cost to be valued.

❖ Rebuilding costs to be valued (initially at 'Day One' rates). Care must be taken here to include for any special features that are to be included to enable replacement of the property on a like for like basis. Examples include facade treatments such as stonework embellishments or internal features such as specialist decorations.

❖ Extent of the valuation to be discussed and agreed with the client: whether tenant's fixtures and fittings are to be valued; whether a basic landlord fit out is to be included; or a shell only valuation with all other items to be included under separate policies. This may be done on agreement with the client or by reference to leases which state the obligations of the landlord and tenant.

❖ Professional fees to be included at an appropriate level, depending on the complexity and location of the property.

❖ Geographical location factors to be accounted for either in rebuilding rates or separately by reference to recognised indices.

❖ Local authority planning and building regulation fees must be included as they are an unavoidable expense.

If the valuation is being projected to cover the period of the policy (as opposed to Day One valuation) then account should be made for the:

❖ period of the policy;

❖ design period;

❖ planning period;

❖ construction period; and

❖ void (letting) period (if required by the owner).

This may result in projecting costs for anything up to and beyond a three year period. In addition, as with any construction scheme, a contingency may be included.

In summary, a Day One valuation may increase by upwards of 30% on the basic rebuild costs to take account of the issues listed above. Property owners should always seek a realistic valuation of their property to avoid being over or under-insured. At best the premiums may be based on an exaggerated value and at worst, following destruction, there will be insufficient funds to reconstruct.

APC student help

The RICS Assessment of Professional Competence

What is it?

The Assessment of Professional Competence (APC) is a route to professional membership of the Royal Institution of Chartered Surveyors (RICS). There are 21 APC pathways, which relate to land, property, construction and the environment. For example, Watts have a graduate training programme specifically for graduates following the Building Surveying, Quantity Surveying and Project Management pathways.

Successfully completing the APC entitles RICS members to practice as qualified chartered surveyors and put the letters MRICS after their names. There are a number of routes to membership and details of these, the APC pathways and specific requirements are set out on the RICS website.

What does it involve?

Candidates are required to be in suitable employment with a firm that has an RICS approved structured training agreement. They will complete a period of structured training, normally for a minimum of 24 months, although this depends upon the entry route. During this period they are allocated an APC Counsellor and Supervisor who will give them guidance on their training and day-to-day work.

The APC training is competency-based and candidates are required to demonstrate that they have the skills and abilities to satisfy specific competencies. Details of requirements for each pathway are set out in *RICS APC/ATC Requirements and competencies*, July 2006.

Assessment takes the form of a submission and professional interview. Candidates are required to make a presentation to a panel of RICS assessors and answer detailed questions relating to their work experience and wider issues.

In addition to achieving specific competency levels, candidates are required to demonstrate that they are:

- ❖ confident to work unsupervised;
- ❖ a good ambassador for the profession;
- ❖ aware of the professional and commercial implications of their work;
- ❖ able to understand their clients' and employer's objectives; and
- ❖ up to date with relevant technical and legal matters.

How do candidates enrol?

To apply for the APC candidates should contact RICS who will send them a résumé form to fill out and return. Once RICS has assessed their eligibility it will send candidates the relevant application form.

Ten APC tips

1. Choose your employer wisely – Attempt to gauge a firm's commitment to graduate training by enquiring about the level of support and training offered. It is also essential to gain the correct spread of work experience during your training period to satisfy relevant competency requirements.

2. Get organised – The timing of your APC application and other submissions can be critical. For example, a delay in your enrolment could hold up your final assessment by six months. Clarify requirements and diarise key dates and milestones.

3. Carefully consider competency choice – You should do some research and set about gaining good advice in relation to competency choices from your employer and colleagues who have recently undertaken their APC. It is essential to ensure that there is a 'fit' with the range and nature of work you will be undertaking.

4. Get out and about – There is no substitute for quality one-to-one on-the-job training; so try to ensure that you make the most of shadowing opportunities from the outset of your training period.

5. Take ownership of your training – Make time to administer your APC paperwork and proactively set about identifying and planning your own training needs and work experience requirements. Your Supervisor and Counsellor should help with this.

6. Network and get advice – Join in with company activities, speak to colleagues about their experience of the APC, consult with your local RICS APC Doctor, and get involved with RICS MATRICS, the organisation for young chartered surveyors, trainees and graduates. You will benefit from advice, broaden your perspective of the profession and, as importantly, have fun and make lifelong friendships.

7. Professional approach – Keeping abreast of current trends and hot topics is essential. Reading relevant property and industry magazines and keeping up to date with changes in legislation, etc. will help build your confidence as a rounded professional.

8. Personal development – You will need to develop personal skills during the course of your training period in preparation for the final assessment. Good time management, organisation and presentation skills are essential. These cannot be attained at the last minute.

9. Technical competence – Continually develop your technical ability. Be resourceful, grow interest in your subject area, attend seminars and undertake structured reading relevant to your workload.

10. Prepare for the final assessment – Ask experienced colleagues to conduct a mock final assessment interview. Receive feedback, refine your presentation and repeat as necessary.

Contact details

Royal Institution of Chartered Surveyors

RICS Contact Centre

Surveyor Court

Westwood Way

Coventry CV4 8JE

Website: www.rics.org and www.rics.org/matrics

Email: contactrics@rics.org

Telephone: +44 (0)870 333 1600

Fax: +44 (0)20 7334 3811

Graduate Recruitment

Watts Academy

Watts

1 Great Tower Street

London EC3R 5AA

Website: watts-international.com

Email: jane.marr@watts-int.com
Telephone: +44 (0)20 7280 8000
Fax: +44 (0)20 7280 8001

Useful references

These guides are all available to download free on the RICS website:

- ❖ *RICS APC/ATC Requirements and competencies*, July 2006
- ❖ *RICS APC Candidate's guide – graduate route to membership*, July 2006
- ❖ *RICS APC Guide for supervisors, counsellors and employers – graduate route to membership*, July 2006

Technical resources

Conversion formulae

Within the lists below, to convert to metric, divide by the factor shown; and to convert from metric multiply by the factor shown.

Length

miles: kilometres	1.6093
yards: metres	0.9144
feet: metres	0.3048
inches: millimetres	25.4

Area

square miles: square kilometres	2.59
square miles: hectares	258.999
acres: square metres	4046.86
acres: hectares	0.4047
square yards: square metres	0.8361
square feet: square metres	0.0929
square inches: square millimetres	645.16

Volume

cubic yards: cubic metres	0.7646
cubic feet: cubic metres	0.0283
cubic inches: cubic centimetres	16.3871

Capacity

gallons: litres	4.546
US gallons: litres	3.785
quarts: litres	1.137
pints: litres 0.568 gills: litres	0.142

Mass

tons: kilogrammes	1016.05
tons: tonnes	1.0160
hundredweights: kilogrammes	50.8023
quarters: kilogrammes	12.7006
stones: kilogrammes	6.3503
pounds: kilogrammes	0.4536
ounces: grammes	28.3495

Temperature

$$°C = 5/9 \ (°F) - 32$$
$$°F = 9/5 \ (°C) + 32$$

Useful information sources

Agencies and Public Bodies
T: 020 7276 2040
Web: www.civilservice.gov.uk/other/agencies

Association for Project Management
T: 08454 581944 Web: www.apm.org.uk

Association of British Insurers
Web: www.abi.org.uk

Association of Building Engineers
T: 01604 404121 Web: www.abe.org.uk

Association of Consultant Approved Inspectors
T: 01435 862487 Web: www.acai.org.uk

Barbour Expert-online to the built environment
T: 01344 884 999 Web: www.barbour-index.co.uk

Boundary Problems
T: 023 8036 1344 Web: www.boundary-problems.co.uk

BRE Certification Ltd
T: 01923 664100 Web: www.brecertification.co.uk

BREEAM
T: 01923 664462 Web: www.breeam.org

British Cement Association
T: 01276 608700 Web: www.cementindustry.co.uk

British Council for Offices
T: 020 7283 4588 Web: www.bco.org.uk

British Geological Survey
T: 0115 936 3143 Web: www.bgs.ac.uk

British Institute of Facilities Management
T: 01799 508606 Web: www.bifm.org.uk

British Property Federation
T: 020 7828 0111 Web: www.bpf.org.uk

British Standards Institution
T: 020 8996 9000 Web: www.bsi-global.com

Building
T: 020 7921 5000 Web: www.building.co.uk

Building Conservation
T: 01747 871717 Web: www.buildingconservation.com

Building Cost Information Service Ltd
T: 020 7695 1500 Web: www.bcis.co.uk

Building Maintenance Information
T: 020 7695 1500 Web: www.bcis.co.uk

Building Research Establishment
T: 01923 664000 Web: www.bre.co.uk

Building Services Research and Information Association
T: 01344 465600 Web: www.bsria.co.uk

Businessparks.net
T: 020 8658 8000 Web: www.businessparks.net

Centre for Accessible Environments
T: 020 7840 0125 Web: www.cae.org.uk

Centre for Window and Cladding Technology
T: 01225 386541 Web: www.cwct.co.uk

Chartered Institute of Arbitrators
T: 020 7421 7444 Web: www.arbitrators.org

Chartered Institute of Building
T: 01344 630700 Web: www.ciob.org.uk

Commission for Architecture and the Built Environment
T: 020 7070 6700 Web: www.cabe.org.uk

Compliance+
T: 020 7549 3300 Web: www.ciria.org/complianceplus/

Concrete Repair Association
T: 01252 739145 Web: www.concreterepair.org.uk

Concrete Society
T: 01276 607140 Web: www.concrete.org.uk

Construction Best Practice Program
T: 0845 605 55 56 Web: www.constructing excellence.org.uk

Construction Europe
T: 01892 784088 Web: www.khl.com

Construction Health and Safety Group
T: 01932 561871 Web: www.chsg.co.uk

Construction Industry Council
T: 020 7399 7400 Web: www.cic.org.uk

Construction Industry Research and Information Association (CIRIA)
T: 020 7549 3300 Web: www.ciria.org.uk

Construction Line
T: 0870 240 0152 Web: www.constructionline.co.uk

Construction Plus
T: 0906 326 3766 Web: www.constructionplus.co.uk

Construction Research and Innovation Strategy Panel (CRISP)
T: 020 7592 1100 Web: www.ncrisp.org.uk

Construct Sustainability
Web: www.constructsustainably.co.uk

Contamlinks
Web: www.contamlinks.co.uk

Corrosion Prevention Association
T: 01252 739144 Web: www.corrosionprevention.org.uk

Countyweb
T: Freephone 0800 980 2425 or 01926 431552
Web: www.countyweb.co.uk

Court Service
T: 020 7189 2000 Web: www.courtservice.gov.uk

DDA Tax Guidance
T: 0845 010 9000
Web: www.inlandrevenue.gov.uk/specialist/disability-act-guidance.htm

Department for Environment, Food and Rural Affairs (Defra)
T: 08459 335577 Web: www.defra.gov.uk

Design Council
T: 020 7420 5200 Web: www.designcouncil.org.uk

DfES Public Private Partnerships
Web: www.dfes.gov.uk/ppppfi

Disability Rights Commission
T: 08457 622633 Web: www.drc-gb.org

Energy Watch
T: 08459 06 07 08 Web: www.energywatch.org.uk

English Heritage
T: 08703 331181 Web: www.english-heritage.org.uk

Environment Agency
T: 08708 506506 Web: www.environment-agency.gov.uk

Environmental Organisation Web Directory
Web: www.webdirectory.com

European Forecasting Group for the Construction Industry
Web: www.euroconstruct.org

Fire Protection Association
T: 01608 812500 Web: www.thefpa.co.uk

Glass & Glazing Federation
T: 0870 0424255 Web: www.ggf.org.uk

Health and Safety Executive
T: 0845 345 0055 Web: www.hse.gov.uk

HM Land Registry
T: 020 7917 8888 Web: www.landreg.gov.uk

HM Treasury – PFI
T: 020 7270 4558 Web: www.hm-treasury.gov.uk

House Builders Federation
T: 020 7960 1600 Web: www.hbf.co.uk

Information for Industry
T: 020 7549 8607 Web: www.connectingbusiness.com

Institution of Civil Engineering Surveyors
T: 0161 972 3100 Web: www.ices.org.uk

Institution of Structural Engineers
T: 020 7235 4535 Web: www.istructe.org.uk

Integrated Facilities Management
T: 020 8922 7491 Web: www.i-fm.net

isurv – surveyors' information centre
T: 020 7695 1777 Web: www.isurv.co.uk

Joint Contracts Tribunal
T: 020 7637 8650 Web: www.jctltd.co.uk

Landlord Zone
T: 0845 260 4420 Web: www.landlordzone.co.uk

Lead Development Association
T: 020 7499 8422 Web: www.ldaint.org

Mastic Asphalt Council
T: 01424 814400 Web: www.masticasphaltcouncil.co.uk

National Green Specification
Web: www.greenspec.co.uk

National Radiological Protection
T: 020 7759 2700/2701 Web: www.hpa.org.uk/radiation/

National Trust
T: 01793 817400 Web: www.nationaltrust.org.uk

NetRegs
T: 0870 8506 506 Web: www.netregs.gov.uk

Department for Communities and Local Government
T: 020 7944 4400 Web: www.communities.gov.uk

Official Journal of the European Communities
T: 01224 636999 Web: www.ojec.com

PPP Forum
T: 020 7842 5610 Web: www.pppforum.com/

Public Private Finance
T: 020 7970 4827 Web: www.publicprivatefinance.com

Pyramus & Thisbe
T: 028 4063 2082 Web: www.partywalls.org.uk

Radon Centres Ltd
T: 01604 494118 Web: www.radon.co.uk

RIBA Bookshop
T: 020 7256 7222 Web: www.ribabookshop.com

RICS Books
T: 0870 333 1600 (option 3) Web: www.ricsbooks.com

Royal Forestry Society
T: 01442 822028 Web: www.rfs.org.uk

Royal Institute of British Architects
T: 020 7580 5533 Web: www.riba.org

Royal Institution of Chartered Surveyors (RICS)
T: 0870 333 1600 Web: www.rics.org

Royal Institution of Chartered Surveyors in Scotland
T: 0131 225 7078 Web: www.rics.org

Service Charges Guide
Web: www.servicechargeguide.propertymall.com

SIMAP
Web: www.simap.eu.int/

Society of Construction Law
T: 01235 770606 Web: www.scl.org.uk

Society of Expert Witnesses
T: 0163 866 0684 Web: www.sew.org.uk

Society of Property Researchers
T: 01206 298205 Web: www.sprweb.co.uk

Stone Federation Great Britain
T: 01303 856123 Web: www.stone-federationgb.org.uk

Tenders Electronic Daily (TED)
Web: http://ted.publications.eu.int/official/

The Stationery Office Bookshop
T: 0870 242 2345 Web: www.tsoshop.co.uk

The Survey Association
T: 0163 664 2840 Web: www.tsa-uk.org.uk

Timber Research and Development Association
T: 01494 569600 Web: www.trada.co.uk

Timber Trade Federation
T: 020 7839 1891 Web: www.ttf.co.uk

UK Online Government
Web: www.direct.gov.uk

UK Taxation Directory
Web: www.uktax.demon.co.uk

Whole Life Cost Forum
Web: www.wlcf.org.uk

Contributors to the Watts Pocket Handbook

External contributors

The scope of the Watts Pocket Handbook would not be possible without the cooperation of external professionals who have dedicated their expertise and valued time to produce specialist information for inclusion in the publication. For this help and support, Watts would like to express their sincere appreciation to the following:

Architectural and design criteria
Basic design data
Building types

Robert Clements
Tooley and Foster Partnership
21 Berners Street
London W1T 3LP
T: 020 7636 4050
F: 020 7636 4077
E: rclements@
tooleyfoster.com

Architectural and design criteria
Modern methods of construction
Commercial and industrial property
Real Estate Investment Trusts (REITs)
Flooding
Compensation for flooding
Flooding and its impact on property
Flood plans
Forecasting floods
Planning to avoid flooding
Protecting property from floods
The surveyor's role in flooding
Housing and residential property
Housing Health and Safety Rating System

Lesley Davis
Davis Ayling Media Limited
Genista Cottage
Stane Street
Westhampnett
Chichester PO18 0PA
T: 01243 784054
E: lesley@
davisaylingmedia.co.uk

Building and construction regulations
Part L 2006 compliance
Environmental
Sustainable development

Arlo Mills
Gleeds
95 New Cavendish Street
London W1W 6XF
T: 020 7631 7000
F: 020 7631 7001
E: arlo.mills@gleeds.co.uk

Building services design
Air-conditioning systems
Data installations
Lift terminology
Lighting design
Plant and equipment
Environmental
Energy conservation
Renewable energy

Keith Crosby
Watkins Payne Partnership
51 Staines Road West
Sunbury-on-Thames
Middlesex TW16 7AH
T: 01932 781641
F: 01932 765590
E: kcrosby@ wppgroup.co.uk

Cost management
Capital allowances for taxation purposes
Land remediation allowances

Chris Doyle
Yewell Consulting LLP
1 Hall Road
Wallington
Surrey SM6 0RT
T: 020 8544 4810
F: 020 8544 4811
E: chris.doyle@yewell.co.uk

Cost management
VAT in the construction industry –
zero rating

Adrian Houstoun
Kingston Smith
Devonshire House
60 Goswell Road
London EC1M 7AD
T: 020 7566 3802
F: 020 7566 4010
E: ajh@kingstonsmith.co.uk

Cost management
Tender prices and building cost indices

Joe Martin
Building Cost Information
Service
Royal Institution of Chartered
Surveyors
12 Great George Street
Parliament Square
London SW1P 3AP
T: 020 7695 1500
F: 020 7695 1501
E: bcis@bcis.co.uk

Cost management
Rating revaluation 2005
Legal and lease
Section 18(1) of the Landlord and
Tenant Act 1927

David Shortall
Alexander Reece Thomson
11 Welbeck Street
London W1G 9XZ
T: 020 7486 1681
F: 020 7486 4200
E: davidshortall@
artsurveyors.co.uk

Development and procurement
Procurement and standard form contracts

Joe Bellhouse
Wedlake Bell
52 Bedford Row
London WC1R 4LR
T: 020 7395 3073
F: 020 7406 1602
E: jbellhouse@
wedlakebell.com

Environmental
BREEAM

Mark Worthington
Tooley and Foster Partnership
21 Berners Street
London W1T 3LP
T: 020 7467 9604
F: 020 7636 4077
E: mworthington@
tooleyfoster.com

Legal and lease
Adjudication Under the Scheme for
Construction Contracts – how to
get started
Dispute resolution
Expert witness
The Provisions of Part II Housing Grants,
Construction and Regeneration Act 1996

Suzanne Reeves
Wedlake Bell
52 Bedford Row
London WC1R 4LR
T: 020 7395 3168
F: 020 7406 1602
E: sreeves@wedlakebell.com

Site analysis
Measured surveys

Simon Barnes
Plowman Craven
141 Lower Luton Road
Harpenden
Hertfordshire AL5 5EQ
T: 01582 765566
F: 01582 763180
E: sbarnes@
plowmancraven.co.uk

Town and country planning in England
Appeals and called-in applications
Development applications and fees
Development plans and monitoring
Environmental impact assessments
General Development Order and
Use Classes Order
Planning and Compulsory Purchase
Act 2004
Planning policy guidance notes,
policy statements and circulars

Alan Gunne-Jones
Tribal MJP
70 High Street
Chislehurst
Kent BR7 5AQ
T: 020 8289 1800
F: 020 8289 1200
E: alan.gunne-
jones@tribalmjp.co.uk

Watts' contributors

Access agreements	Aidan Cosgrave, Keith Martin
Achieving excellence in construction	Mike Ridley
Acts of parliament and regulations	Angela Dawson
Airtightness	Trevor Rushton
Alkali aggregate reactions – ASR	Trevor Rushton
Asbestos	Mark Ratcliff, Paul Winstone
A systematic approach to maintenance management	Mike Ridley
BCO best practice for new offices and fitting out works	Rebecca Jermy, Michael Lee
'Best value' in local authorities	Stuart Russell
The Building (Amendment) Regulations 2004	Trevor Rushton
Building into the basement	Allen Gilham
Chemical and physical testing requirements	Trevor Rushton
Chlorides	Trevor Rushton
Collateral warranties and reliance letters	Paul Lovelock
Commercial/industrial surveys	Trevor Rushton
Common defects in commercial and residential properties	Trevor Rushton
Composite panels	Trevor Rushton
Condensation and toxic moulds	Allen Gilham
Condition surveys	Steve Brewer
The Construction (Design and Management) Regulations 1994	Rebecca Bridge, Jeramy Franklin-Buffey, Paul Winstone
The Construction (Health, Safety and Welfare) Regulations 1996	Rebecca Bridge, Jeramy Franklin-Buffey, Paul Winstone
Construction management	Mike Ridley
Construction noise and vibration	Aidan Cosgrave, Keith Martin
The contract administrator's role	Andrew Gear
Contract insurance	Jon Evans
Conversion formulae	Angela Dawson
Corrosion of metals	Phil Kirby, Trevor Rushton
Cost management	Christopher Knott
Curtain walling systems	Trevor Rushton

The RICS Assessment of Professional Competence	Alison Collett, Alastair Hughes, Trevor Rushton
Rights to light	Aidan Cosgrave, Jonathan Nash
Rising damp	Trevor Rushton
Rising groundwater	Trevor Rushton
Site archaeology	Allen Gilham
Soils and foundation design	Trevor Rushton
Soil survey	Trevor Rushton
Sources of information in maintenance management	Angela Dawson
Specifications	Tim French
Specification writing	Tim French
Spontaneous glass fracturing	Trevor Rushton
Subsidence	Trevor Rushton
Surveying safely	Rebecca Bridge, Jeramy Franklin-Buffey, Paul Winstone
Tenant fit out and licences to alter	Michael Kirkman
Tender prices and building cost indices	Tim French
Thin stone cladding	Trevor Rushton
Troublesome plant growth: Giant Hogweed	Trevor Rushton
Troublesome plant growth: Japanese Knotweed	Trevor Rushton
VAT in the construction industry – zero rating	Stuart Russell
Useful information sources	Angela Dawson
Vendor surveys	Trevor Rushton
Watts' publications	Sam Rumens
The Work at Height Regulations 2005	Rebecca Bridge, Jeramy Franklin-Buffey, Paul Winstone
The Workplace Regulations – Glazing	Trevor Rushton
The Workplace Regulations – Falls from height	Rebecca Bridge, Jeramy Franklin-Buffey, Paul Winstone
The Workplace Regulations – Lighting	Neil Wotherspoon, Paul Winstone
The Workplace Regulations – Provision of sanitary facilities	Rebecca Bridge, Jeramy Franklin-Buffey, Paul Winstone

Envest contributors

Contaminated land	Tim Coffin
Environmental Liability Directive	
Environment and specification	
Radon	
Water Framework Directive	

ikon contributors

Urban regeneration	Rob Sully

Watts' publications

For further information on any of the following publications, please contact Samantha Rumens, Production Executive, Watts' Marketing Department. Tel: +44 (0)20 7280 8000.

Watts Bulletin

As a technical companion to the Watts Pocket Handbook, the Watts Bulletin keeps its readership abreast of breaking news and changes in legislation within the property and construction industry. As part of the series, the practice also publishes two special issues a year, on topical subjects.

watts-international.com

Visit watts-international.com for more information on Watts and details of our range of services and our teams. The site is of interest to all stakeholders, from prospective employees to key clients, offering technical information, career opportunities, and case studies on a wide variety of jobs. A detailed search facility makes access to content quick and easy.

Watts Review

Published since 1999, this annual publication follows the format of an annual report and accounts document, updating clients on Watts' performance and development in the last full financial year. Watts Review 2005 – 2006 features both financial and operational highlights, as well as reports from the Chairman and Managing Partner. It also outlines the Group's ambitions for 2006 – 2011 and the continuing expansion of our UK and European network.

Watts Practice Profile

The Practice Profile provides an account of Watts' offices, services, performance and procedures, and is presented as a matter of course when tendering for new business. As a control document for all other marketing publications, it is continually updated. The Practice Profile is tailored to the scope of our UK and European offices, with French, Spanish and German versions available.

See also the RICS Books' publication pages for publications written by Watts' employees as authors and published by RICS Books.

RICS Books' publications

RICS Books publishes a range of authoritative, practical and essential books for surveyors. All books can be purchased by telephoning mail order on 0870 333 1600 (option 3) or by email at mailorder@rics.org.

There is also an online bookshop www.ricsbooks.com with over 8000 relevant publications, contracts and electronic services for property professionals.

Key titles include:

Investigating Hazardous and Deleterious Building Materials

Trevor Rushton

Price: £49.95

Stock code: 9898

Written by Trevor Rushton, Partner at Watts, and published by RICS Books, this book provides a first point of reference and practical guidance to the identification and treatment of problems associated with some types of building materials. It brings together the essentials of a wide range of different materials and forms of construction over the years that:

- ❖ may have been found to be hazardous to persons or to the environment;
- ❖ may have been considered to be deleterious;
- ❖ might have been regarded as being problematical in some way; and
- ❖ would probably be labelled as deleterious if they had their chance again.

It gives advice on:

- ❖ the nature of the material;
- ❖ its normal use;
- ❖ problem areas;
- ❖ methods of diagnosis and analysis; and
- ❖ methods of repair.

Investigating Hazardous and Deleterious Building Materials also examines the history of the use of the materials in question and guidance to the ages and types of building most at risk.

It is essential reading for building surveyors, home inspectors, building engineers, architects, facilities managers, students and other built environment professionals.

About the author

Trevor Rushton FRICS FBEng has over 25 years' experience in commercial building surveying. A Partner at Watts since 1990, Trevor specialises in building engineering and technology and is a prolific writer and speaker on technical topics. He is editor-in-chief of the regular Watts Bulletin publication and has written the chapters on materials and defects for *isurv building surveying* for which he is also one of the consultant editors. Trevor is a Fellow of both the Royal Institution of Chartered Surveyors (RICS) and the Association of Building Engineers (ABE).

Surveying Buildings

Malcolm Hollis

Price: £60

Stock code: 7859

Established as the leading surveying text and a must for all building surveyors and students. It is full of practical advice based on Malcolm Hollis' experience of thousands of real-life surveys. Written in a lively style and packed with colour photographs, diagrams and charts, an essential companion to any building inspection.

Pocket Surveying Buildings

Malcolm Hollis

Price: £22.50

Stock code: 9114

The ideal on-site companion, this book is a handy pocket size and the ideal companion to the main work *Surveying Buildings* by the same author. Practical and user-friendly this book will be an essential companion on all your home inspections.

Diagnosing Damp

Ralph Burkinshaw and Mike Parrett

Price: £47.50

Stock code: 6090

Diagnosing Damp provides you with the knowledge and tools to understand the causes of dampness in buildings and is packed full of features, diagrams and photographs to aid correct diagnosis.

Cracking and Building Movement – Book and CD ROM

Peter R. Dickinson and Nigel Thornton

Price: £49.95

Stock code: 7273

This book provides practising building surveyors, structural engineers and construction professionals with a true one-stop guide to inspection, diagnosis, reporting and repair of cracking problems in buildings.

Homebuyer Survey to Home Condition Report – Making the Change

Stephen Callaghan

Price: £45

Stock code: 9239

This book demonstrates the fundamental differences, and areas of similarity, between the two forms of survey report. By taking a case study property and completing both an RICS Homebuyer Survey and a Home Condition Report on it, he guides the reader, through annotated text, to the important reporting differences that are required.

DDA and Access: a Surveyor's Guide

Written by Mark Ratcliff, Associate at Watts, and published by RICS Books, this book is intended to be a practical guide for surveyors to help them get their heads around the complexities of the DDA and access for disabled users. The guide is intended to provide a source of reference in terms of the application of the DDA and everything a surveyor needs to know about the principles behind access, without needing to become an access specialist. The book is due for publication by RICS Books later in 2007.

HCRwriter.com

Writing up Home Condition Reports will be an essential part of your role as a home inspector and RICS Books is developing an online tool that will make this process efficient and effective. Log in to www.hcrwriter.com to get the latest information and register your interest.

isurv – fast track to best practice information

isurv is an online database of best practice guidance. It has over 120 contributors (including a number from Watts) providing expert commentary on surveying issues, and contains RICS guidance notes, model letters, forms and a case-law database. It is updated twice a month and is an ideal reference resource for surveyors.

For more information on *isurv* and to take out a free trial, please go to www.isurv.co.uk or email isurv@rics.org

Index

Index

Watts' network of offices

International property and construction consultants

Barcelona
Paseo de Gracia 118, Ppal
08008 Barcelona
T: +34 93 255 31 25
F: +34 93 255 31 09
E: barcelona@watts-int.com

Belfast
2–12 Montgomery Street
Belfast BT1 4NX
T: +44 (0)28 9024 8222
F: +44 (0)28 9024 8007
E: belfast@watts-int.com

Berlin
Bleibtreustraße 51a
D–10623 Berlin
T: +49 (0)30 345 0569 0
F: +49 (0)30 345 0569 10
E: berlin@watts-int.com

Birmingham
43 Temple Row
Birmingham
B2 5LS
T: +44 (0)121 237 6095
F: +44 (0)121 237 6100
E: birmingham@watts-int.com

Bristol
33–35 Queen Square
Bristol BS1 4LU
T: +44 (0)117 927 5800
F: +44 (0)117 927 5810
E: bristol@watts-int.com

Dublin
74 Fitzwilliam Lane
Dublin 2
T: +353 (0)1 703 8750
F: +353 (0)1 703 8751
E: dublin@watts-int.com

Düsseldorf
Neuer Zollhof 3
40 221 Düsseldorf
T: +49 (0)211 22 05 9 433
F: +49 (0)211 22 05 9 110
E: dusseldorf@watts-int.com

Edinburgh
29A Stafford Street
Edinburgh EH3 7BJ
T: +44 (0)131 226 9250
F: +44 (0)131 226 7070
E: edinburgh@watts-int.com

Glasgow
176 Bath Street
Glasgow G2 4HG
T: +44 (0)141 353 2211
F: +44 (0)141 353 2277
E: glasgow@watts-int.com

Leeds
Atlas House
31 King Street
Leeds LS1 2HL
T: +44 (0)113 245 3555
F: +44 (0)113 245 1333
E: leeds@watts-int.com

London
1 Great Tower Street
London EC3R 5AA
T: +44 (0)20 7280 8000
F: +44 (0)20 7280 8001
E: london@watts-int.com

Madrid
Zurbano 10, 2°
28010 Madrid
T: +34 91 4355459
F: +34 91 5758267
E: madrid@watts-int.com

Manchester
60 Fountain Street
Manchester M2 2FE
T: +44 (0)161 831 6180
F: +44 (0)161 834 7750
E: manchester@watts-int.com

Munich
Albert-Schweitzer-Straße 66/III
D-81735 München
T: +49 (0)89 67 8 0663 0
F: +49 (0)89 67 8 0663 22
E: munchen@watts-int.com

Paris
140, Avenue des Champs-Elysées
Paris 75008
T: +33 (0)1 70 36 19 80
F: +33 (0)1 70 36 19 82
E: paris@watts-int.com

European Alliances
Watts has strategic alliances with
four other firms on the continent
that operate in Scandinavia,
Holland, Belgium, Poland and the
Czech Republic.
For further information, please
contact:
Peter Primett
Director
T: +44 (0)20 7280 8000

watts-international.com

Watts.